TEST BANK FOR
TUSSY AND GUSTAFSON'S

Prealgebra

SECOND EDITION

Judith M. Jones
Valencia Community College

Australia • Canada • Mexico • Singapore • Spain • United Kingdom • United States

For more information about this or any other Brooks/Cole products, contact:
BROOKS/COLE
511 Forest Lodge Road
Pacific Grove, CA 93950 USA
www.brookscole.com
1-800-423-0563 (Thomson Learning Academic Resource Center)

Printed in the United States of America

10 9 8 7 6 5 4 3 2 1

ISBN: 0-534-3830-0

Table of Contents

Test Form F- Mixed (Free Response/Multiple Choice)
Test Form G- Mixed (Free Response/Multiple Choice)
Test Form H- Mixed (Free Response/Multiple Choice)

Chapter 6
Test Form A- Free Response
Test Form B- Free Response
Test Form C- Mixed (Free Response/Multiple Choice)
Test Form D- Multiple Choice
Test Form E- Multiple Choice
Test Form F- Mixed (Free Response/Multiple Choice)
Test Form G- Mixed (Free Response/Multiple Choice)
Test Form H- Mixed (Free Response/Multiple Choice)

Chapter 7
Test Form A- Free Response
Test Form B- Free Response
Test Form C- Mixed (Free Response/Multiple Choice)
Test Form D- Multiple Choice
Test Form E- Multiple Choice
Test Form F- Mixed (Free Response/Multiple Choice)
Test Form G- Mixed (Free Response/Multiple Choice)
Test Form H- Mixed (Free Response/Multiple Choice)

Chapter 8
Test Form A- Free Response
Test Form B- Free Response
Test Form C- Mixed (Free Response/Multiple Choice)
Test Form D- Multiple Choice
Test Form E- Multiple Choice
Test Form F- Mixed (Free Response/Multiple Choice)
Test Form G- Mixed (Free Response/Multiple Choice)
Test Form H- Mixed (Free Response/Multiple Choice)

Chapter 9
Test Form A- Free Response
Test Form B- Free Response
Test Form C- Mixed (Free Response/Multiple Choice)
Test Form D- Multiple Choice
Test Form E- Multiple Choice
Test Form F- Mixed (Free Response/Multiple Choice)
Test Form G- Mixed (Free Response/Multiple Choice)
Test Form H- Mixed (Free Response/Multiple Choice)

1. Is 3.5 greater or smaller than 1.5?

2. Write the following number in standard notation:

7 ten thousands + 8 thousands + 5 hundreds + 3 tens + 2 ones.

3. Write the following number in standard notation:

Forty-three thousand nine hundred.

4. Add:

$17 + 29$

5. Subtract:

$770 - (324 - 40)$

6. In 1995, the monthly circulation of a magazine grew by 24085. In 1996, the monthly circulation decreased by 45221. If the monthly circulation in 1994 was 1540693, what was it in 1996?

Enter your answer without commas.

7. EATING HABITS The following list shows the 6 countries with the largest per person annual consumption of meat. Complete the table below presenting the data in order, beginning with the largest per-person consumption (place 1). (The abbreviation "lb" means "pounds.")

Australia: 251 lb
Austria: 232 lb
Canada: 213 lb
Cyprus: 239 lb
Denmark: 219 lb
United States: 260 lb

Place	Annual consumption of meat (lb)
1	
2	
3	
4	
5	
6	

8. Multiply:

$6 \cdot (5 \cdot 2)$

9. Multiply:

$$\begin{array}{r} 74 \\ \times\ 52 \\ \hline \end{array}$$

10. Divide:

$54 \div 18$

11. Do the following division and give the quotient and the remainder:

$24\overline{)593}$

12. A rock band gave two concerts in 23 cities. Approximately 1700 fans attended each concert. How many persons heard the group?

13. When using the division method to find the prime factorization of 78384, what is an obvious number choice with which to start the division process?

14. Write 385 in prime-factored form.

15. Evaluate the expression:

$13 - 11 + 1$

16. Evaluate the expression:

$4^3 \cdot 3$

17. Evaluate the expression:

$86 - 7\left[17 - (6 + 3)\right]$

18. The scores received by a junior diver are as follows:

6	3	2	7	8	4

The formula for computing the overall score for the dive is as follows:

1. Throw out the lowest score.
2. Throw out the highest score.
3. Divide the sum of the remaining scores by 4.

Find the diver's score.

19. Find the solution of the equation:

$y - 10 = 0.$

20. Use the addition or subtraction property of equality to solve the equation:

$x - 10 = 4.$

21. Use the addition or subtraction property of equality to solve the equation:

$x + 1 = 11.$

22. The sound intensity of a jet engine is 118 decibels.
What noise level will an airplane mechanic experience if the ear plugs she is wearing reduce the sound intensity by 43 decibels?

23. Use the division or the multiplication property of equality to solve the equation.

$3v = 63$

24. Use the division or the multiplication property of equality to solve the equation.

$\frac{z}{4} = 3$

25. The attendance at an elementary school open house was only half of what the principal had expected. If 170 people visited the school that evening, how many had she expected to attend?

Answers

1. 3.5 > 1.5

2. 78532

3. 43900

4. 46

5. 486

6. 1519557

7. 1, 260, 2, 251, 3, 239, 4, 232, 5, 219, 6, 213

8. 60

9. 3848

10. 3

11. 24, 17

12. 78200

13. 2

14. $11 \cdot 5 \cdot 7$

15. 3

16. 192

17. 30

18. 5

19. $y=10$

20. $x=14$

21. $x=10$

22. 75

23. 21

24. 12

25. 340

1. Is 1.9 greater or smaller than 1.1?

2. Write the following number in standard notation:

5 ten thousands + 9 thousands + 2 hundreds + 3 tens + 7 ones.

3. Write the following number in standard notation:

Twenty-one thousand six hundred.

4. Add:

$25 + 29$

5. Subtract:

$711 - (282 - 83)$

6. A savings account contained $443. After a deposit of $56 and a withdrawal of $181, how much is in the account?

7. EATING HABITS The following list shows the 6 countries with the largest per person annual consumption of meat. Complete the table below presenting the data in order, beginning with the largest per-person consumption (place 1). (The abbreviation "lb" means "pounds.")

Australia: 251 lb
Austria: 229 lb
Canada: 213 lb
Cyprus: 236 lb
Denmark: 223 lb
United States: 274 lb

Place	Annual consumption of meat (lb)
1	
2	
3	
4	
5	
6	

8. Multiply:

$6 \cdot (5 \cdot 2)$

9. Multiply:

$$\begin{array}{r} 61 \\ \times 42 \\ \hline \end{array}$$

10. Divide:

$90 \div 9$

11. Do the following division and give the quotient and the remainder:

$19\overline{)412}$

12. A jazz quartet gave two concerts in 39 cities. Approximately 1000 fans attended each concert. How many persons heard the group?

13. Find the prime factors of 55 and 66. What prime factor do they have in common?

14. Write 154 in prime-factored form.

15. Evaluate the expression:

$20 - 17 + 2$

16. Evaluate the expression:

$$9 + \left(7^2 - \frac{175}{5}\right)$$

17. Evaluate the expression:

$$70 - 2\left[18 - \left(5 + 4\right)\right]$$

18. Use the following bar graph to find the average number of therms of natural gas used per month. Round the result to the nearest integer.

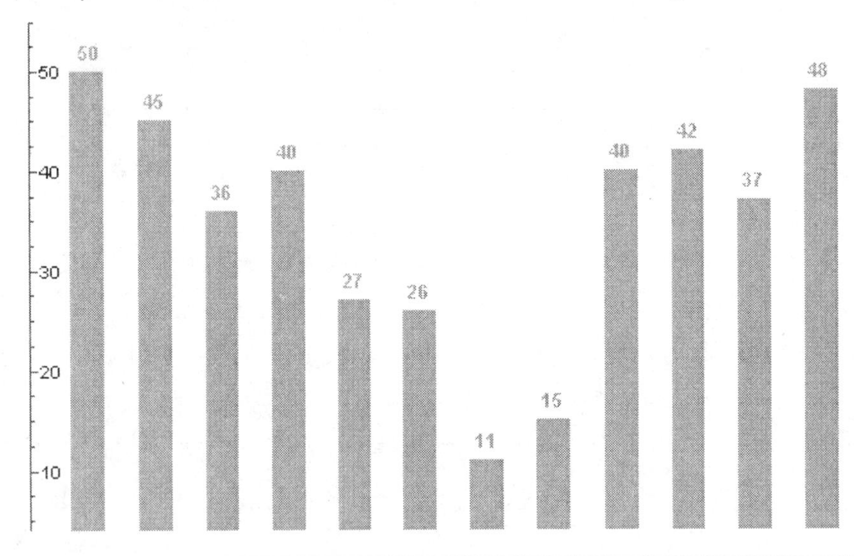

19. Find the solution of the equation:

$y - 2 = 0.$

20. Use the addition or subtraction property of equality to solve the equation:

$x - 10 = 6.$

21. Find the solution of the equation:

$49 = 38 + b.$

22. A man needs $274 for a new set of golf clubs. How much more money does he need if he now has $220?

23. Use the division or the multiplication property of equality to solve the equation.

$2x = 120$

24. Use the division or the multiplication property of equality to solve the equation.

$$1 = \frac{v}{24}$$

25. 15 employees of a grocery store pooled their money to buy $150 worth of lottery tickets each week, with the understanding they would split the prize equally if they happened to win. One week they did have the winning ticket and won $529500. What was each employee's share of the winnings?

Answers

1. 1.9 > 1.1

2. 59237

3. 21600

4. 54

5. 512

6. 318

7. 1, 274, 2, 251, 3, 236, 4, 229, 5, 223, 6, 213

8. 60

9. 2562

10. 10

11. 21, 13

12. 78000

13. 11

14. $7 \cdot 11 \cdot 2$

15. 5

16. 23

17. 52

18. 34.75

19. y=2

20. x=16

21. b=11

22. x=54

23. 60

24. 24

25. 35300

1. A total of 338 girls tried out for a city volleyball program. How many girls should be put on each team roster if the following requirements must be met?
1. All the teams are to have the same number of players.
2. A reasonable number of players on a team is 11 to 14.
3. For scheduling purposes, there must be an even number of teams.

Select the correct answer:

( ) 13
( ) 14
( ) 12
( ) 11

2. Is 4.7 greater or smaller than 1.7?

3. True or False:

Since 9 < 24, it is also true that 24 < 9.

True or False?

( ) True
( ) False

4. Write the following number in standard notation:

2 ten thousands + 6 thousands + 3 hundreds + 9 tens + 4 ones.

5. Write the following number in standard notation.

Nine million four hundred thousand eight hundred

Select the correct answer:

( ) 940800
( ) 94000800
( ) 980400
( ) 9400800
( ) 9800400

6. Add:

$\left(17 + 81\right) + 51$

7. Subtract:

554 - (388 - 28)

Select the correct answer:

( ) 914
( ) 194
( ) 204
( ) 138

8. Find the length of the house shown in the picture, where $a = 17, b = 20, c = 12, d = 12$.

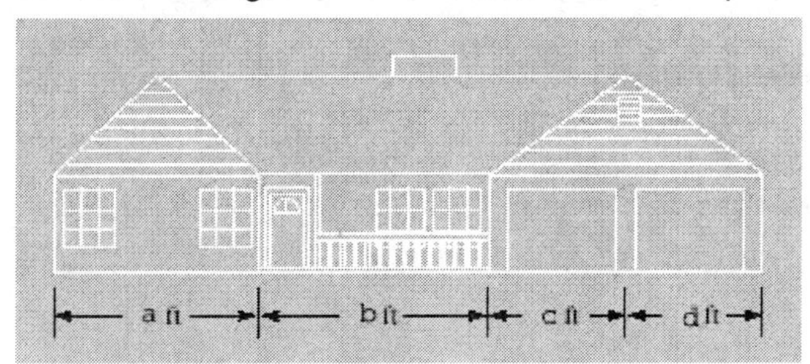

9. True or false:

$8 \cdot (2 \cdot 9) = 143$

( ) True
( ) False

10. Multiply:

$$\begin{array}{r} 84 \\ \times 43 \\ \hline \end{array}$$

11. Divide:

$$\frac{340}{20}$$

Select the correct answer:

( ) 27
( ) 34
( ) 16
( ) 18
( ) 17

12. A first grade class received 98 halfpint cartons of milk to distribute evenly to the 19 students. How many cartons were left over?

13. Find the prime factors of 10 and 385. What prime factor do they have in common?

Select the correct answer:

( ) 22
( ) 55
( ) 10
( ) 2
( ) 5
( ) 77
( ) 11
( ) 7

14. Write 3969 in prime-factored form.

15. True or False:

$15 - 5 + 20 = 30$

( ) True
( ) False

16. Evaluate the following expression:

$14^2 - 6(4)(3)$

17. The list below shows the number of people watching *Who Wants to Be a Millionaire?* on five weeknights in November of 1999. How large was the average audience?

Monday	26400000
Tuesday	24400000
Wednesday	22800000
Thursday	25700000
Friday	21300000

18. True or False:

The solution of the equation:
$\boldsymbol{x - 6 = 0}$ is $\boldsymbol{x = 6}$

( ) True
( ) False

19. Find the solution of the equation:

$174 = x - 159$

20. Find the solution of the equation:

$27 = 20 + b$

Select the correct answer.

( ) none of these choices
( ) b = - 47
( ) b = 47
( ) b = 7

21. After a week of playing Sega's*Sonic Adventure*, a boy scored 12747 points in one game - an improvement of 5245 points over the very first time he played. What was his score for his first game?

22. Use the division or the multiplication property of equality to solve the equation.

$20 = 2y$

23. Use the division or the multiplication property of equality to solve the equation.

$249 = \frac{y}{3}$

24. Lengthy delays and skyrocketing costs caused a rapid-transit construction project to go over budget by a factor of 10. The final audit showed the project costing $500 million. What was the initial cost estimate?

25. PRESIDENTS The following list shows the 5 youngest U.S. presidents and their ages (in years/days) when they took office.

W. Clinton 46 yr/181 days
T. Roosevelt 42 yr/319 days
J. Kennedy 43 yr/319 days
U. Grant 46 yr/319 days
G. Cleveland 47 yr/60 days

The youngest president is W. Clinton.
True or False?

( ) True
( ) False

Answers

1. 13

2. $4.7 > 1.7$

3. false

4. 26394

5. 9400800

6. 149

7. 194

8. 61

9. false

10. 3612

11. 17

12. 3

13. 5

14. $3^4 \cdot 7^2$

15. true

16. 124

17. 24120000

18. true

19. $x=333$

20. $b = 7$

21. 7502

22. 10

23. 747

24. 50

25. (none)

1. True or False:

3.3 > 3.3

( ) True
( ) False

2. True or False:

5 ten thousands + 8 thousands + 6 hundreds + 9 tens + 3 ones is 58693

( ) True
( ) False

3. Write the number in standard notation.
Fifty-one thousand six hundred.

Select the correct answer:

( ) 56001
( ) 51060
( ) 5160
( ) 51600

4. True or False:

$19 + 27 = 36$

( ) True
( ) False

5. Subtract:

590 - (570 - 83)

Select the correct answer:

( ) -63
( ) 1077
( ) 113
( ) 103

6. True or False:

In 1994, the monthly circulation of a magazine grew by 17269. In 1995, the monthly circulation decreased by 42512. If the monthly circulation in 1993 was 1012330, in 1995 monthly circulation was 987087.

( ) True
( ) False

7. True or false:

$5 \cdot (6 \cdot 2) = 59$

( ) True
( ) False

8. EATING HABITS The following list shows the 6 countries with the largest per person annual consumption of meat. (The abbreviation "lb" means "pounds.")

Australia: 251 lb
Austria: 234 lb
Canada: 213 lb
Cyprus: 239 lb
Denmark: 221 lb
United States: 279 lb

True or False:

Denmark has the fourth highest annual per-person consumption of meat.

( ) True
( ) False

9. True or false:

$$\begin{array}{r} 32 \\ \times 65 \\ \hline 2090 \end{array}$$

( ) True
( ) False

10. True or false:

$18 \div 6 = 3$

( ) True
( ) False

11. True or False:The following division has a quotient of 21 and a remainder of 4.

$38\overline{)802}$

( ) True
( ) False

12. A rock band gave two concerts in 23 cities. Approximately 1000 fans attended each concert. How many persons heard the group?

Select the correct answer:

( ) 23000
( ) 45990
( ) 46000
( ) 46100
( ) 22990

13. When using the division method to find the prime factorization of 68156, what is an obvious choice with which to start the division process?

Select the correct answer:

( ) 5
( ) 7
( ) 10
( ) 3
( ) 2

14. Write 42 in prime-factored form.

Select the correct answer:

( ) $1 \cdot 7 \cdot 3$
( ) $2 \cdot 3 \cdot 7$
( ) $2 \cdot 3 \cdot 8$
( ) $3 \cdot 3 \cdot 7$
( ) $4 \cdot 2 \cdot 7$

15. True or False:

$17 - 4 + 19 = 32$

( ) True
( ) False

16. True or false:

$3^2 \cdot 2 = 18$

( ) True
( ) False

17. Evaluate the following expression:

$64 - 2\left[38 - \left(5 + 5\right)\right]$

Select the correct answer:

( ) 3
( ) 8
( ) 6
( ) 18
( ) 13

18. The scores received by a junior diver are as follows:

7	5	2	7	8	1

The formula for computing the overall score for the dive is as follows:
1. Throw out the lowest score.
2. Throw out the highest score.
3. Divide the sum of the remaining scores by 4.

True or false:

The diver's score is 6.

( ) True
( ) False

19. True or False:

The solution of the equation:
$a - 6 = 0$ is $a = 6$

( ) True
( ) False

20. Use the addition or subtraction property of equality to solve the equation:

$y - 9 = 5$

Select the correct answer.

( ) y = 14
( ) none of those
( ) y = -4
( ) y = - 14

21. Use the addition or subtraction property of equality to solve the equation:

$y + 5 = 7$

Select the correct answer.

( ) y = - 12
( ) y = 12
( ) y = 2
( ) none of these choices

22. The sound intensity of a jet engine is 106 decibels.
What noise level will an airplane mechanic experience if the ear plugs she is wearing reduce the sound intensity by 43 decibels?

Select the correct answer.

( ) 149 decibels
( ) 63 decibels
( ) 106 decibels
( ) none of these choices
( ) 43 decibels

23. Use the division or the multiplication property of equality to solve the equation.
What is the result?

$4x = 204$

Select the correct answer.

( ) 50
( ) 51
( ) 816
( ) 817

24. Use the division or the multiplication property of equality to solve the equation. What is the result?

$$\frac{v}{3} = 9$$

Select the correct answer.

( ) 0.333333
( ) 28
( ) 1.333333
( ) 27
( ) 3

25. The attendance at an elementary school open house was only half of what the principal had expected. If 160 people visited the school that evening, how many had she expected to attend?

Select the correct answer.

( ) 319
( ) 480
( ) 160
( ) 81
( ) 320
( ) 162
( ) 80

Answers

1. true

2. true

3. 51600

4. false

5. 103

6. true

7. false

8. false

9. false

10. true

11. true

12. 46000

13. 2

14. $2 \cdot 3 \cdot 7$

15. true

16. true

17. 8

18. false

19. true

20. $y = 14$

21. $y = 2$

22. 63 decibels

23. 51

24. 27

25. 320

1. True or False:

4.5 > 4.3

( ) True
( ) False

2. True or False:

4 ten thousands + 3 thousands + 6 hundreds + 5 tens + 8 ones is 43658

( ) True
( ) False

3. Write the number in standard notation.
Fifty-eight thousand seven hundred.

Select the correct answer:

( ) 5870
( ) 58070
( ) 58700
( ) 57008

4. True or False:

$13 + 25 = 28$

( ) True
( ) False

5. Subtract:

644 - (357 - 20)

Select the correct answer:

( ) 317
( ) 307
( ) 981
( ) 267

6. A savings account contained $371. After a deposit of $83 and a withdrawal of $132, how much is in the account?

Select the correct answer:

( ) $332
( ) $586
( ) $596
( ) $322

7. True or false:

$9 \cdot (7 \cdot 3) = 188$

( ) True
( ) False

8. EATING HABITS The following list shows the 6 countries with the largest per person annual consumption of meat. (The abbreviation "lb" means "pounds.")

Australia: 252 lb
Austria: 232 lb
Canada: 215 lb
Cyprus: 239 lb
Denmark: 219 lb
United States: 270 lb

True or False:

Denmark has the fourth highest annual per-person consumption of meat.

( ) True
( ) False

9. True or false:

$$\begin{array}{r} 74 \\ \times 19 \\ \hline 1416 \end{array}$$

( ) True
( ) False

10. True or false:

$70 \div 10 = 7$

( ) True
( ) False

11. True or False:The following division has a quotient of 20 and a remainder of 6.

$11\overline{)226}$

( ) True
( ) False

12. A rock band gave two concerts in 23 cities. Approximately 2100 fans attended each concert. How many persons heard the group?

Select the correct answer:

( ) 96590
( ) 48290
( ) 96600
( ) 96700
( ) 48300

13. Find the prime factors of 77 and 110. What prime factor do they have in common?

Select the correct answer:

( ) 11
( ) 77
( ) 2
( ) 55
( ) 35
( ) 5
( ) 10
( ) 7

14. Write 105 in prime-factored form.

Select the correct answer:

( ) $7 \cdot 5 \cdot 3$
( ) $6 \cdot 7 \cdot 3$
( ) $7 \cdot 5 \cdot 4$
( ) $6 \cdot 3 \cdot 5$
( ) $5 \cdot 8 \cdot 3$

15. True or False:

$$13 - 5 + 9 = 17$$

( ) True
( ) False

16. Evaluate the following expression:

$$7 + \left(9^3 - \frac{136}{4}\right)$$

Select the correct answer:

( ) 700
( ) 707
( ) 702
( ) 701
( ) 712

17. Evaluate the following expression:

$$46 - 2\left[18 - (5 + 6)\right]$$

Select the correct answer:

( ) 42
( ) 27
( ) 30
( ) 37
( ) 32

18. Use the following bar graph to find the average number of therms of natural gas used per month.

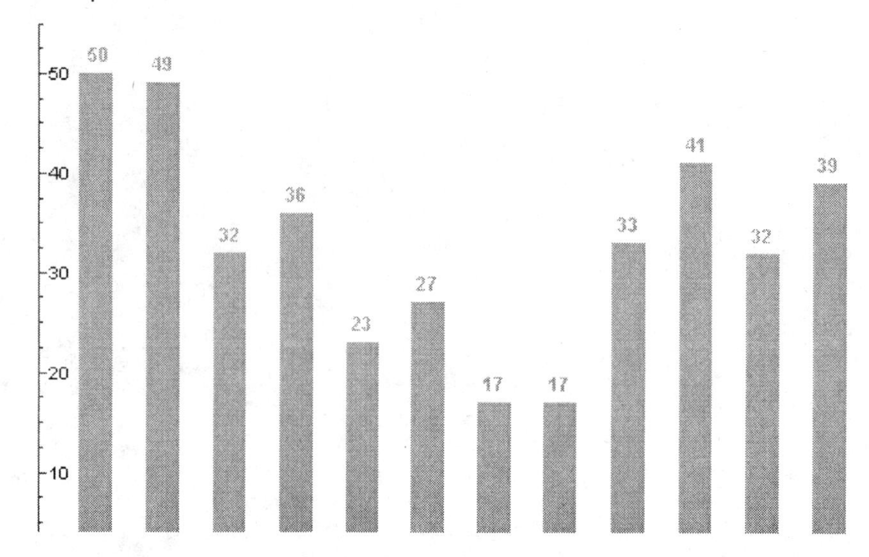

Select the correct answer:

( ) 43
( ) 31
( ) 23
( ) 34
( ) 33

19. True or False:

The solution of the equation:
$b - 6 = 0$ is $b = 6$

( ) True
( ) False

20. Use the addition or subtraction property of equality to solve the equation:

$z - 10 = 9$

Select the correct answer.

( ) z = 19
( ) z = -1
( ) z = - 19
( ) none of those

21. Find the solution of the equation:

$40 = 31 + b$

Select the correct answer.

( ) b = 71
( ) none of these choices
( ) b = 9
( ) b = - 71

22. A man needs $235 for a new set of golf clubs. How much more money does he need if he now has $214?

Select the correct answer.

( ) $ 21
( ) - $ 449
( ) $ 449
( ) - $ 21
( ) none of these choices

23. Use the division or the multiplication property of equality to solve the equation. What is the result?

$$2z = 180$$

Select the correct answer.

( ) 91
( ) 360
( ) 90
( ) 359

24. Use the division or the multiplication property of equality to solve the equation. What is the result?

$$1 = \frac{x}{34}$$

Select the correct answer.

( ) 34
( ) -0.970588
( ) 1
( ) 0.029412
( ) 33

25. 15 employees of a grocery store pooled their money to buy $147 worth of lottery tickets each week, with the understanding they would split the prize equally if they happened to win. One week they did have the winning ticket and won $421500. What was each employee's share of the winnings?

Select the correct answer.

( ) $2810
( ) $28101
( ) $25895
( ) $28200
( ) $28100
( ) $2205
( ) $2809

Answers

1. true

2. true

3. 58700

4. false

5. 307

6. $322

7. false

8. false

9. false

10. true

11. true

12. 96600

13. 11

14. $7 \cdot 5 \cdot 3$

15. true

16. 702

17. 32

18. 33

19. true

20. $z = 19$

21. $b = 9$

22. $ 21

23. 90

24. 34

25. $28100

1. Is 3.9 greater or smaller than 2.3?

2. Write the following number in standard notation:

5 ten thousands + 4 thousands + 2 hundreds + 8 tens + 9 ones.

3. Write the following number in standard notation:

Fifty-eight thousand six hundred.

4. Add:

$13 + 25$

5. Subtract:

$918 - (523 - 21)$

6. In 1995, the monthly circulation of a magazine grew by 24315. In 1996, the monthly circulation decreased by 28656. If the monthly circulation in 1994 was 1195808, what was it in 1996?

Enter your answer without commas.

7. EATING HABITS The following list shows the 6 countries with the largest per person annual consumption of meat. Complete the table below presenting the data in order, beginning with the largest per-person consumption (place 1). (The abbreviation "lb" means "pounds.")

Australia: 250 lb
Austria: 235 lb
Canada: 211 lb
Cyprus: 236 lb
Denmark: 219 lb
United States: 264 lb

Place	Annual consumption of meat (lb)
1	
2	
3	
4	
5	
6	

8. Multiply:

$9 \cdot (4 \cdot 2)$

9. Multiply:

$$\begin{array}{r} 94 \\ \times\ 72 \\ \hline \end{array}$$

10. Divide:

$91 \div 7$

11. Do the following division and give the quotient and the remainder:

$33\overline{)1000}$

12. A jazz quartet gave two concerts in 32 cities. Approximately 1100 fans attended each concert. How many persons heard the group?

13. When using the division method to find the prime factorization of 54934, what is an obvious number choice with which to start the division process?

14. Write 105 in prime-factored form.

Select the correct answer:

( ) $5 \cdot 4 \cdot 7$
( ) $3 \cdot 5 \cdot 8$
( ) $6 \cdot 3 \cdot 7$
( ) $3 \cdot 5 \cdot 7$
( ) $2 \cdot 7 \cdot 5$

15. True or False:

$19 - 8 + 5 = 16$

( ) True
( ) False

16. True or false:

$3^3 \cdot 7 = 189$

( ) True
( ) False

17. Evaluate the following expression:

$60 - 2\left[27 - \left(4 + 9\right)\right]$

Select the correct answer:

( ) 27
( ) 32
( ) 30
( ) 42
( ) 37

18. The scores received by a junior diver are as follows:

6	7	2	5	8	6

The formula for computing the overall score for the dive is as follows:
1. Throw out the lowest score.
2. Throw out the highest score.
3. Divide the sum of the remaining scores by 4.

True or false:

The diver's score is 7.

( ) True
( ) False

19. True or False:

The solution of the equation:
$a - 2 = 0$ is $a = 2$

( ) True
( ) False

20. Use the addition or subtraction property of equality to solve the equation:

$a - 8 = 5$

Select the correct answer.

( ) a = -3
( ) a = 13
( ) a = - 13
( ) none of those

21. Use the addition or subtraction property of equality to solve the equation:

$b + 3 = 8$

Select the correct answer.

( ) b = 11
( ) b = 5
( ) b = - 11
( ) none of these choices

22. The sound intensity of a jet engine is 111 decibels.
What noise level will an airplane mechanic experience if the ear plugs she is wearing reduce the sound intensity by 42 decibels?

Select the correct answer.

( ) 153 decibels
( ) none of these choices
( ) 42 decibels
( ) 69 decibels
( ) 111 decibels

23. Use the division or the multiplication property of equality to solve the equation.
What is the result?

$6v = 426$

Select the correct answer.

( ) 2556
( ) 71
( ) 72
( ) 2555

24. Use the division or the multiplication property of equality to solve the equation.
What is the result?

$\frac{y}{4} = 6$

Select the correct answer.

( ) 24
( ) 1.5
( ) 1.666667
( ) 0.666667
( ) 25

25. The attendance at an elementary school open house was only half of what the principal had expected. If 168 people visited the school that evening, how many had she expected to attend?

Select the correct answer.

( ) 170
( ) 84
( ) 168
( ) 336
( ) 337
( ) 83
( ) 504

Answers

1. 3.9 > 2.3

2. 54289

3. 58600

4. 38

5. 416

6. 1191467

7. 1, 264, 2, 250, 3, 236, 4, 235, 5, 219, 6, 211

8. 72

9. 6768

10. 13

11. 30, 10

12. 70400

13. 2

14. $3 \cdot 5 \cdot 7$

15. true

16. true

17. 32

18. false

19. true

20. a = 13

21. b = 5

22. 69 decibels

23. 71

24. 24

25. 336

1. True or False:

0.9 > 0.7

( ) True
( ) False

2. True or False:

4 ten thousands + 3 thousands + 7 hundreds + 2 tens + 8 ones is 43728

( ) True
( ) False

3. Write the number in standard notation.
Fifty-one thousand nine hundred.

Select the correct answer:

( ) 5190
( ) 51090
( ) 51900
( ) 59001

4. True or False:

11 + 15 = 16

( ) True
( ) False

5. Subtract:

866 - (737 - 20)

Select the correct answer:

( ) 1583
( ) 109
( ) 149
( ) 159

6. True or False:

In 1991, the monthly circulation of a magazine grew by 12745. In 1992, the monthly circulation decreased by 33637. If the monthly circulation in 1990 was 1411198, in 1992 monthly circulation was 1390306.

( ) True
( ) False

7. True or false:

$$9 \cdot (7 \cdot 2) = 125$$

( ) True
( ) False

8. True or false:

$$\begin{array}{r} 15 \\ \times 34 \\ \hline 520 \end{array}$$

( ) True
( ) False

9. EATING HABITS The following list shows the 6 countries with the largest per person annual consumption of meat. (The abbreviation "lb" means "pounds.")

Australia: 253 lb
Austria: 231 lb
Canada: 213 lb
Cyprus: 240 lb
Denmark: 222 lb
United States: 274 lb

True or False:

Denmark has the fourth highest annual per-person consumption of meat.

( ) True
( ) False

10. True or false:

$52 \div 4 = 13$

( ) True
( ) False

11. True or False:The following division has a quotient of 22 and a remainder of 20.

$31\overline{)702}$

( ) True
( ) False

12. A rock band gave two concerts in 46 cities. Approximately 1000 fans attended each concert. How many persons heard the group?

Select the correct answer:

( ) 46000
( ) 91990
( ) 92100
( ) 92000
( ) 45990

13. When using the division method to find the prime factorization of 65128, what is an obvious choice with which to start the division process?

Select the correct answer:

( ) 3
( ) 10
( ) 2
( ) 7
( ) 5

Write 165 in prime-factored form.

14. Evaluate the following expression:

$20 - 8 + 11$

15. Evaluate the following expression:

$4^2 \cdot 3$

16. Evaluate the following expression:

$89 - 3\left[35 - (8 + 4)\right]$

17. The scores received by a junior diver are as follows:

6	3	2	6	8	5

The formula for computing the overall score for the dive is as follows:

1. Throw out the lowest score.
2. Throw out the highest score.
3. Divide the sum of the remaining scores by 4.

Find the diver's score.

18. Find the solution of the equation:

$z - 3 = 0$

19. Use the addition or subtraction property of equality to solve the equation:

$y - 10 = 3$.

20. Use the addition or subtraction property of equality to solve the equation:

$a + 2 = 9$

21. The sound intensity of a jet engine is 102 decibels.
What noise level will an airplane mechanic experience if the ear plugs she is wearing reduce the sound intensity by 31 decibels?

22. Use the division or the multiplication property of equality to solve the equation.

$3y = 24$

23. Use the division or the multiplication property of equality to solve the equation.

$\frac{a}{3} = 10$

24. The attendance at an elementary school open house was only half of what the principal had expected. If 265 people visited the school that evening, how many had she expected to attend?

Answers For *Copy 1*

1. true

2. true

3. 51900

4. false

5. 149

6. true

7. false

8. false

9. false

10. true

11. true

12. 92000

13. 2

14. 23

15. 48

16. 20

17. 5

18. $z=3$

19. $y=13$

20. $a=7$

21. 71

22. 8

23. 30

24. 530

1. Information is often transmitted in code. Many codes involve writing products of large primes, because they are difficult to factor. To see how difficult, try finding two prime factors of 6059. (Hint: Both primes are greater than 70.) Separate your answer with a comma.

2. A total of 154 girls tried out for a city volleyball program. How many girls should be put on each team roster if the following requirements must be met?
1. All the teams are to have the same number of players.
2. A reasonable number of players on a team is 5 to 8.
3. For scheduling purposes, there must be an even number of teams.

Select the correct answer:

( ) 6
( ) 7
( ) 8
( ) 5

3. Round $346830 to the nearest $10000.

Select the correct answer:

( ) $347000
( ) $340000
( ) $346000
( ) $350000
( ) $300000
( ) $400000

4. Find the perimeter of the following rectangle, where a = 25 and b = 10

a feet (ft)

b ft

Choose your answer from below.

Select the correct answer:

( ) 140 feet
( ) 70 feet
( ) 35 feet
( ) 20 feet
( ) 250 feet
( ) 50 feet

5. A high school PE teacher had the students in her class form 4-person teams for a basketball tournament. 32 teams participated in the tournament.
True or False:
There were 96 students in the PE class.

( ) True
( ) False

6. True or false:

$8 \cdot (2 \cdot 9) = 143$

( ) True
( ) False

7. Use the addition or subtraction property of equality to solve the equation:

$0 = y - 6$

8. Use the addition or subtraction property of equality to solve the equation:

$0 = c - 11$.

Select the correct answer.

( ) c = - 11
( ) c = 11
( ) none of these choices
( ) c = 0

9. True or False:

In 1997, 4455 fewer Dalmatians were registered than in the year when they were at their height of popularity.

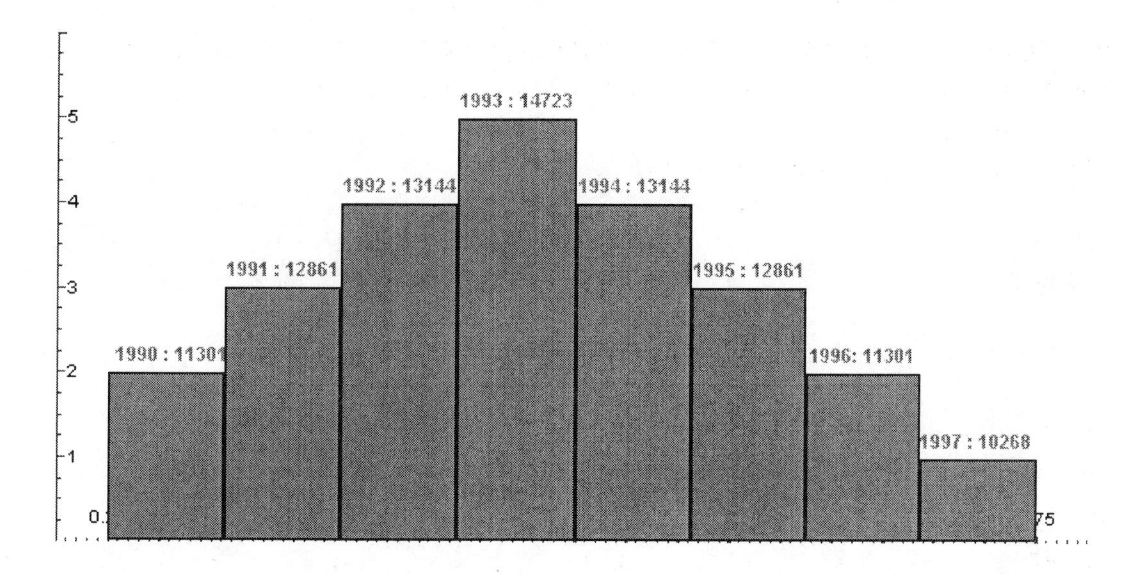

( ) True
( ) False

10. Use the following bar graph to find the average number of therms of natural gas used per month.

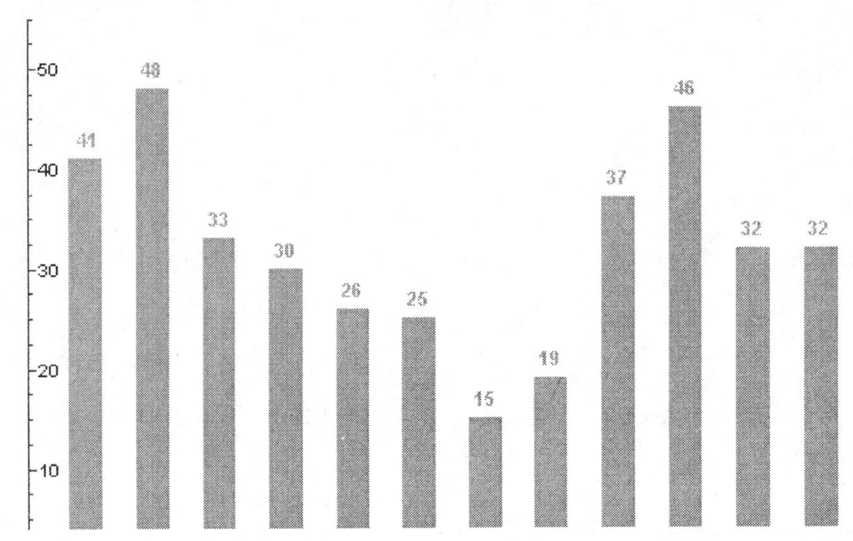

Select the correct answer:

( ) 30
( ) 32
( ) 22
( ) 33
( ) 42

11. True or False:
The solution of the equation $50 = 5z$ is 10.

( ) True
( ) False

12. When using the division method to find the prime factorization of 29042, what is an obvious choice with which to start the division process?

Select the correct answer:

( ) 2
( ) 7
( ) 5
( ) 10
( ) 3

13. How much ribbon is needed to wrap the package shown in the illustration if 14 inches of ribbon are needed to make the bow, l= 11, w= 5 and h= 3?

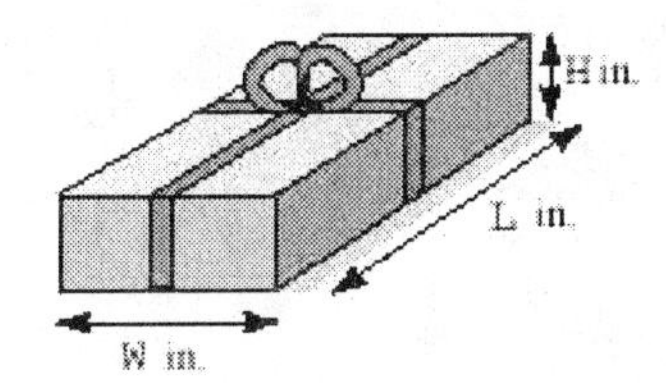

14. Round $68437 to the nearest $100.

Select the correct answer:

( ) $69000
( ) $68500
( ) $68000
( ) $68400

15. The scores received by a junior diver are as follows:

3	4	2	3	8	6

The formula for computing the overall score for the dive is as follows:

1. Throw out the lowest score.
2. Throw out the highest score.
3. Divide the sum of the remaining scores by 4.

True or false:

The diver's score is 5.

( ) True
( ) False

16. Round 70481 to the nearest thousand.

Select the correct answer:

( ) 71000
( ) 70000
( ) 70400
( ) 70500

17. Use the division or the multiplication property of equality to solve the equation.

$70 = 7a$

18. True or False:

A department head prepared an annual budget with the line items shown in the illustration. The projected number of dollars to be spent is 63810.

Line item	Amount
Equipment	12081
Contractual	15069
Travel	12466
Supplies	7900
Development	16294
Maintenance	11170

( ) True
( ) False

19. How much padded rope is needed to create the square boxing ring in the illustration if each side is 25 feet long?

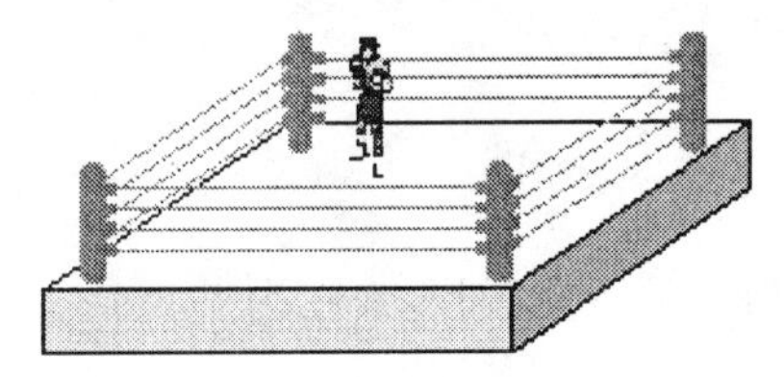

Select the correct answer:

( ) 100 feet
( ) 400 feet
( ) 101 feet
( ) 375 feet
( ) 401 feet

20. True or False:

18 - 8 + 1 = 11

( ) True
( ) False

21. Find the solution of the equation:

$50 = 20 + c$

22. True or False:
If we divide z by 6 and then divide that product by 6, the result is $6z$.

( ) True
( ) False

23. Use the following bar graph to find the average number of therms of natural gas used per month.

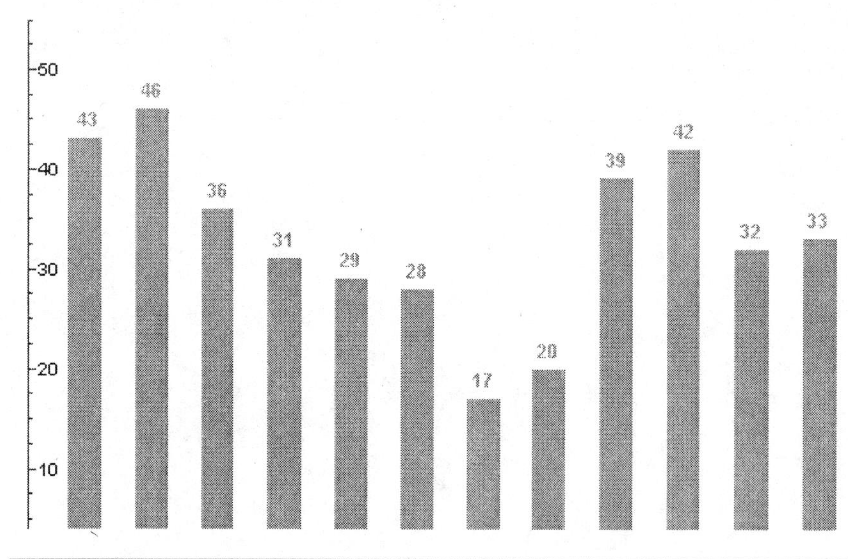

24. Evaluate the following expression:

$$13 - \frac{48}{8} + 9 \cdot 7$$

Select the correct answer:

( ) 65
( ) 69
( ) 80
( ) 72
( ) 70

25. The list below shows the number of people watching *Who Wants to Be a Millionaire?* on five weeknights in November of 1999. How large was the average audience?

Monday	26200000
Tuesday	24300000
Wednesday	22100000
Thursday	25300000
Friday	21200000

Select the correct answer:

( ) 24820500
( ) 23815000
( ) 23818900
( ) 22820000
( ) 23820000
( ) 23820100

Answers

1. 83, 73

2. 7

3. $350000

4. 70 feet

5. false

6. false

7. y=6

8. c = 11

9. true

10. 32

11. true

12. 2

13. 58

14. $68400

15. false

16. 70000

17. 10

18. false

19. 400 feet

20. true

21. c=30

22. false

23. 33

24. 70

25. 23820000

1. On one lie detector test a suspected burglar scored -19, which indicates deception. However, on a second test, he scored -4, which is inconclusive. Find the difference in the scores.

2. Simplify the expression.

$-\left(-106\right)$

3. Which one of the symbols, "<" or ">," inserted in the blank would make a true statement?

-75 ______ -131

Enter the entire inequality as your answer.

4. Use the two expressions below and one of the symbols, "<" or ">," to write an inequality.

$-\left|-273\right| \quad 1$

5. Find the following sum:

11 + (-7).

6. Evaluate the following expression:

17 + (-9) - (-11) - 19.

7. The bar chart below shows a week of daily reports listing the height of a river in comparison to flood stage. Fill the table with values of the daily height in relation to the flood stage using signed numbers.

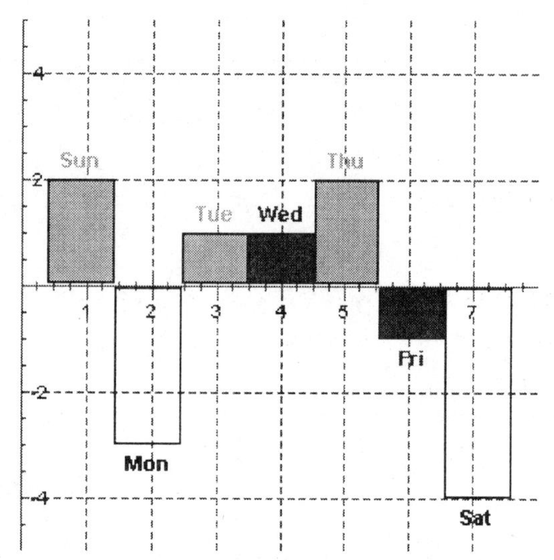

Day	Height
Sun	
Mon	
Tue	
Wed	
Thu	
Fri	
Sat	

8. Evaluate the following sum:

[25 + (-5)] - [-8 - (-29)].

9. Find the difference:

$-27 - 27$.

10. Evaluate the expression:

$(13 - 14) - (4 - 10)$.

11. Rashawn flew from his New York home to Hawaii for a week of vacation. He left blizzard conditions and a temperature of -2° F, and stepped off the airplane into 61° F weather. What temperature change did he experience?

12. Find the product: $10(-9)$

13. Evaluate the expression: $(-6)(-8)(3)(-1)$

14. Find the product: $(-5)(0)(9)$

15. Find the quotient, if possible: $\frac{-88}{-11}$

16. Find the quotient, if possible: $\frac{-18}{-1}$

17. A mule train is to travel from a stable on the rim of the canyon to a camp on the canyon floor, approximately 3200 feet below the rim. If the guide wants the mules to be rested after every 800 feet of descent, how many stops will be made on the trip?

18. Evaluate: $-24 \div (-2)4$

19. Evaluate: $(9-10)^2-(8-6)^2$

20. Evaluate: $\dfrac{-20-(-63)}{4^2-2}$

21. Evaluate: $5(5)-3|-7|^2$

22. Solve the equation:

$x+16=-43$.

23. Solve the equation:

$-7a=-49$.

24. Solve the equation:

$-2=\dfrac{c}{-10}$.

25. Solve the equation:

$\frac{h}{-6} + 5 = 19$.

Answers

1. 15

2. 106

3. $-75 > -131$

4. $-|-273| < 1$

5. 4

6. 0

7. Sun, 2, Mon, -3, Tue, 1, Wed, 1, Thu, 2, Fri, -1, Sat, -4

8. -1

9. -54

10. 5

11. 63

12. -90

13. -144

14. 0

15. 8

16. 18

17. 4

18. 3

19. -3

20. $3\frac{1}{14}$

21. -122

22. -59

23. 7

24. 20

25. h=-84

1. Simplify the expression.

$-(-66)$

2. Which one of the symbols, "<" or ">," inserted in the blank would make a true statement?

-201 _____ -273

Enter the entire inequality as your answer.

3. Use the two expressions below and one of the symbols, "<" or ">," to write an inequality.

$-|-52| \quad 1$

4. Find the following sum:

-16 + (-16).

5. Evaluate the following expression:

-8 + (-20) - (-25) - 18.

6. Evaluate the following sum:

[-30 + (-1)] - [-9 - (-10)].

7. The following bar chart shows the daily high temperature in degrees Fahrenheit. Fill the table with values of the temperature for each month to obtain a line graph of the same information.

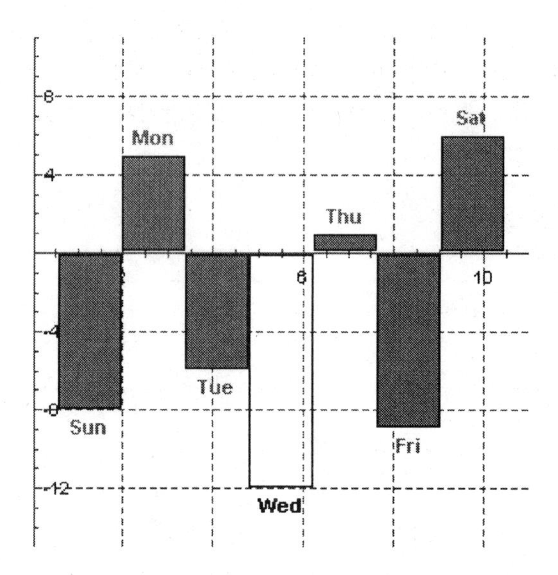

Day	Temperature
Sun	
Mon	
Tue	
Wed	
Thu	
Fri	
Sat	

8. Find the difference:

- 13 - 13 .

9. Evaluate the expression:

(15 - 12) - (4 - 9).

10. A submarine was traveling 1700 feet below the ocean's surface when the radar system warned of an impending collision with another sub. The captain ordered the navigator to dive an additional 300 feet and then level off.

Find the depth of the submarine after the dive.

11. Find the product: $7(-10)$

12. Evaluate the expression: $(-6)(-3)(10)(-1)$

13. Find the product: $(-14)(0)(30)$

14. A levy protects a town in a low-lying area from flooding. According to geologists, the banks of the levy are eroding at a rate of 10 feet per year. If something isn't done to correct the problem, what signed number indicates how much of the levy will erode during the next decade?

15. Find the quotient, if possible: $\frac{-128}{-16}$

16. Find the quotient, if possible: $\frac{-21}{-1}$

17. Over a week's time, engineers at a city water reservoir released enough water to lower the water level 77 feet. On average, how much did the water level change each day during this period?

18. Evaluate: $-48 \div (-8)2$

19. Evaluate: $(4 - 5)^2 - (10 - 7)^2$

20. Evaluate: $\dfrac{-1 - (-50)}{6^2 - 20}$

21. Evaluate: $9(2) - 3|-2|^2$

22. Solve the equation:

$x + 13 = -47$.

23. Solve the equation:

$-9b = -27$.

24. Solve the equation:

$-17 = \dfrac{a}{-17}$.

25. Solve the equation:

$$\frac{h}{-12}+2=3.$$

Answers

1. 66

2. -201 > -273

3. $-|-52| < 1$

4. -32

5. -21

6. -32

7. Sun, -8, Mon, 5, Tue, -6, Wed, -12, Thu, 1, Fri, -9, Sat, 6

8. -26

9. 8

10. -2000

11. -70

12. -180

13. 0

14. -100

15. 8

16. 21

17. -11

18. 3

19. -8

20. $3\frac{1}{16}$

21. 6

22. -60

23. 3

24. 289

25. h=-12

1. Which one of the symbols, "<" or ">," inserted in the blank would make a true statement?

-39 _____ -125

Enter the entire inequality as your answer.

2. What symbol must we insert in the blank to make a true statement.

$-|-182| \quad 1$

( ) >
( ) <

3. Find the following sum:

14 + (-22).

4. Evaluate the following expression:

-17 + (-5) - (-26) - 10.

( ) 24
( ) 14
( ) -38
( ) -6

5. Evaluate the following sum:

[4 + (-2)] - [-25 - (-29)].

6. On a financial balance sheet, debts (negative numbers) are denoted within parentheses. Assets (positive numbers) are written without parentheses. What is the 1990 fund balance for the preshool whose financial records are shown in table below?

Fund balances	**$**
Classroom supplies	458
Emergency needs	4269
Holiday program	(239)
Insurance	3865
Janitorial	(5318)
Licensing	3550
Maintenance	(546)

( ) -2021
( ) 6039
( ) 2021
( ) -6039
( ) -1407

7. Find the difference:

- 20 - 20 .

8. Find the difference:

28 - 28 .

( ) 0
( ) -56
( ) 56

9. Evaluate the expression:

(14 - 10) - (5 - 11).

10. On one lie detector test a suspected burglar scored - 16, which indicates deception. However, on a second test, he scored -4, which is inconclusive. Find the difference in the scores.

( ) - 12
( ) 12
( ) 20
( ) - 20

11. True or False:

$4(-5) = 20$

( ) True
( ) False

12. Evaluate the expression: $(-8)(-6)(5)(-1)$

13. True or False:

$(-19)(0)(18) = 0$

( ) True
( ) False

14. A health care provider for a company estimates that 83 hours per week are lost by employees suffering from stress-related or preventable illness. In a 52-week year, how many hours are lost?

( ) -4306 hours
( ) -4315 hours
( ) -4416 hours
( ) -4316 hours

15. Find the quotient, if possible: $\frac{-187}{-17}$

16. Find the quotient. $\frac{-6}{-1}$

( ) 6
( ) 1
( ) -6
( ) -1
( ) 0

17. On Monday, the value of Jane's 145 shares of stock was at an all-time high. By Friday, the value had fallen $3335. What was her per-share loss that week?

18. Evaluate: $-200 \div (-10)5$

19. Evaluate: $(10 - 4)^2 - (9 - 7)^2$

( ) 34
( ) 36
( ) 42
( ) 19
( ) 29
( ) 23
( ) 32

20. Evaluate: $7(4) - 6|-10|^2$

21. Solve the equation:

$x + 13 = -49$.

22. True or False:

The solution of the equation $-3y = -6$ is: -2.

( ) True
( ) False

23. Solve the equation:

$-12 = \frac{z}{-13}$.

24. True or False:

The solution of the equation:

$\frac{h}{-2} + 20 = 4$ is ***h*= 32**.

( ) True
( ) False

25. True or False:

Simplifying the expression $-(-34)$ we get 34.

( ) True
( ) False

Answers For *Copy 1*

1. -39 > -125

2. <

3. -8

4. -6

5. -2

6. 6039

7. -40

8. 0

9. 10

10. 12

11. false

12. -240

13. true

14. -4316 hours

15. 11

16. 6

17. -23

18. 4

19. 32

20. -572

21. -62

22. true

23. 156

24. true

25. true

1. Evaluate the expression:

$[-12 + (-13)] - (-15)$.

( ) -40
( ) 14
( ) 40
( ) 10
( ) -10
( ) 16

2. True or False:

Simplifying the expression $-(-45)$ we get 45.

( ) True
( ) False

3. Choose the symbol to fill in the blank to make a true statement.

-10 ____ -5

( ) <
( ) >

4. What symbol must we insert in the blank to make a true statement.

$-|-290| \quad 1$

( ) >
( ) <

5. Evaluate the following expression:

$-24 + (-4) - (-4) - 15$.

( ) -1
( ) -9
( ) -17
( ) -39

6. Find the sum of **-8 + (-18)**.

( ) 26
( ) -25
( ) -26
( ) 10

7. True or False:

[11 + (-1)] - [-5 - (-24)] = -8.

( ) True
( ) False

8. A financier's lunchtime workout includes jogging up 24 stories of stairs in a high rise office building. If he starts on the fourth level below ground in the underground parking garage, on what story of the building will he finish his workout?

( ) 20th story
( ) 24th story
( ) 28th story

9. Find the difference:

- 17 - 17 .

( ) 34
( ) 0
( ) -34

10. Find the difference:

10 - 10 .

( ) 20
( ) 0
( ) -20

11. Evaluate the expression:

$(6 - 10) - (1 - 19)$.

( ) -22
( ) 16
( ) 14
( ) -24

12. Rashawn flew from his New York home to Hawaii for a week of vacation. He left blizzard conditions and a temperature of - 1° F, and stepped off the airplane into 94° F weather. What temperature change did he experience?

( ) 93°
( ) 95°
( ) -93°
( ) -95°

13. True or False:

$4(-8) = 32$

( ) True
( ) False

14. True or False:

$(-3)(-2)(4)(-1) = 24$

( ) True
( ) False

15. True or False:

$(-12)(0)(8) = 0$

( ) True
( ) False

16. Find the quotient. $\frac{-10}{-2}$

( ) -10
( ) 2
( ) -2
( ) 5
( ) -5

17. Find the quotient. $\frac{-8}{-1}$

( ) 8
( ) 1
( ) -1
( ) -8
( ) 0

18. True or False:

A mule train is to travel from a stable on the rim of the canyon to a camp on the canyon floor, approximately 2400 feet below the rim. If the guide wants the mules to be rested after every 600 feet of descent, the party will be make 4 stops on the trip.

( ) True
( ) False

19. Evaluate: $-48 \div (-2)8$

( ) -1
( ) 5
( ) -6
( ) -8
( ) 13
( ) 10
( ) 3

20. Evaluate: $(9 - 8)^2 - (4 - 5)^2$

( ) -5
( ) 0
( ) 7
( ) -13
( ) -8
( ) 3
( ) 11

21. Evaluate: $2(4) - 2|-3|^2$

( ) -19
( ) -3
( ) -7
( ) 0
( ) -10
( ) -15
( ) -23

22. Evaluate: $\dfrac{-5-(-38)}{5^2-15}$

( ) $3\frac{4}{10}$
( ) $3\frac{3}{11}$
( ) $3\frac{3}{9}$
( ) $3\frac{5}{11}$
( ) $3\frac{3}{10}$
( ) $3\frac{4}{11}$
( ) $3\frac{4}{9}$

23. Solve the equation:
$x + 9 = -26$.

( ) $x = 35$
( ) $x = -17$
( ) $x = -35$
( ) $x = 17$

24. True or False:

The solution of the equation $-9z = -126$ is: -14.

( ) True
( ) False

25. True or False:

The solution of the equation: $-20 = \frac{a}{-8}$ is $a = 160$.

( ) True
( ) False

Answers

1. -10

2. true

3. <

4. <

5. -39

6. -26

7. false

8. 20th story

9. -34

10. 0

11. 14

12. 95°

13. false

14. false

15. true

16. 5

17. 8

18. true

19. 3

20. 0

21. -10

22. $3\frac{3}{10}$

23. $x = -35$

24. true

25. true

1. True or False:

Simplifying the expression $-(-118)$ we get 118.

( ) True
( ) False

2. Choose the symbol to fill in the blank to make a true statement.

-9 ____ -8

( ) >
( ) <

3. What symbol must we insert in the blank to make a true statement.
$-|-259| \quad 1$

( ) >
( ) <

4. Find the sum of**16 + (-4)**.

( ) -12
( ) 13
( ) 12
( ) 20

5. Evaluate the following expression:

-28 + (-3) - (-15) - 21.

( ) -37
( ) 5
( ) -25
( ) 11

6. True or False:

[26 + (-5)] - [-19 - (-26)] = 15.

( ) True
( ) False

7. After a heavy rainstorm, a river that had been 2 feet under flood stage rose 11 feet in a 48-hour period. Which of the following numbers is the height of the river after the storm in comparison to flood stage?

( ) 11
( ) 13
( ) 9

8. Find the difference:

- 5 - 5 .

( ) 0
( ) -10
( ) 10

9. Evaluate the expression:

(8 - 11) - (5 - 18).

( ) -16
( ) -26
( ) 10
( ) 20

10. A submarine was traveling 1800 feet below the ocean's surface when the radar system warned of an impending collision with another sub. The captain ordered the navigator to dive an additional 200 feet and then level off.
Find the depth of the submarine after the dive.

( ) 2000 ft
( ) 1600 ft
( ) - 1600 ft
( ) -2000 ft

11. True or False:

$$(-20)(0)(27) = 0$$

( ) True
( ) False

12. True or False:

$$8(-6) = 48$$

( ) True
( ) False

13. True or False:

$$(-4)(-9)(5)(-1) = 180$$

( ) True
( ) False

14. A levy protects a town in a low-lying area from flooding. According to geologists, the banks of the levy are eroding at a rate of 5 feet per year. If something isn't done to correct the problem, what signed number indicates how much of the levy will erode during the next decade?

( ) -50 ft
( ) -60 ft
( ) -20 ft

15. Find the quotient. $\frac{-3}{-1}$

( ) -3
( ) 1
( ) 0
( ) -1
( ) 3

16. Find the quotient. $\frac{-48}{-8}$

( ) 8
( ) 6
( ) -8
( ) -6
( ) -48

17. Over a week's time, engineers at a city water reservoir released enough water to lower the water level 49 feet. On average, how much did the water level change each day during this period?

( ) 49 ft
( ) 7 ft
( ) -8 ft
( ) -7 ft
( ) 8 ft

18. Evaluate: $-28 \div (-7)2$

( ) 8
( ) -11
( ) -3
( ) 3
( ) -6
( ) 2
( ) 12

19. Evaluate: $(3 - 7)^2 - (10 - 5)^2$

( ) -8
( ) -2
( ) -21
( ) -9
( ) 2
( ) -18
( ) -14

20. Evaluate: $\frac{-4 - (-35)}{4^2 - 7}$

( ) $3\frac{5}{9}$

( ) $3\frac{4}{8}$

( ) $3\frac{6}{10}$

( ) $3\frac{4}{10}$

( ) $3\frac{5}{8}$

( ) $3\frac{5}{10}$

( ) $3\frac{4}{9}$

21. Evaluate: $9(7) - 3|-9|^2$

( ) -191
( ) -180
( ) -173
( ) -170
( ) -189
( ) -179
( ) -183

22. Solve the equation:
$x + 19 = -31$.

( ) $x = -12$
( ) $x = 12$
( ) $x = 50$
( ) $x = -50$

23. True or False:

The solution of the equation $-7z = -91$ is: -13.

( ) True
( ) False

24. True or False:

The solution of the equation: $-12 = \frac{z}{-8}$ is $z = 96$.

( ) True
( ) False

25. True or False:

The solution of the equation:

$\frac{h}{-6} + 19 = 13$ is $\boldsymbol{h} = \mathbf{36}$.

( ) True
( ) False

Answers

1. true

2. <

3. <

4. 12

5. -37

6. false

7. 9

8. -10

9. 10

10. -2000 ft

11. true

12. false

13. false

14. -50 ft

15. 3

16. 6

17. -7 ft

18. 2

19. -9

20. $3\frac{4}{9}$

21. -180

22. $x = -50$

23. true

24. true

25. true

1. After a heavy rainstorm, a river that had been 3 feet under flood stage rose 25 feet in a 48-hour period. Find the height of the river after the storm in comparison to flood stage.

2. True or False:

$|-4| = 4$

( ) True
( ) False

3. Which number is farther from 6 on the number line, 14 or -3?

4. Find the product: $6(-3)$

5. True or False:

$(-3)(-3)(-3)(-3)(-3) = 243$

( ) True
( ) False

6. Find the difference:

15 - 15 .

( ) -30
( ) 30
( ) 0

7. The illustration and the table below show the predicted Fahrenheit temperatures for a day in mid-January. According to this prediction, what is the coldest it should get in New York?

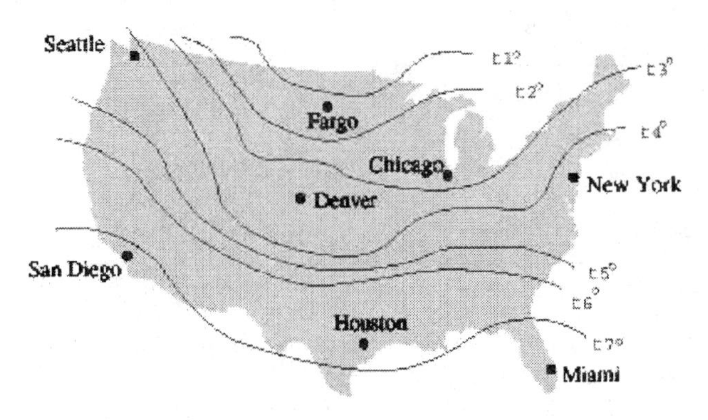

Variable	Temperature
*t*1	-15
*t*2	-10
*t*3	5
*t*4	10
*t*5	20
*t*6	25
*t*7	40

( ) 20
( ) 10
( ) -10
( ) 25
( ) -15
( ) 40
( ) 5

8. True or False:

The quotient of $\frac{-5390}{-70}$ is 78.

( ) True
( ) False

9. Find each sum using a number line.

$-4+(-4)$	
$10+(-9)$	
$-2+(10)$	

10. Which of the following expressions is written correctly?

( ) 2 + (-7)
( ) 2 + -7

11. Evaluate: $\frac{-9-25}{-7-4}$

12. Which is a related division statement for
$10(-9) = -90$?

( ) $\frac{-90}{9} = 10$
( ) $10 \cdot 9 = 90$
( ) $\frac{-90}{-9} = 10$

13. During a 5-hour period, the temperature steadily dropped. (See Illustration)What was the average change in the temperature per hour over this 5-hour time span?

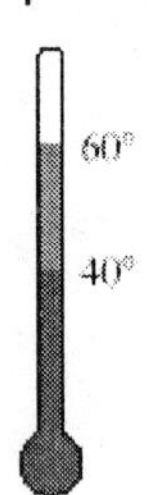

14. Rashawn flew from his New York home to Hawaii for a week of vacation. He left blizzard conditions and a temperature of - 8° F, and stepped off the airplane into 90° F weather. What temperature change did he experience?

( ) - 82°
( ) 82°
( ) - 98°
( ) 98°

15. Evaluate the expression:

- 827 - 1469 - (- 428).

( ) 2724
( ) -1868
( ) 1868
( ) -214
( ) -2724
( ) 0

16. True or False:

0 > -171

( ) True
( ) False

17. Evaluate: $(-2-2)^2-(-7)$

18. Engineers have decided that part of a roller coaster ride will consist of a steep plunge from a peak 118 feet high. The car will then come to a screeching halt in a cave. (See illustration.)

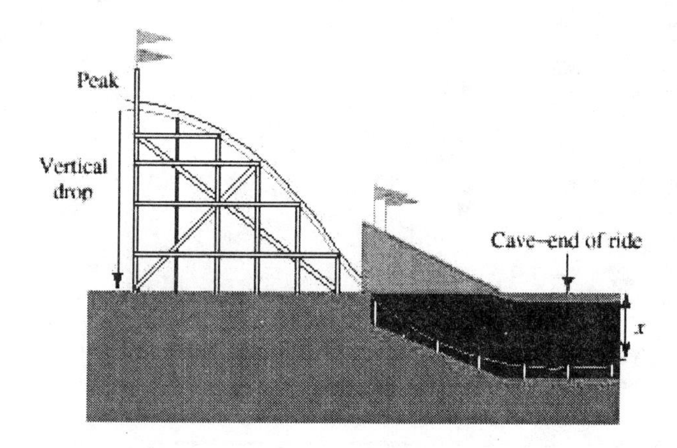

How far below ground should the cave be if engineers want the overall drop in height to be 155 feet?

( ) 273 ft
( ) 37 ft
( ) 118 ft
( ) 34 ft
( ) 40 ft

19. The expression**2 + - 1**is not written corectly. Write the expression correctly.

20. The bar chart below shows a week of daily reports listing the height of a river in comparison to flood stage. Fill the table with values of the daily height in relation to the flood stage using signed numbers.

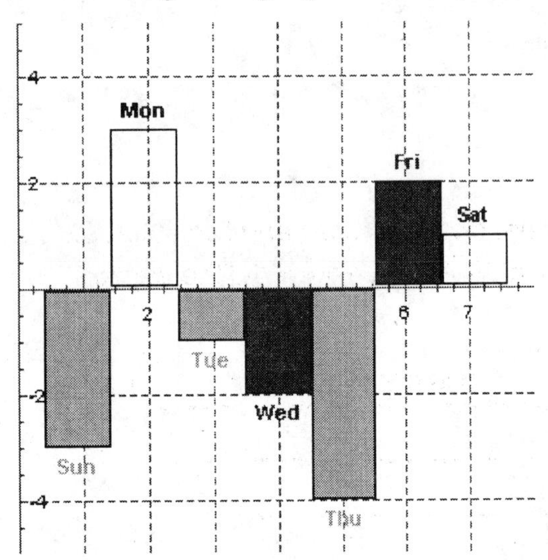

Day	Height
Sun	
Mon	
Tue	
Wed	
Thu	
Fri	
Sat	

21. Find the sum using a number line and choose the correct answer.

-2 + (-10).

( ) -12
( ) 8
( ) -8
( ) 2

22. A movie studio produced four films, two financial successes and two failures. The profits and losses of the films are shown in the table below. Find the studio's profit, if any, for the year.

Film	Millions of dollars
Drama	14
Comedy	-13
Action	29
Music	-12

23. If z is any number except zero, what is $\frac{0}{z}$?

24. At the midway point of the season, a basket-ball team finds itself 10 games behind the league leader. Team management decides to trade for a talented player, in hopes of making up at least half of the deficit in the standings by the end of the year. Where in the league standings does management expect to finish at season's end?

( ) 10
( ) -5
( ) -6
( ) 5
( ) -10

25. After its first year of business, a manufacturer of smoke detectors found its market share 32 points behind the industry leader. Five years later, it trailed the leader by only 5 points. How many points of market share did the company pick up over this five-year span?

Answers

1. 22

2. true

3. -3

4. -18

5. false

6. 0

7. 10

8. false

9. $-4+(-4)$, -8, $10+(-9)$, 1, -2+10, 8

10. 2 + (-7)

11. $3\frac{1}{11}$

12. $\frac{-90}{-9} = 10$

13. -4

14. 98°

15. -1868

16. true

17. 23

18. 37 ft

19. $2+(-1)$

20. Sun, -3, Mon, 3, Tue, -1, Wed, -2, Thu, -4, Fri, 2, Sat, 1

21. -12

22. 18000000

23. 0

24. -5

25. 27

1. True or False:

Simplifying the expression $-(-229)$ we get 229.

( ) True
( ) False

2. Which one of the symbols, "<" or ">," inserted in the blank would make a true statement?

-128 _____ -155

Enter the entire inequality as your answer.

3. What symbol must we insert in the blank to make a true statement.

$-|-44| \quad 1$

( ) <
( ) >

4. Find the sum of **-24 + (-14)**.

( ) -38
( ) 38
( ) -37
( ) -10

5. Evaluate the following expression:

30 + (-18) - (-10) - 18.

6. True or False:

[-17 + (-14)] - [-16 - (-30)] = -44.

( ) True
( ) False

7. On a financial balance sheet, debts (negative numbers) are denoted within parentheses. Assets (positive numbers) are written without parentheses. What is the 1980 fund balance for the school whose financial records are shown in the table below?

Fund balances	**$**
Classroom supplies	528
Emergency needs	4269
Holiday program	(453)
Insurance	5959
Janitorial	(1983)
Licensing	3801
Maintenance	(267)

8. Find the difference:

- 27 - 27 .

( ) 54
( ) 0
( ) -54

9. Find the difference:

24 - 24 .

10. Evaluate the expression:

(5 - 13) - (8 - 23).

( ) -39
( ) -23
( ) 23
( ) 7

11. On one lie detector test a suspected burglar scored -16, which indicates deception. However, on a second test, he scored -2, which is inconclusive. Find the difference in the scores.

12. True or False:

$6(-9) = 54$

( ) True
( ) False

13. Evaluate the expression: $(-3)(-5)(6)(-1)$

14. True or False:

$(-7)(0)(11) = 0$

( ) True
( ) False

15. A health care provider for a company estimates that 60 hours per week are lost by employees suffering from stress-related or preventable illness. Consider a 50 week year, and use a signed number to express how many hours are lost in that year.

16. Find the quotient. $\frac{-70}{-10}$

( ) 10
( ) -70
( ) -10
( ) -7
( ) 7

17. Find the quotient. $\frac{-6}{-1}$

( ) -6
( ) -1
( ) 0
( ) 6
( ) 1

18. On Monday, the value of Susan's 255 shares of stock was at an all-time high. By Friday, the value had fallen $4590. What was her per-share loss that week?

19. Evaluate: $-96 \div (-6)8$

( ) 3
( ) 2
( ) 9
( ) -10
( ) -7
( ) 12
( ) -2

20. Evaluate: $(8 - 4)^2 - (7 - 10)^2$

21. Evaluate: $8(5) - 5|-6|^2$

( ) -131
( ) -139
( ) -147
( ) -140
( ) -150
( ) -136
( ) -143

22. Solve the equation:
$x + 8 = -38$.

23. True or False:

The solution of the equation $-2z = -30$ is: -15.

( ) True
( ) False

24. Solve the equation:
$-16 = \frac{c}{-9}$.

25. In its first year of business, a nursery suffered a loss due to frost damage, ending the year $15900 in the red. In the second year, it made a sizable profit. If the total profit for the first two years in business was $24430, how much profit was made the second year?

( ) $8530
( ) - $8530
( ) 24430
( ) $40330
( ) - $40330

Answers For *Copy 1*

1. true

2. -128 > -155

3. <

4. -38

5. 4

6. false

7. 11854

8. -54

9. 0

10. 7

11. 14

12. false

13. -90

14. true

15. -3000

16. 7

17. 6

18. -18

19. 2

20. 7

21. -140

22. -46

23. true

24. 144

25. $40330

1. True or False:

$2(-4) = 8$

( ) True
( ) False

2. True or False:

The solution of the equation: $-17 = \frac{x}{-2}$ is $x = 34$.

( ) True
( ) False

3. Evaluate the expression:

$-1000 - 1655 - (-371)$.

( ) -2284
( ) 2284
( ) -3026
( ) 0
( ) 3026
( ) -284

4. Evaluate the expression: $(-6)(-8)(-9)$

( ) -432
( ) 434
( ) -434
( ) 432

5. Evaluate the expression:

$-5 - (-5) - 11$.

6. A politician proposed a two-year plan for cutting a county's $40 million budget deficit, as shown in the table below. If this plan is put into effect, what will be the change (in millions of dollars) in the county's financial status in two years?

	Plan	**Prediction**
1st year	Raise taxes, drop subsidy programs	Will cut deficit in half
2nd year	Search out waste and fraud	Will cut remaining deficit in half

7. Over a week's time, engineers at a city water reservoir released enough water to lower the water level 77 feet. On average, how much did the water level change each day during this period?

8. Find the product: $3(-4)$

9. The bar chart below shows a week of daily reports listing the height of a river in comparison to flood stage.

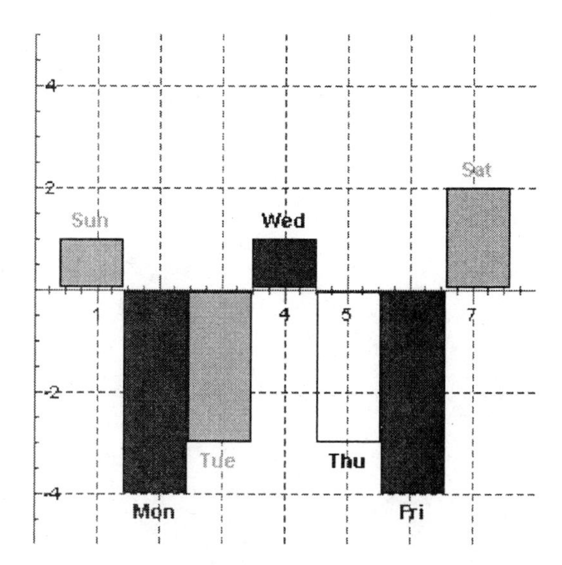

Which of the following statements are correct?

[ ] The height of the river on Thu was 1.
[ ] The height of the river on Tue was -3.
[ ] The height of the river on Fri was -4.
[ ] The height of the river on Wed was -3.
[ ] The height of the river on Sun was 1.
[ ] The height of the river on Sat was 2.
[ ] The height of the river on Mon was -3.

10. Evaluate: $\left|-3-(-8)\right|$

( ) 11
( ) -4
( ) 5
( ) 15
( ) 8
( ) -7
( ) 0

11. Find the absolute value:

$|9|$

12. The expression **10 + - 8** is not written corectly. Write the expression correctly.

13. Use a calculator to find the power $(-22)^4$.

( ) -234256
( ) -10648
( ) 10648
( ) 234256
( ) -5153632

14. Evaluate: $-7\left(\frac{6}{-2}\right) - (-1)^{15}$

( ) 31
( ) 23
( ) 22
( ) 14
( ) 12
( ) 29
( ) 17

15. The opposite of - 4 is _______.

16. Find the product of -2 and the opposite of 3.

17. After a heavy rainstorm, a river that had been 2 feet under flood stage rose 30 feet in a 48-hour period. Find the height of the river after the storm in comparison to flood stage.

18. The illustration and the table below show the predicted Fahrenheit temperatures for a day in mid-January. According to this prediction, what is the coldest it should get in Seattle?

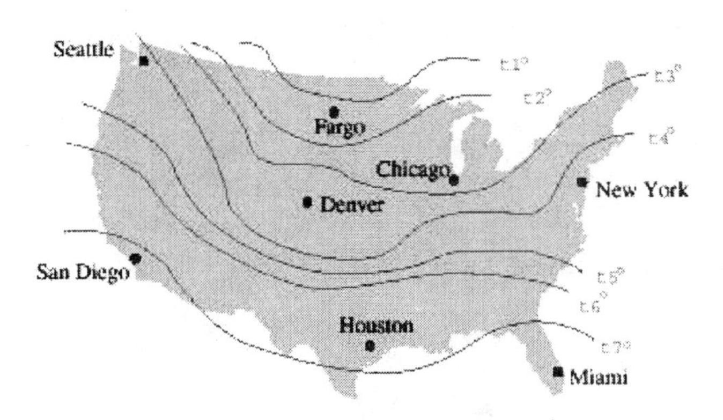

Variable	Temperature
*t*1	-15
*t*2	-5
*t*3	0
*t*4	5
*t*5	15
*t*6	30
*t*7	35

19. True or False:

A mule train is to travel from a stable on the rim of the canyon to a camp on the canyon floor, approximately 4200 feet below the rim. If the guide wants the mules to be rested after every 600 feet of descent, the party will be make 7 stops on the trip.

( ) True
( ) False

20. True or False:

$(-5)(-2)(3)(-1) = 30$

( ) True
( ) False

21. Which of the following numbers is the additive identity?

10, 1, |1|, -5, 0, -29, -10

22. Engineers have decided that part of a roller coaster ride will consist of a steep plunge from a peak 116 feet high. The car will then come to a screeching halt in a cave. (See illustration.)

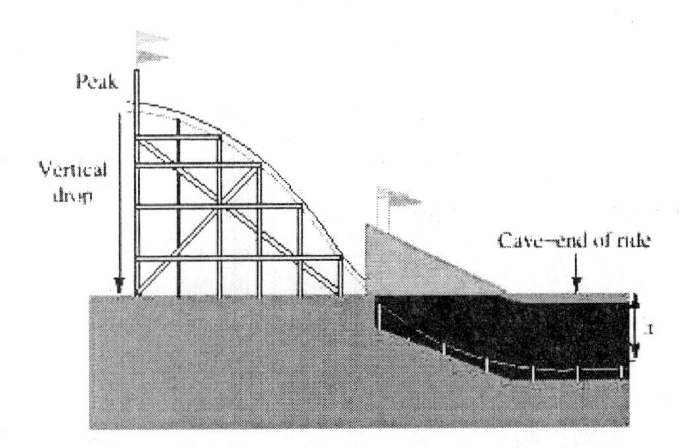

How far below ground should the cave be if engineers want the overall drop in height to be 185 feet?

( ) 301 ft
( ) 74 ft
( ) 64 ft
( ) 69 ft
( ) 116 ft

23. Use a calculator to evaluate the expression: $(32)(-35)(-59)$

( ) -2065
( ) -66080
( ) -1888
( ) 66080
( ) 1888

24. True or False:

The quotient of $\frac{-88}{-22}$ is 4.

( ) True
( ) False

25. Which of the following contains a minus sign?

( ) $16 - 4$
( ) -16
( ) $-(-16)$

Answers

1. false

2. true

3. -2284

4. -432

5. -11

6. $30000000

7. -11

8. -12

9. The height of the river on Tue was -3.IThe height of the river on Fri was -4.IThe height of the river on Sun was 1.IThe height of the river on Sat was 2.

10. 5

11. 9

12. $10+(-8)$

13. 234256

14. 22

15. 4

16. 6

17. 28

18. 5

19. true

20. false

21. 0

22. 69 ft

23. 66080

24. true

25. 16 - 4

1. Translate the following phrase to an algebraic expression.
The difference of y and 30

2. Translate the following phrase to an algebraic expression.
y decreased by 3.

3. The height of a hedge was w feet before a gardener cut 4 feet off of the top.

Write an algebraic expression that describes the new height of the trimmed hedge.

4. Translate the following phrase to an algebraic expression.
The quotient of 6 and z is reduced by 3.

5. Evaluate the expression:

$-7z$ for $z = -2$

6. Evaluate the expression:

$\frac{w - 10}{3}$ for $w = 19$

7. Evaluate the algebraic expression:

$\frac{7y - 9s}{-10}$ for $y = 30$ and $s = 30$

8. A jewelry store buys bracelets for $78 and marks them up $6. What is the retail price of a ring?

9. Simplify:

$7(-7t)(3)$

10. Simplify the following expression. Use the distributive property to remove the parentheses.

$5(x+3)$

11. Write the following expression without using the parentheses.

$-(7m+2)$

12. Identify the coefficient of each term in the table below.

Term	Coefficient
$19x$	
b	
$-dx$	
$-15b$	

13. Complete the table below by identifying the components of each term.

Term	Numerical coefficient	Variable part
$-7z$		
$-20t$		
c		
$-13cz$		

14. The heights of two trees are shown in the illustration below. Find the sum of their heights, if $h=c$, and $H=c+20$.

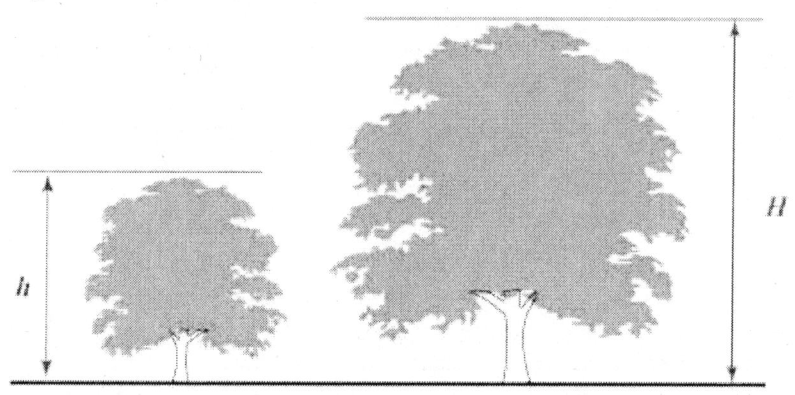

15. Simplify the following expression by combining like terms, if possible.

$6a-3a$

16. Simplify the following expression by combining like terms, if possible.

$-4z+10-4b-4z+2$

17. Simplify the following expression by combining like terms, if possible.

$5\,(9x + 6) - 2\,(10x + 7)$

18. Solve the equation by combining like terms.

$8y + 4y = 24$

19. Solve the equation by eliminating a variable term on one side of the equation.

$-6a + 75 = 9a$

20. Solve the equation by removing parentheses.

$-5(t - 5) = 0$

21. Solve the equation by removing parentheses.

$8 - (s - 3) = -5$

22. Every month, a salesman adds 9 new accounts. How many new accounts will he add in m months?

23. A shoe salesman receives a commission for every pair of shoes he sells. Complete the following table.

Shoe ID Number	Number sold	Commission per shoe ($)	Total commission ($)
1	11	6	
2	8	3	
3	x	7	
4	10-v	4	

24. A student plans to pay back a $660 loan with monthly payments of $40. How many payments has she made if the debt has been reduced to $420?

25. In an effort to cut costs, a corporation has decided to lay off 4 employees every month until the number of employees totals 120. If 320 people are now employed, how many months will it take to reach the employment goal?

Answers

1. y-30

2. y-3

3. w-4

4. $\frac{6}{z}-3$

5. 14

6. 3

7. 6

8. 84

9. $-147t$

10. $5x+15$

11. $-7m-2$

12. $19x$, 19, b, 1, $-dx$, -1, $-15b$, -15

13. $-7z$, -7, z, $-20t$, -20, t, c, 1, c, $-13cz$, -13, cz

14. $2c+20$

15. $3a$

16. $-8z-4b+12$

17. $25x+16$

18. 2

19. 5

20. 5

21. 16

22. $9m$

23. 1, 11, 6, 66, 2, 8, 3, 24, 3, x, 7, $7x$, 4, 10-v, 4, $4(10-v)$

24. 6

25. 50

1. Translate the following phrase to an algebraic expression.
The difference of z and 16

2. Translate the following phrase to an algebraic expression.
The sum of d and 38.

3. Translate the following phrase to an algebraic expression.
z decreased by 48.

4. A graduating class of w people took buses that held 30 students each to an all night graduation party. How many buses were needed to transport the class?

5. Translate the following phrase to an algebraic expression.
The quotient of 9 and z is reduced by 9.

6. Evaluate the expression:

$-6w$ for $w = -5$

7. Evaluate the expression:

$\frac{w - 2}{4}$ for $w = 18$

8. Evaluate the algebraic expression:

$\frac{10x - 2t}{-10}$ for $x = 20$ and $t = 40$

9. Find the sale price of a pair of skis that normally sells for $247 but is discounted $40.

10. Simplify:

$4(3t)(4)$

11. Simplify the following expression. Use the distributive property to remove the parentheses.

$4(p - 3)$

12. Write the following expression without using the parentheses.

$-(6p + 3)$

13. Identify the coefficient of each term in the table below.

Term	Coefficient
$-3a$	
t	
$-da$	
$-10t$	

14. Complete the table below by identifying the components of each term.

Term	Numerical coefficient	Variable part
$-3a$		
$5n$		
z		
$-19za$		

15. The heights of two trees are shown in the illustration below. Find the sum of their heights, if $h = b$, and $H = b + 9$.

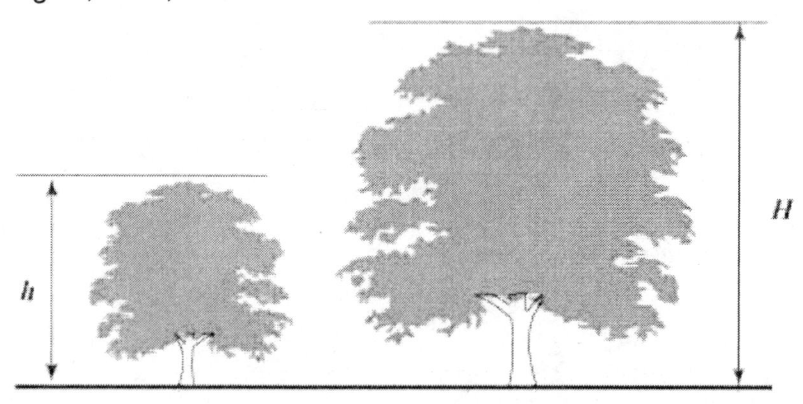

16. Simplify the following expression by combining like terms, if possible.

$-6c - 9c$

17. Simplify the following expression by combining like terms, if possible.

$2a + 7 - 2t - 10a + 1$

18. Simplify the following expression by combining like terms, if possible.

$7(5a + 9) - 4(4a + 3)$

19. Solve the equation by combining like terms.

$3y + 10y = 65$

20. Solve the equation by eliminating a variable term on one side of the equation.

$-2b + 70 = 8b$

21. Solve the equation by removing parentheses.

$-5(x - 9) = 0$

22. Solve the equation by removing parentheses.

$10 - (s - 9) = -2$

23. Every month, a salesman adds 5 new accounts. How many new accounts will he add in x months?

24. The following illustration shows a rack that contains dress shoes and athletic shoes. If there areapairs of dress shoes in the rack, how many pairs of athletic shoes are there in the rack?

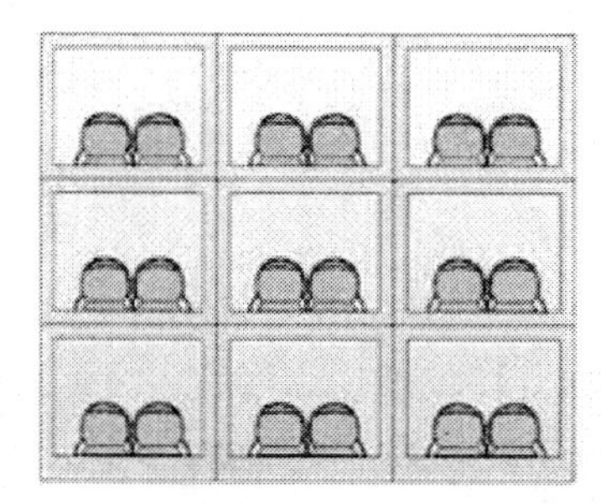

25. To get a heavy-equipment operator's certificate, 40 hours of on-the-job training are required. If a woman has completed 24 hours, and the training sessions last for 4 hours, how many more sessions must she take to get the certificate?

Answers

1. $z-16$

2. $d+38$

3. $z-48$

4. $\frac{w}{30}$

5. $\frac{9}{z}-9$

6. 30

7. 4

8. -12

9. 207

10. $48t$

11. $4p-12$

12. $-6p-3$

13. $-3a$, -3, t, 1, $-da$, -1, $-10t$, -10

14. $-3a$, -3, a, $5n$, 5, n, z, 1, z, $-19za$, -19, za

15. $2b+9$

16. $-15c$

17. $-8a-2t+8$

18. $19a+51$

19. 5

20. 7

21. 9

22. 21

23. $5x$

24. 9-a

25. 4

1. The illustration below shows the commute to work (in miles) for two men who work in the same office. Answer True or False:

Mr.Lamb lives 15 miles farther from the office than Mr. Lopez.

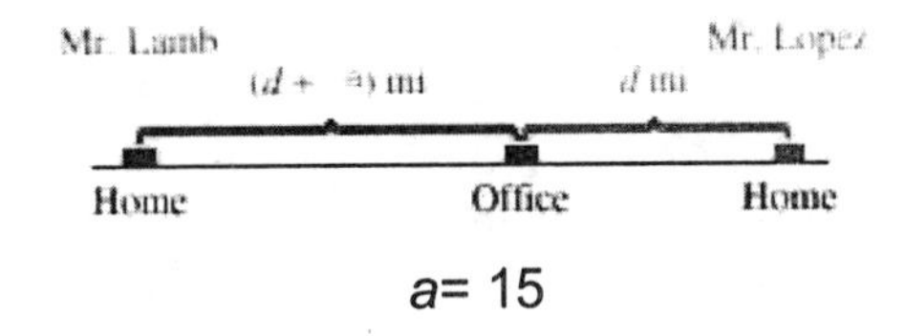

a= 15

( ) True
( ) False

2. Suppose thatzinches of tape have been used off the roll shown in the illustration below. How many inches of tape are left on the roll, if*a*= 300 inches?

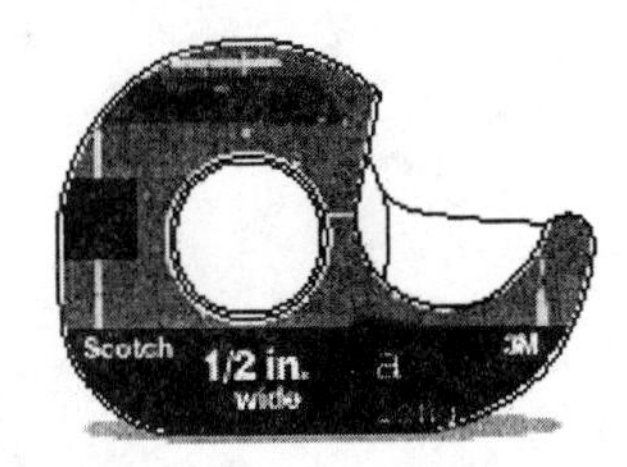

3. True or False:

$z\times(5) = 5z$

( ) True
( ) False

4. The height of a hedge was y feet before a gardener cut 3 feet off of the top. What is the new height of the trimmed hedge?

Select the correct answer.

( ) 3y
( ) y - 3
( ) y + 3

5. Evaluate the expression:

$4(t - 5)$ for $t = 4$

6. Evaluate the expression:

$3t + t^2$ for $t = 5$

Select the correct answer.

( ) 15
( ) 40
( ) 30

7. Evaluate the algebraic expression:

$a^2 - b^2$ for $a = 7$ and $b = 9$

8. A jewelry store buys a pair of earrings for $194 and marks it up $6. Answer True or False:

The retail price of this pair of earrings is $188.

( ) True
( ) False

9. Which of the following expressions are examples of the left distributive property?

[ ] $8(3 + x)$
[ ] $5(3 + t)$
[ ] $(7 + a)9$
[ ] $(6 + t)9$
[ ] $(7 + x)6$

10. Simplify:

$-3(4t)$

11. Simplify:

$7(-6x)(-4)$

Select the correct answer.

( ) $28x$
( ) $167x$
( ) $42x$
( ) $169x$
( ) $24x$
( ) $168x$

12. The following expression is the result of an application of the distributive property. What was the original algebraic expression?

$4(9a) + 4(2)$

13. True or False:

The numerical coefficient of the term $10n$is 10.

( ) True
( ) False

14. Simplify and complete the expression:

$7(b+5) - 4b = 7b + ? - 4b = 3b + 35$. What is the missing value?

15. Simplify the following expression by combining like terms, if possible.

$16y + (-16y)$

Select the correct answer.

( ) -32
( ) 0
( ) $32y$

16. The appropriate size of a square dance floor for a given number of dancers can be determined from the table shown below. Find the perimeter of each of the dance floors listed and complete the table.

Number of slow dancers	Number of fast dancers	Length of side of floor (ft)	Perimeter of floor (ft)
5	4	9	
12	13	16	
19	17	29	

17. Solve the equation by combining like terms.

$6z - 10z = -24$

Select the correct answer.

( ) $z = 36$
( ) $z = 60$
( ) $z = 6$

18. Solve the equation by eliminating a variable term on one side of the equation:

$7s - 10 = 5s - 20$

19. True or False:

$-45 = 9(a + 9)$

$a = 14$

( ) True

( ) False

20. Solve the equation.

$10t + 10(t - 2) = 60$

21. Every month, a salesman adds 6 new accounts. How many new accounts will he add in x months?

Select the correct answer.

( ) $7x$

( ) $5x$

( ) $3x$

( ) $2x$

( ) $4x$

( ) $6x$

22. The perimeter of a rectangle is 110 ft. Width is t. Heigth is $4t$.
Filling in the blanks, write a full statement about the perimeter of the rectangle:

$2 \cdot \square + 2 \cdot \square = 110$ Write out the complete equation in the answer field.

23. A student plans to pay back a $570 loan with monthly payments of $20. How many payments has she made if the debt has been reduced to $450?

Select the correct answer.

( ) 5
( ) 2
( ) 6
( ) 9
( ) 6
( ) 8

24. A landscaper buried a water line around a rectangular-shaped lawn to serve as a supply line for a sprinkler system. The length of the lawn is 2 times its width. If 90 feet of pipe was used to do the job, what is the width of the lawn?

25. A preschool charges $5 for a child to attend its morning session or $20 to attend the afternoon session. No child can attend both. 30 children are enrolled in the preschool. If the daily receipts are $435, how many children attend the morning session?

Select the correct answer.

( ) 4
( ) 5
( ) 12
( ) 16
( ) 11
( ) 3

Answers For

1. true

2. 300-z

3. true

4. y - 3

5. -4

6. 40

7. -32

8. false

9. 8(3 +*x*)|5(3 +*t*)

10. $-12t$

11. 168*x*

12. $4(9a+2)$

13. true

14. 35

15. 0

16. 5, 4, 9, 36, 12, 13, 16, 64, 19, 17, 29, 116

17. *z*= 6

18. -5

19. false

20. 4

21. 6*x*

22. $2\ell + 2 \cdot 4\ell = 110$

23. 6

24. 15

25. 11

1. Translate the phrase to an algebraic expression.

The difference of w and 10.

Select the correct answer.

( ) 10 - w
( ) 10 + w
( ) w - 10

2. Translate the following phrase to an algebraic expression.

The sum of z and 45.

Select the correct answer.

( ) $\frac{z}{45}$
( ) z- 45
( ) z+ 45

3. Translate the following phrase to an algebraic expression.

q decreased by 40.

Select the correct answer.

( ) q - 40
( ) 40 - q
( ) q + 40

4. The height of a hedge wasxfeet before a gardener cut 4 feet off of the top. What is the new height of the trimmed hedge?

Select the correct answer.

( ) 4x
( ) x - 4
( ) x + 4

5. Translate the following phrase to an algebraic expression.

The quotient of 8 and w is reduced by 3.

Select the correct answer.

( ) $\frac{8}{w} + 3$
( ) $\frac{8}{w} - 3$
( ) $8 \cdot w - 3$

6. Evaluate the expression:

- 4*t*for*t*= - 5

Select the correct answer.

( ) -20
( ) 4
( ) 20

7. Evaluate the expression:

$\frac{w - 4}{2}$ for*w*= 10

Select the correct answer.

( ) 6
( ) 7
( ) 3

8. True or False:

$\frac{7y - 8s}{-8} = -41$ for*y*= 8 and*s*= 48

( ) True
( ) False

9. A jewelry store buys a bracelet for $125 and marks it up $20. Answer True or False:

The retail price of this bracelet is $105.

( ) True
( ) False

10. Simplify:

$5(7t)(3)$

Select the correct answer.

( ) $106t$
( ) $21t$
( ) $104t$
( ) $15t$
( ) $105t$
( ) $35t$

11. Simplify the following expression. Use the distributive property to remove the parentheses.

$3(p- 4)$

Select the correct answer.

( ) $3p- 12$
( ) $12p- 3$
( ) $3p- 3$
( ) $3p- 4$
( ) $12p- 4$
( ) $12p- 12$

12. Write the following expression without using parentheses.

$-(6x+4)$

Select the correct answer.

( ) $6x-4$
( ) $-6x-4$
( ) $-4x+6$
( ) $-4x-6$
( ) $-6x+4$
( ) $4x-6$

13. What is the coefficient of the following term?

$19xy$

Select the correct answer.

( ) 19
( ) xy
( ) $19y$
( ) x

14. What is the variable part of the following term?

$-12nx$

Select the correct answer.

( ) x
( ) -12
( ) nx
( ) n

15. The heights of two trees are shown in the illustration below. Find the sum of their heights, if $h=c$, and $H=c+8$.

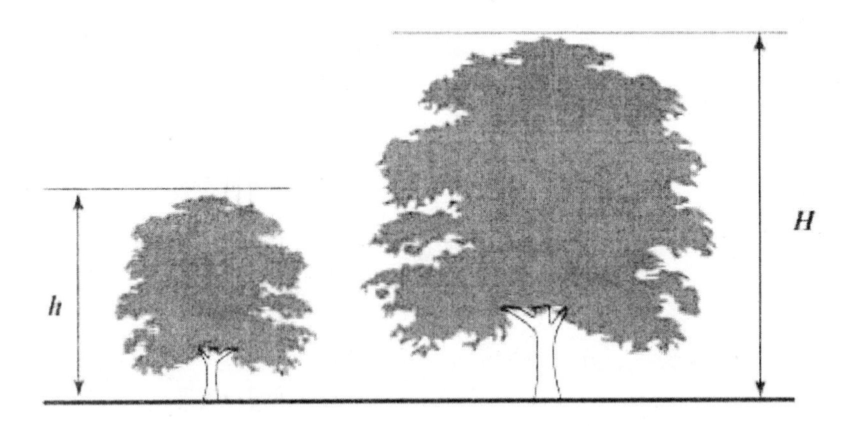

Select the correct answer.

( ) 8
( ) $c+8$
( ) c
( ) $2c+8$

16. Simplify the following expression by combining like terms, if possible.

$2y-4y$

Select the correct answer.

( ) $-2y$
( ) -2
( ) $6y$

17. Simplify the following expression by combining like terms, if possible.

$7a + 8 - 4b - 5a + 5$

Select the correct answer.

( ) $3a - 2b + 12$
( ) $2a - 4b + 13$
( ) none of these
( ) $12a - 4b + 8$

18. Simplify the following expression by combining like terms, if possible.

$3(9b + 7) - 4(6b + 2)$

Select the correct answer.

( ) $3b - 29$
( ) $51b + 13$
( ) none of these
( ) $3b + 13$

19. Solve the equation by combining like terms.
$7s + 2s = 72$

Select the correct answer.

( ) $s = 56$
( ) $s = 16$
( ) $s = 8$

20. Solve the equation.

$-2a + 56 = 6a$

Select the correct answer.

( ) $a = 14$
( ) $a = 7$
( ) $a = -7$

21. True or False:

$-6(z-6)=0$
$z=6$

( ) True
( ) False

22. True or False:

$4-(b-7)=-10$
$b=7$

( ) True
( ) False

23. Every month, a salesman adds 6 new accounts. How many new accounts will he add in u months?

Select the correct answer.

( ) $4u$
( ) $6u$
( ) $10u$
( ) $7u$
( ) $8u$
( ) $9u$

24. A shoe salesman receives a commission for every pair of shoes he sells.

Type of shoe	Number sold	Commission per shoe ($)
Child's	8 - a	3

What is the salesman's total commission?

Select the correct answer.

( ) $3(8 - a)$
( ) $8(a - 3)$
( ) $3(a - 8)$
( ) $8(3 - a)$

25. A student plans to pay back a $620 loan with monthly payments of $30. How many payments has she made if the debt has been reduced to $470?

Select the correct answer.

( ) 7
( ) 3
( ) 5
( ) 4
( ) 8
( ) 1

Answers

1. w - 10

2. $z + 45$

3. q - 40

4. x - 4

5. $\frac{8}{w} - 3$

6. 20

7. 3

8. true

9. false

10. $105t$

11. $3p - 12$

12. $-6x - 4$

13. 19

14. nx

15. $2c + 8$

16. $-2y$

17. $2a - 4b + 13$

18. $3b + 13$

19. $s = 8$

20. $a = 7$

21. true

22. false

23. $6u$

24. $3(8 - a)$

25. 5

1. Translate the phrase to an algebraic expression.

The difference of d and 45.

Select the correct answer.

( ) 45 - d
( ) d - 45
( ) 45 + d

2. Translate the following phrase to an algebraic expression.

The sum of w and 37.

Select the correct answer.

( ) $\frac{w}{37}$
( ) w- 37
( ) w+ 37

3. Translate the following phrase to an algebraic expression.

d decreased by 28.

Select the correct answer.

( ) d + 28
( ) 28 - d
( ) d - 28

4. A graduating class of w people took buses that held 35 students each to an all night graduation party. How many buses were needed to transport the class?

Select the correct answer.

( ) $\frac{35}{w}$

( ) $35w$

( ) $\frac{w}{35}$

5. Translate the following phrase to an algebraic expression.

The quotient of 8 and z is reduced by 3.

Select the correct answer.

( ) $\frac{8}{z} - 3$

( ) $\frac{8}{z} + 3$

( ) $8 \cdot z - 3$

6. Evaluate the expression:

$-9y$ for $y = -4$

Select the correct answer.

( ) 9
( ) -36
( ) 36

7. Evaluate the expression:

$\frac{t - 2}{2}$ for $t = 10$

Select the correct answer.

( ) 8
( ) 6
( ) 4

8. True or False:

$\frac{9x - 7t}{-3} = 74$ for $x = 27$ and $t = 3$

( ) True
( ) False

9. A pair of shoes is normally sold for $260 but is discounted $20. Answer True or False:

The sale price is $240.

( ) True
( ) False

10. Simplify:

$7(-4p)(6)$

Select the correct answer.

( ) $-24p$
( ) $169p$
( ) $167p$
( ) $42p$
( ) $-28p$
( ) $-168p$

11. Simplify the following expression. Use the distributive property to remove the parentheses.

$3(t+7)$

Select the correct answer.

( ) $21t+21$
( ) $21t+3$
( ) $21t+7$
( ) $3t+3$
( ) $3t+21$
( ) $3t+7$

12. Write the following expression without using parentheses.

$-(3a+2)$

Select the correct answer.

( ) $-3a+2$
( ) $-3a-2$
( ) $-2a-3$
( ) $3a-2$
( ) $2a-3$
( ) $-2a+3$

13. What is the coefficient of the following term?

$5ay$

Select the correct answer.

( ) ay
( ) $5y$
( ) 5
( ) a

14. What is the variable part of the following term?

13*tz*

Select the correct answer.

( ) *z*
( ) *tz*
( ) *t*
( ) 13

15. The heights of two trees are shown in the illustration below. Find the sum of their heights, if*h*=*c*, and*H*=*c*+ 14.

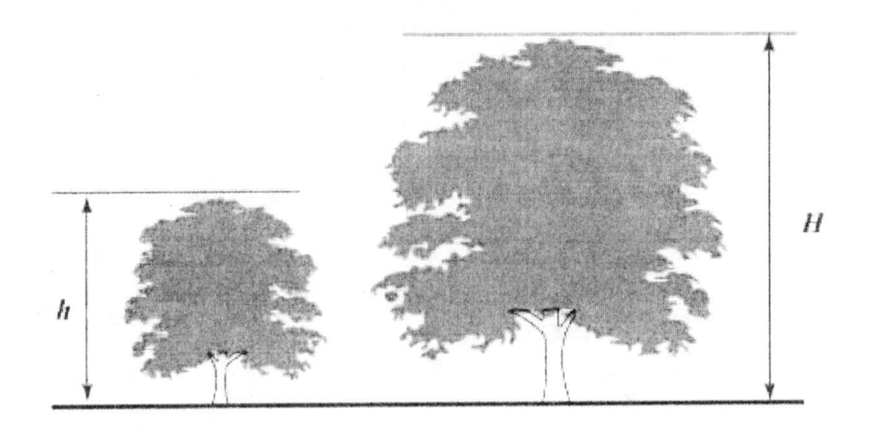

Select the correct answer.

( ) 14
( ) 2*c*+ 14
( ) *c*
( ) *c*+ 14

16. Simplify the following expression by combining like terms, if possible.

$2a - 4a$

Select the correct answer.

( ) -2
( ) $6a$
( ) $-2a$

17. Simplify the following expression by combining like terms, if possible.

$9z + 8 - 2y - 3z + 3$

Select the correct answer.

( ) none of these
( ) $12z - 2y + 8$
( ) $6z - 2y + 11$
( ) $7z - 6y + 10$

18. Simplify the following expression by combining like terms, if possible.

$5(9y + 6) - 3(8y + 2)$

Select the correct answer.

( ) $21y + 24$
( ) none of these
( ) $69y + 24$
( ) $21y - 36$

19. Solve the equation by combining like terms.
$10y + 9y = 76$

Select the correct answer.

( ) $y = 4$
( ) $y = 36$
( ) $y = 40$

20. Solve the equation.

$-9x + 104 = 4x$

Select the correct answer.

( ) $x = -8$
( ) $x = 8$
( ) $x = 72$

21. True or False:

$-4(t - 8) = 0$
$t = 8$

( ) True
( ) False

22. True or False:

$2 - (t - 8) = -7$
$t = 1$

( ) True
( ) False

23. Every month, a salesman adds 10 new accounts. How many new accounts will he add in*a*months?

Select the correct answer.

( ) $3a$
( ) $10a$
( ) $6a$
( ) $16a$
( ) $14a$
( ) $4a$

24. The following illustration shows a rack that contains dress shoes and athletic shoes. If there arexpairs of dress shoes in the rack, how many pairs of athletic shoes are there in the rack?

Select the correct answer.

( ) 18 -x
( ) 9 -x
( ) x- 9
( ) x- 18

25. To get a heavy-equipment operator's certificate, 47 hours of on-the-job training are required. If a woman has completed 23 hours, and the training sessions last for 4 hours, how many more sessions must she take to get the certificate?

Select the correct answer.

( ) 4
( ) 10
( ) 9
( ) 6
( ) 7
( ) 1

Answers

1. $d - 45$

2. $w + 37$

3. $d - 28$

4. $\frac{w}{35}$

5. $\frac{8}{z} - 3$

6. 36

7. 4

8. true

9. true

10. $-168p$

11. $3t + 21$

12. $-3a - 2$

13. 5

14. tz

15. $2c + 14$

16. $-2a$

17. $6z - 2y + 11$

18. $21y + 24$

19. $y = 4$

20. $x = 8$

21. true

22. false

23. $10a$

24. $9 - x$

25. 6

1. Simplify the following expression. Use the distributive property to remove the parentheses.

$3(p + 2)$

Select the correct answer.

( ) $3p + 2$
( ) $3p + 6$
( ) $6p + 2$
( ) $6p + 6$
( ) $3p + 3$
( ) $6p + 3$

2. Translate the following phrase to an algebraic expression.
The product of 23 and x is increased by 26.

3. True or False:

$5(8a + 8) = 2(10a - 20)$
$a = 4$

( ) True
( ) False

4. Simplify:

$4p(8u)$

Select the correct answer.

( ) $8pu$
( ) $32pu$
( ) $16pu$
( ) $4pu$
( ) $33pu$
( ) $31pu$

5. True or False:

$10 - (x - 8) = -8$
$x = 10$

( ) True
( ) False

6. Evaluate the expression:

$2w^2$ for $w = 4$

Select the correct answer.

( ) 8
( ) 128
( ) 32

7. True or False:

$-3(8t - 3) = 57$
$t = -2$

( ) True
( ) False

8. Translate the following phrase to an algebraic expression.
The difference of d and 28

9. The following illustration shows a rack that contains dress shoes and athletic shoes. If there are t pairs of dress shoes in the rack, how many pairs of athletic shoes are there in the rack?

10. Find the sale price of a pair of boots that normally sells for $185 but is discounted $30.

11. Simplify the following expression. Use the distributive property to remove the parentheses.

$10(2t+5y+7)$

Select the correct answer.

( ) $70t+20y+50$
( ) $50t+20y+70$
( ) $70t+50y+20$
( ) $20t+50y+70$
( ) $50t+70y+20$
( ) $20t+70y+50$

12. As part of redecorating, crown molding was installed around the base of the ceiling of a room. 240 feet of molding was needed for the project. Find the width of the room if its length is 5 times its width.

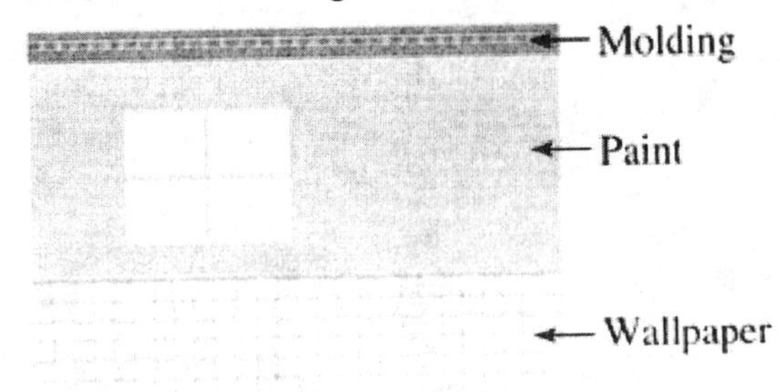

13. A 72-seat passenger plane has 7 times as many economy seats as first-class seats. Find the number of first-class seats.

Select the correct answer.

( ) 14
( ) 15
( ) 9
( ) 13
( ) 7
( ) 1

14. Suppose thatzinches of tape have been used off the roll shown in the illustration below. How many inches of tape are left on the roll, if*a*= 430 inches?

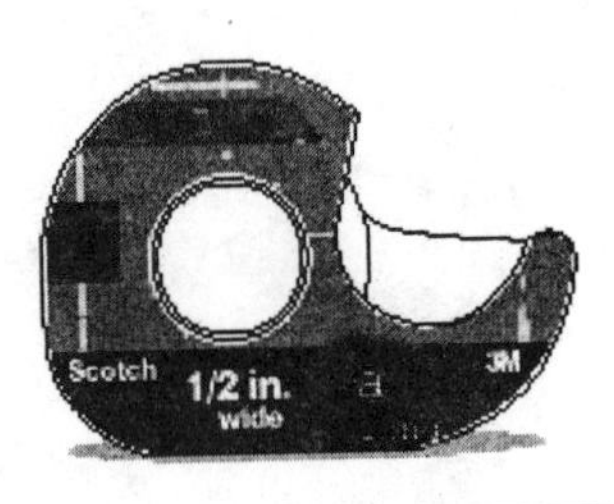

15. In the following expression, which factor is distributed?

$(a+3)(-8)$

Select the correct answer.

( ) 3
( ) -24
( ) -8
( ) -3
( ) 24
( ) 8

16. Solve the equation by eliminating a variable term on one side of the equation.

$7z+30=2z+15$

17. Write the following expression without using parentheses.

$-(-4x+9b-6)$

18. Evaluate the expression:

$6z+z^2$ for $z=5$

Select the correct answer.

( ) 55
( ) 30
( ) 30

19. Simplify and complete the following solution. What is the missing value?

$4(y-6)+7y=4y+\ ?\ -24=11y-24$

Select the correct answer.

( ) $16y$
( ) $3y$
( ) $7y$
( ) 1

20. Write the following expression without using parentheses.

$-(-10x-9)$

21. Evaluate the expression:

$|2x-18|$ for $x=4$

Select the correct answer.

( ) 10
( ) -10
( ) 14

22. True or False:

$a+8$ is a simpler form of the expression $a-(-2)$.

( ) True
( ) False

23. Simplify:

$-4x(6y)$

24. Use the distributive property to complete the following expression. Write the simplified expression.

$14(x - 3) = ?$

25. Evaluate the expression:

$y^2 - 5y + 8$ for $y = 5$

Select the correct answer.

( ) 28
( ) 8
( ) 0

Answers

1. $3p + 6$

2. $23x + 26$

3. false

4. $32pu$

5. false

6. 32

7. true

8. d-28

9. 9-t

10. 155

11. $20t + 50y + 70$

12. 20

13. 9

14. 430-z

15. -8

16. -3

17. $4x - 9b + 6$

18. 55

19. $7y$

20. $10x + 9$

21. 10

22. true

23. $-24xy$

24. $14x - 14 \cdot 3$

25. 8

1. Solve the equation by removing parentheses.

$8 - (x + 9) = -6$

2. Solve the equation by combining like terms.

$t + 10 + t = 28$

3. After receiving their tax refund, a husband and wife split the refunded money equally. The husband then gave $60 of his money to charity, leaving him with $70. What was the amount of the tax refund check?

Select the correct answer.

( ) $188
( ) $203
( ) $260
( ) $328
( ) $463
( ) $199

4. Simplify the following expression. Use the distributive property to remove the parentheses.

$5(2x + 10b + 6)$

5. A thermometer manufacturer wishes to scale a thermometer in both degrees Celsius and degrees Fahrenheit. Find the missing Celsius degree measures in the illustration below, if $x = 127.4$, $y = 123.8$, and $z = 44.6$.

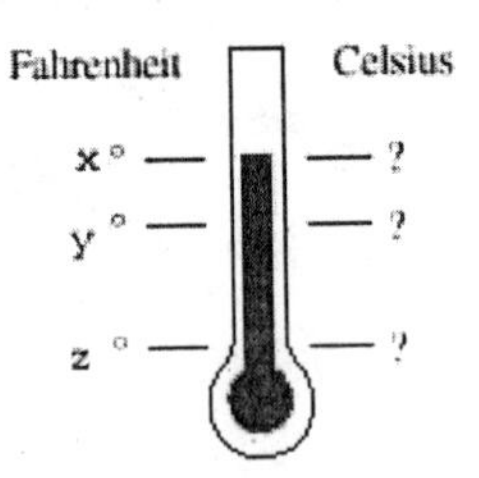

Fahrenheit	Celsius
127.4	
123.8	
44.6	

6. Evaluate the algebraic expression:

$\frac{9x - 4t}{-4}$ for $x = 12$ and $t = 32$

7. Solve the equation.

$2y + 2(y - 9) = 22$

8. Solve the equation by eliminating a variable term on one side of the equation.

$2z + 9 = 3z$

9. The weights of two mixtures, measured in ounces, are compared on a balance, as shown in the illustration. By how much mixture is A heavier?

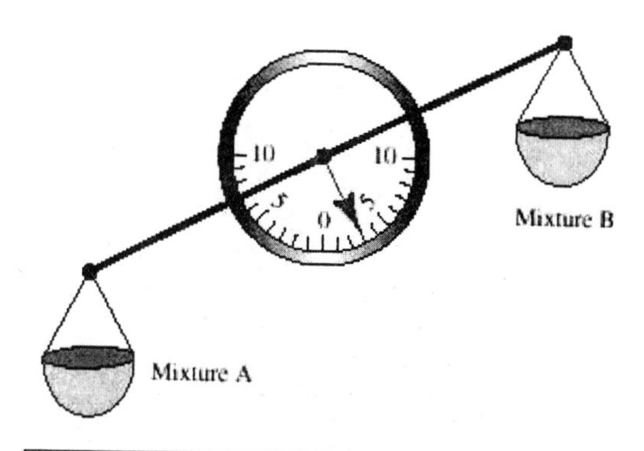

10. As part of redecorating, crown molding was installed around the base of the ceiling of a room. 240 feet of molding was needed for the project. Find the width of the room if its length is 5 times its width.

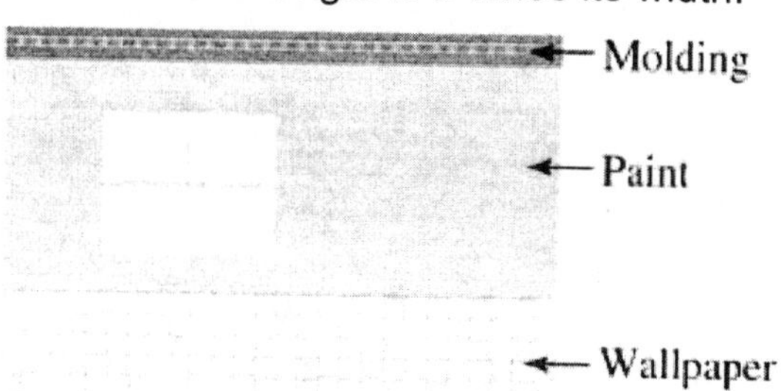

11. Evaluate the expression:

$z^2 - 6z + 10$ for $z = 1$

12. True or False:

$-|7a - 8k + 6| = -5$ for $a = 3$ and $k = 4$.

( ) True
( ) False

13. Solve the equation.

$3(8y + 4) = 2(9y - 6)$

14. True or False:

$2 - (a - 9) = -7$
$a = 0$

( ) True
( ) False

15. A landscape architect has designed a planter surrounding two birch trees, as shown in the illustration below. The planter is to be outlined with redwood edging in the shape of a rectangle and two squares. If the material costs $0.57 a running foot, how much will the redwood for this project cost?

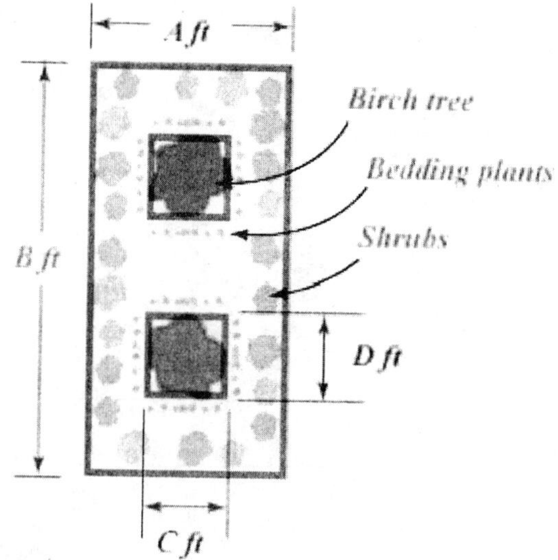

A= 70,*B*= 100,*C*= 5,*D*= 35

Select the correct answer.

( ) $285.00
( ) $433.20
( ) $188.10
( ) $239.40

16. If we letxrepresent the height of the elm tree, write an algebraic expression for the height of the birch tree.

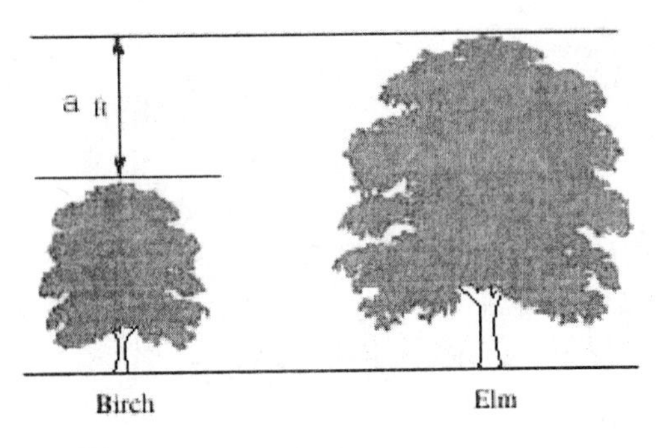

a= 34

17. Simplify:

5(- 2a)(3)

Select the correct answer.

( ) - 30a
( ) - 10a
( ) - 6a
( ) 31a
( ) 29a
( ) 15a

18. How many years are in 4 decades?

Select the correct answer.

( ) 400 years
( ) 4 years
( ) 40 years

19. Write the following expression without using parentheses.

$-(-7m-6)$

20. Simplify:

$x-(-7)$

21. In the illustration below, we can let q represent the height of the elm tree. Answer True or False:

The height of the birch tree can be represented by the algebraic expression $q-31$.

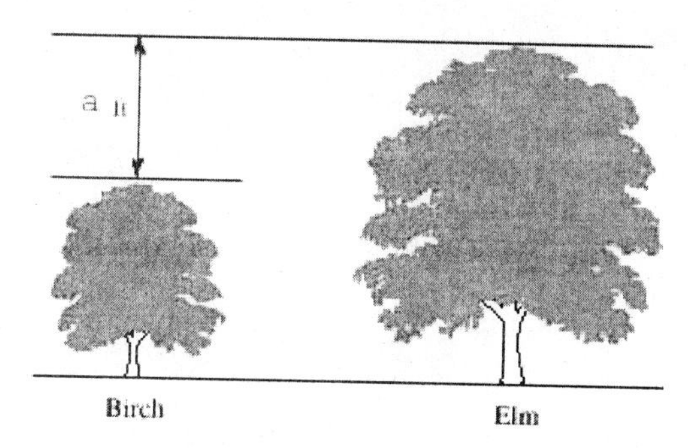

$a=31$

( ) True
( ) False

22. True or False:

$3(t+3)=15$
$t=2$

( ) True
( ) False

23. Solve the equation by combining like terms.

$8a - 4a = 36$

Select the correct answer.

( ) $a = 9$
( ) $a = 72$
( ) $a = 36$

24. The illustration below shows the distance (in miles) that two men live from the office. Find the total distance the men travel from home to office, if $B = c$, and $A = c + 2$.

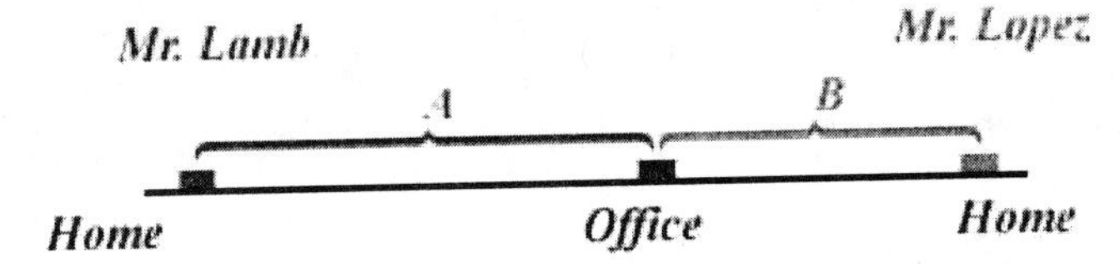

Select the correct answer.

( ) $2c + 2$
( ) 2
( ) $c + 2$
( ) c

25. True or False:

$m + 2$ is a simpler form of the expression $m - (-4)$.

( ) True
( ) False

Answers

1. 5

2. 9

3. $260

4. $10x+50b+30$

5. 127.4, 53, 123.8, 51, 44.6, 7

6. 5

7. 10

8. 9

9. 3

10. 20

11. 5

12. true

13. -4

14. false

15. $285.00

16. x-34

17. $-30a$

18. 40 years

19. $7m+6$

20. x+7

21. true

22. true

23. $a = 9$

24. $2c + 2$

25. true

1. What is the numerical coefficient of the term $-4b$?

2. Simplify the following expression by combining like terms, if possible.

$5x + 7 - 4y - 7x + 9$

3. Simplify the following expression by combining like terms, if possible.

$-8x - 9x$

Select the correct answer.

( ) -17
( ) $1x$
( ) $-17x$

4. Evaluate the expression:

$x^2 - 4x + 6$ for $x = 3$

5. A student plans to pay back a $670 loan with monthly payments of $30. How many payments has she made if the debt has been reduced to $490?

Select the correct answer.

( ) 9
( ) 6
( ) 5
( ) 3
( ) 8
( ) 4

6. Suppose that z inches of tape have been used off the roll shown in the illustration below. How many inches of tape are left on the roll, if a = 360 inches?

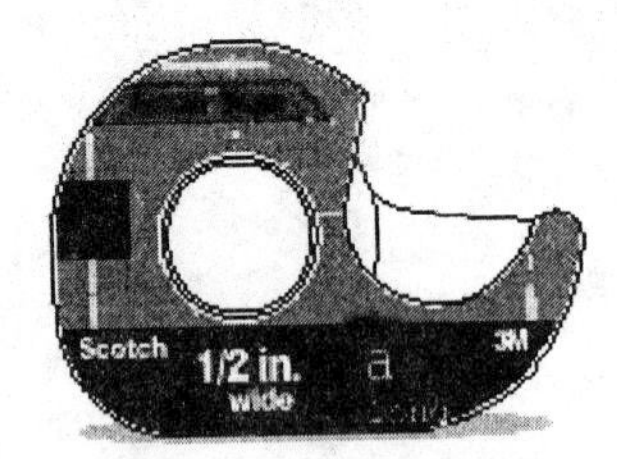

Select the correct answer.

( ) 360+z
( ) 360z
( ) 360-z

7. Evaluate the expression:

$6x + 17$ for $x = 4$

8. A landscape architect has designed a planter surrounding two birch trees, as shown in the illustration below. The planter is to be outlined with redwood edging in the shape of a rectangle and two squares. If the material costs \$0.28 a running foot, how much will the redwood for this project cost?

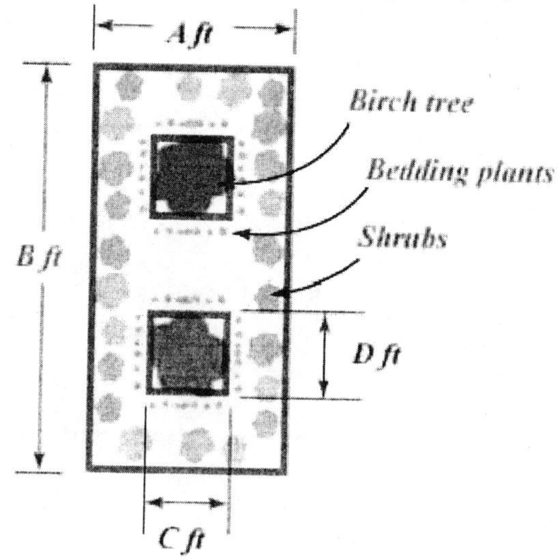

$A = 50, B = 60, C = 35, D = 5$

Select the correct answer.

( ) \$75.60
( ) \$106.40
( ) \$84.00
( ) \$145.60

9. What is the variable part of the following term?

12*yx*

Select the correct answer.

( ) *y*
( ) *x*
( ) 12
( ) *yx*

10. A graduating class ofxpeople took buses that held 35 students each to an all night graduation party. How many buses were needed to transport the class?

11. In an effort to cut costs, a corporation has decided to lay off 4 employees every month until the number of employees totals 105. If 345 people are now employed, how many months will it take to reach the employment goal?

12. Evaluate the expression:

$7t+t^2$fort= 3

13. Simplify:

3(6*a*)

Select the correct answer.

( ) 3*a*
( ) 18*a*
( ) 17*a*
( ) 9*a*
( ) 6*a*
( ) 19*a*

14. The perimeter of a rectangle is 140 ft. Width is*t*. Heigth is 5*t*.
Filling in the blanks, write a full statement about the perimeter of the rectangle:

2 · □ + 2 · □ = 140 Write out the complete equation in the answer field.

15. A landscaper buried a water line around a rectangular-shaped lawn to serve as a supply line for a sprinkler system. The length of the lawn is 3 times its width. If 200 feet of pipe was used to do the job, what is the width of the lawn?

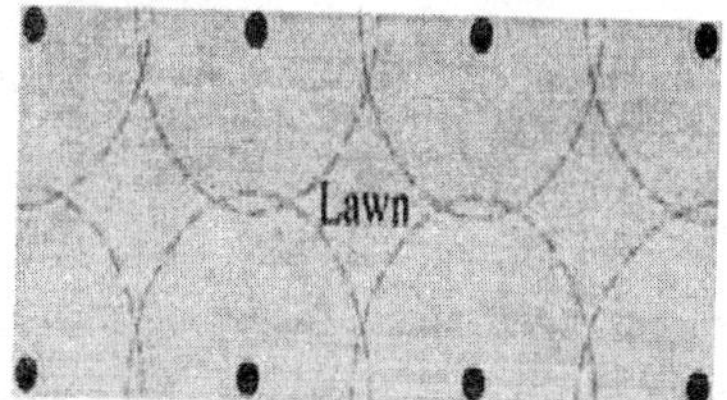

16. True or False:

- 5(4*x*- 5) = 105
x= - 4

( ) True
( ) False

17. The following expression is the result of an application of the distributive property. What was the original algebraic expression?

$4(2p) - 4(3q) + 4(10)$

Select the correct answer.

( ) $4(10p + 2q - 3)$
( ) $4(3p - 2q + 10)$
( ) $4(2p - 10q + 3)$
( ) $4(2p - 3q + 10)$
( ) $4(3p + 10q - 2)$
( ) $4(10p + 3q - 2)$

18. Translate the following phrase to an algebraic expression.

The quotient of 8 and q is reduced by 3.

Select the correct answer.

( ) $\frac{8}{q} + 3$
( ) $\frac{8}{q} - 3$
( ) $8 \cdot q - 3$

19. Find the sale price of a pair of boots that normally sells for $169 but is discounted $20.

20. Simplify the following expression. Use the distributive property to remove the parentheses.

$2(7x+6q-5k)$

Select the correct answer.

( ) $10x-14q+12k$
( ) $12x+10q-14k$
( ) $14x+12q-10k$
( ) $14x-10q+12k$
( ) $12x+14q-10k$
( ) $10x-12q+14k$

21. A student figures that she has q hours to study for a government final. She wants to spread the studying evenly over a 7-day period. Write an expression for how many hours she should study each day.

Select the correct answer.

( ) $\frac{7}{q}$
( ) $7q$
( ) $\frac{q}{7}$

22. Translate the following phrase to an algebraic expression.

The sum of z and 25.

Select the correct answer.

( ) $z+25$
( ) $z-25$
( ) $\frac{z}{25}$

23. A shoe salesman receives a commission for every pair of shoes he sells.

Type of shoe	Number sold	Commission per shoe ($)
Sandal	6 - m	3

What is the salesman's total commission?

Select the correct answer.

( ) $3(m-6)$
( ) $3(6-m)$
( ) $6(3-m)$
( ) $6(m-3)$

24. Simplify:

$4x(9n)$

Select the correct answer.

( ) $36xn$
( ) $35xn$
( ) $37xn$
( ) $4xn$
( ) $9xn$
( ) $18xn$

Answers

1. -4

2. $-2x-4y+16$

3. $-17x$

4. 3

5. 6

6. $360-z$

7. 41

8. $106.40

9. yx

10. $\frac{x}{35}$

11. 60

12. 30

13. $18a$

14. $2t+2\cdot 5t=140$

15. 25

16. true

17. $4(2p-3q+10)$

18. $\frac{8}{q}-3$

19. 149

20. $14x+12q-10k$

21. $\frac{q}{7}$

22. $z + 25$

23. $3(6 - m)$

24. $36xn$

1. If possible, simplify this fraction to its lowest terms:

$$\frac{52}{169}$$

2. Multiply. Write your answer in lowest terms.

$$\left(-\frac{6}{14}\right) \times \left(-\frac{7}{18}\right).$$

3. Multiply. Write your answer in lowest terms.

$$\frac{4a^8}{45} \times \left(\frac{9a}{16a^4}\right).$$

4. If possible, simplify this fraction to its lowest terms:

$$\frac{30y^2}{5y^8}$$

5. This illustration shows the party affiliation of the governors of the 50 states.

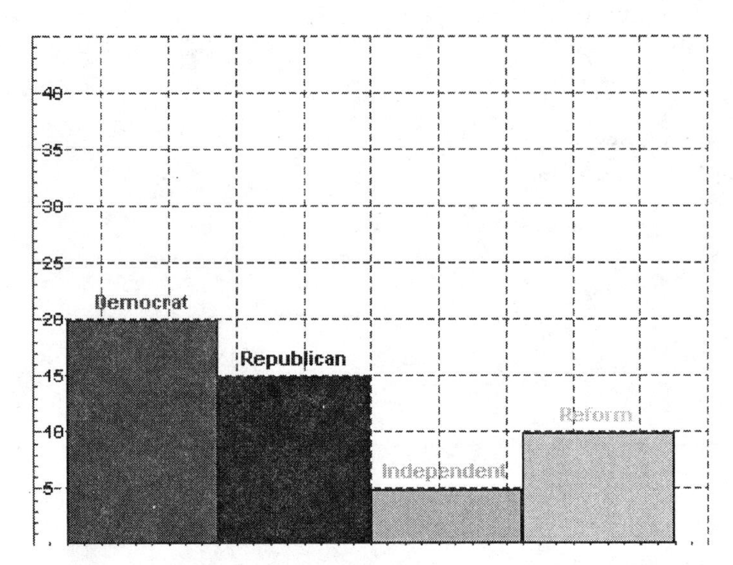

Using your cursor, match the affiliation to its corresponding correct fraction.

Democrats	$\frac{15}{50}$
Republicans	$\frac{20}{50}$
Independant	$\frac{10}{50}$
Reform	$\frac{5}{50}$

6. A tennis ball is dropped from a height of *H* inches. Each time it hits the ground, it bounces to one-third of the height of its previous bounce. See the illustration and find the three missing bounce heights, where *H* = 54.

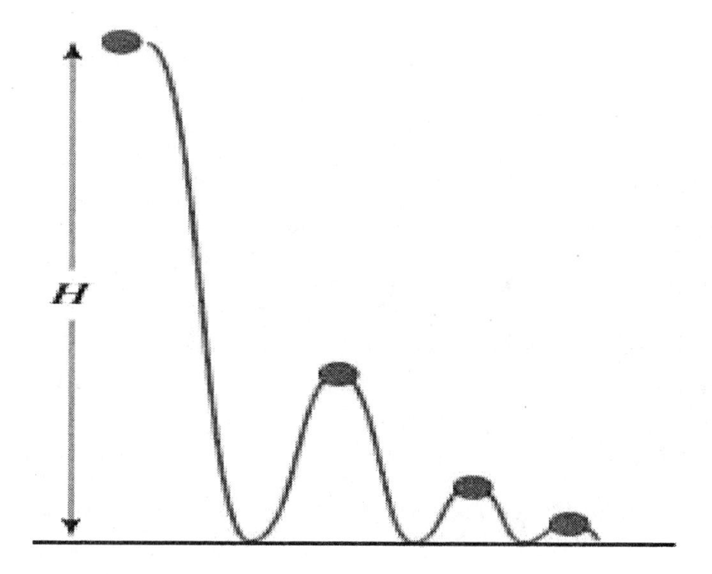

7. Find the quotient.

$$\frac{13}{2} \div \left(-\frac{7}{5}\right)$$

8. Find the quotient.

$$\frac{5t^3}{11v^5} \div \frac{13t}{5v}$$

9. FURNITURE

A production process applies several layers of a clear acrylic coat to outdoor furniture to help protect it from the weather. If each protective coat is $\frac{7}{40}$ inch thick, how many applications will be needed to build up $\frac{7}{5}$ inch of clear finish?

10. Consider the fraction $\frac{3}{11}$. By what should we multiply the numerator and denominator of this fraction to express it as an equivalent fraction with a denominator of $22z$?

11. Complete the operation below and simplify if necessary.

$$\frac{19}{z} - \frac{12}{z}$$

12. Complete the operation and simplify if necessary.

$$-5 + \frac{2}{3}$$

13. In the illustration below the divisions on the face of the meter represent fractions. If the arrow moves up 5 marks, what value will it register?

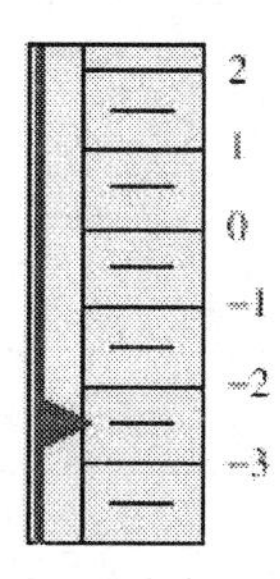

14. Write the following mixed number as an improper fraction:

$-6\frac{1}{5}$

15. Evaluate the power and write your answer as an improper fraction.

$\left(3\frac{1}{5}\right)^2$

16. Find the sum and simplify if necessary.

$13\frac{2}{5} + 8\frac{1}{7}$

17. Find the difference.

$18\frac{1}{8} - 3$

18. AIR TRAVEL

A businesswoman's flight leaves Atlanta at 2 P.M. and arrives in Hartford at 8:45 P.M. Express the duration of the flight as a mixed number.

19. Evaluate the expression and simplify if necessary.

$\frac{4}{7}\left(-\frac{1}{3}\right) + \frac{4}{5}$

20. Evaluate the following algebraic expression for $b = \frac{1}{3}$ and $c = \frac{4}{7}$

$\frac{1}{4}b^2 + c$

21. Simplify the following complex fraction: $\frac{\frac{2}{3}}{\frac{4}{5}}$

Express your answer as a mixed number if possible.

22. Evaluate the expression and simplify if necessary.

$$\frac{\frac{1}{4}+\frac{5}{8}}{\frac{1}{4}-\frac{5}{8}}$$

23. Solve the equation: $\frac{2}{9}p = 8$

24. Solve the equation: $11p + 5 = 0$

Answers

1. $\frac{4}{13}$

2. $\frac{1}{6}$

3. $\frac{a^5}{20}$

4. $\frac{6}{y^6}$

5. Democrats -> 20/50, Republicans -> 15/50, Independant -> 5/50, Reform -> 10/50

6. 2, 6, 18

7. $-\frac{65}{14}$

8. $\frac{25t^2}{143v^4}$

9. 8

10. $2z$

11. $\frac{7}{z}$

12. $\frac{-13}{3}$

13. 0

14. $-\frac{31}{5}$

15. $\frac{256}{25}$

16. $21\frac{19}{35}$

17. $15\frac{1}{8}$

18. $6\frac{3}{4}$

19. $\frac{8}{21}$

20. $\frac{151}{252}$

21. $\frac{10}{12}$

22. $\frac{28}{-12}$

23. 36

24. $-\frac{5}{11}$

1. If possible, simplify this fraction to its lowest terms:

$$\frac{52}{169}$$

2. If possible, simplify this fraction to its lowest terms:

$$\frac{130b^5}{13b^7}$$

3. Complete the table by finding the amount of the job that will be completed by each person working alone for the given number of hours.

Name	Total time complete the job alone	Time worked alone	Amount of job completed
Bob	8	7	
Ali	8	1	

4. Multiply. Write your answer in lowest terms.

$$\left(-\frac{19}{30}\right) \times \left(-\frac{10}{38}\right).$$

5. Multiply. Write your answer in lowest terms.

$$\frac{2y^4}{12} \times \left(\frac{3y}{10y^3}\right).$$

6. A tennis ball is dropped from a height of H inches. Each time it hits the ground, it bounces to one-third of the height of its previous bounce. See the illustration and find the three missing bounce heights, where $H = 135$.

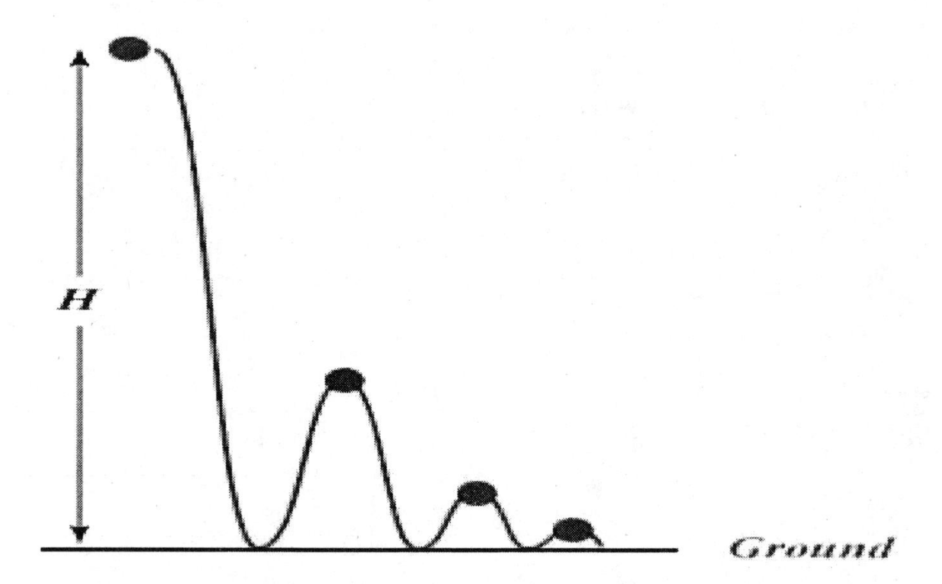

7. Find the quotient.

$$\frac{1}{13} \div \left(-\frac{11}{3}\right)$$

8. Find the quotient.

$$\frac{5f^5}{13b^3} \div \frac{11f}{7b}$$

9. UNDERGROUND CABLE

How many days will it require to install an underground TV cable from the broadcasting station to the subdivision for each of the proposed routes described in the table below?

Proposal	Amount of cable installed per day	Cable required
Route 1	$\frac{8}{4}$ of a mile	120 miles
Route 2	$\frac{5}{4}$ of a mile	85 miles

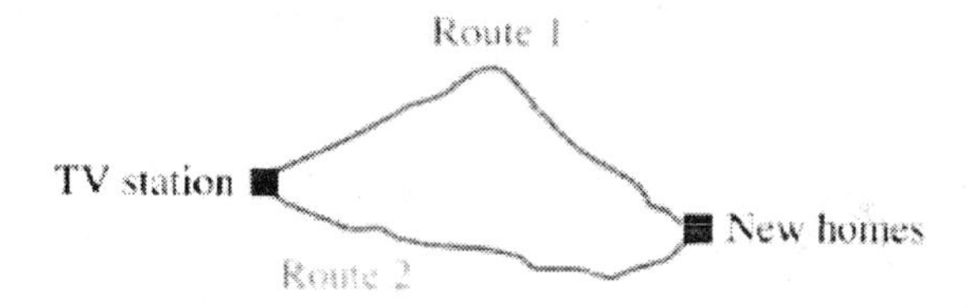

10. Consider the fraction $\frac{3}{5}$. By what should we multiply the numerator and denominator of this fraction to express it as an equivalent fraction with a denominator of $10y$?

11. Complete the operation below and simplify if necessary.

$$\frac{18}{z} - \frac{10}{z}$$

12. Complete the operation and simplify if necessary.

$$-7 + \frac{2}{7}$$

13. In the illustration below the divisions on the face of the meter represent fractions. If the arrow moves up 5 marks, what value will it register?

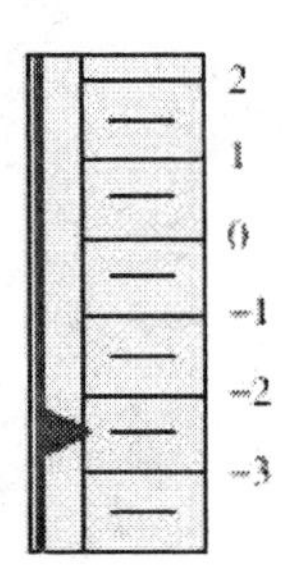

14. Write the following mixed number as an improper fraction:

$$-9\frac{2}{3}$$

15. Evaluate the power and write your answer as an improper fraction.

$$\left(1\frac{1}{3}\right)^2$$

16. Find the sum and simplify if necessary.

$$12\frac{3}{7} + 9\frac{1}{11}$$

17. Find the difference.

$$18\frac{1}{11} - 8$$

18. Evaluate the expression and simplify if necessary.

$$\frac{4}{7}\left(-\frac{2}{5}\right) + \frac{2}{5}$$

19. Evaluate the following algebraic expression for $b = \frac{1}{3}$ and $c = \frac{4}{5}$

$$\frac{1}{4}b^2 + c$$

20. Simplify the following complex fraction: $\dfrac{\frac{2}{3}}{\frac{6}{5}}$

Express your answer as a mixed number if possible.

21. Evaluate the expression and simplify if necessary.

$$\dfrac{\frac{3}{4}+\frac{5}{8}}{\frac{3}{4}-\frac{5}{8}}$$

22. To improve reading skills, elementary school children read silently at the end of the school day for $\frac{7}{8}$ of an hour on Mondays and for $\frac{5}{8}$ of an hour on Fridays. For the month of January, how many hours did the children read silently in class? Use the following calendar for help.

S	M	T	W	T	F	S
	1	2	3	4	5	6
7	8	9	10	11	12	13
14	15	16	17	18	19	20
21	22	23	24	25	26	27
28	29	30	31			

23. Solve the equation: $\frac{1}{10}m = 3$

24. Solve the equation: $11a = 5a - 2$

25. A theater usher at a Broadway musical finds that $\frac{2}{3}$ of the patrons attending a performance are in their seats by show time. The remaining 20 people are seated after the opening number. If the show is always a complete sellout, how many seats does the theater have?

Answers

1. $\frac{4}{13}$

2. $\frac{10}{b^2}$

3. Bob, 8, 7, $\frac{7}{8}$, Ali, 8, 1, $\frac{1}{8}$

4. $\frac{1}{6}$

5. $\frac{y^2}{20}$

6. 5, 15, 45

7. $-\frac{3}{143}$

8. $\frac{35t^4}{143b^2}$

9. 60, 68

10. $2y$

11. $\frac{8}{z}$

12. $\frac{-47}{7}$

13. 0

14. $-\frac{29}{3}$

15. $\frac{16}{9}$

16. $21\frac{40}{77}$

17. $10\frac{1}{11}$

18. $\frac{2}{35}$

19. $\frac{149}{180}$

20. $\frac{10}{18}$

21. $\frac{44}{4}$

22. $\frac{440}{64}$

23. 30

24. $-\frac{2}{6}$

25. 60

1. If possible, simplify this fraction to its lowest terms:

$$\frac{116}{377}$$

2. If possible, simplify this fraction to its lowest terms:

$$\frac{78x^{2}}{13x^{5}}$$

3. Multiply. Write your answer in lowest terms.

$$\left(-\frac{8}{36}\right) \times \left(-\frac{18}{32}\right).$$

4. Multiply. Write your answer in lowest terms.

$$\frac{9c^{5}}{21} \times \left(\frac{3c}{81c^{3}}\right).$$

5. A tennis ball is dropped from a height of *H* inches. Each time it hits the ground, it bounces to one-third of the height of its previous bounce. See the illustration and find the three missing bounce heights, where $H = 135$.

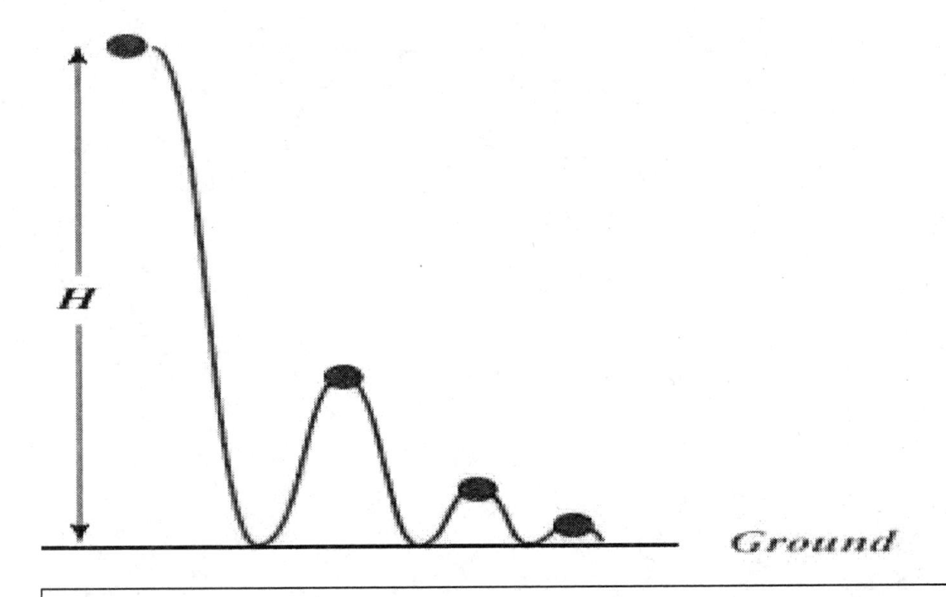

6. Find the quotient.

$$\frac{5}{3} \div \left(-\frac{1}{5}\right)$$

7. Find the quotient.

$$\frac{2t^5}{13s^5} \div \frac{5t}{3s}$$

8. A hardware chain purchases large amounts of nails and packages them in $\frac{7}{3}$ pound bags for sale. How many of these bags of nails can be obtained from 8603 pounds of nails?

9. Consider the fraction $\frac{4}{5}$. By what should we multiply the numerator and denominator of this fraction to express it as an equivalent fraction with a denominator of $20c$? Check your answer below.

( ) $20c$
( ) $4c$
( ) 4
( ) c
( ) 20

10. What is the result of the operation $\frac{12}{z} - \frac{11}{z}$?

( ) $\frac{1}{z}$
( ) 1
( ) $\frac{23}{z}$

11. True or False?

$$-4 + \frac{3}{5} = \frac{17}{5}$$

( ) True
( ) False

12. True or False?

A truck can safely carry a one- ton load. It can safely deliver $\frac{1}{6}$ ton of sand, $\frac{1}{3}$ ton of gravel , and $\frac{10}{18}$ ton of cement at one time to a job site.

( ) True
( ) False

13. In the illustration below the divisions on the face of the meter represent fractions. If the arrow moves up 7 marks, what value will it register? Check your answer in the table at the bottom of the window.

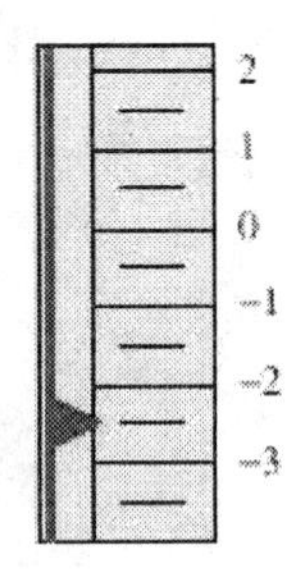

( ) $2\frac{1}{2}$
( ) 1
( ) $1\frac{1}{2}$

14. Write the following mixed number as an improper fraction.

$-1\frac{2}{5}$

Select the correct answer.

( ) $-\frac{7}{5}$

( ) $-\frac{3}{5}$

( ) $\frac{5}{5}$

15. Evaluate the power and write your answer as an improper fraction.

$\left(2\frac{1}{2}\right)^2$

Select the correct answer.

( ) $\frac{16}{4}$

( ) $\frac{25}{4}$

( ) $\frac{9}{4}$

16. Find the area of the license plate in the illustration below if

$a = 4\frac{1}{4}$ and $b = 2\frac{1}{4}$

Select the correct answer.

( ) $\frac{153}{16}$

( ) $\frac{25}{16}$

( ) $\frac{128}{16}$

17. Find the sum.

$6\frac{2}{11} + 8\frac{3}{5}$

Select the correct answer.

( ) $6\frac{43}{55}$

( ) $14\frac{43}{55}$

( ) $2\frac{43}{55}$

18. Find the difference.

$7\frac{1}{6} - 2$

Select the correct answer.

( ) $5\frac{1}{12}$
( ) $5\frac{3}{6}$
( ) $5\frac{1}{6}$

19. True or False? $\frac{4}{5}\left(-\frac{1}{3}\right) + \frac{4}{5} = \frac{8}{15}$

( ) True
( ) False

20. Evaluate the following algebraic expression for $b = \frac{2}{3}$ and $c = \frac{1}{3}$

$\frac{1}{2}b^2 + c$

21. Simplify the following complex fraction: $\dfrac{\frac{1}{5}}{\frac{2}{3}}$

( ) $\frac{5}{6}$
( ) $\frac{2}{15}$
( ) $\frac{3}{10}$
( ) $\frac{10}{3}$
( ) $\frac{15}{2}$

22. Evaluate the expression: $\dfrac{\frac{3}{5}+\frac{1}{4}}{\frac{3}{5}-\frac{1}{4}}$

( ) $\frac{7}{17}$
( ) $\frac{19}{7}$
( ) $\frac{17}{12}$
( ) $\frac{7}{19}$
( ) $\frac{17}{7}$

23. To improve reading skills, elementary school children read silently at the end of the school day for $\frac{5}{8}$ of an hour on Mondays and for $\frac{7}{8}$ of an hour on Fridays. For the month of January, how many hours did the children read silently in class? Use the following calendar for help.

S	M	T	W	T	F	S
	1	2	3	4	5	6
7	8	9	10	11	12	13
14	15	16	17	18	19	20
21	22	23	24	25	26	27
28	29	30	31			

24. Solve the equation: $2f + 13 = 0$

( ) $\frac{2}{13}$

( ) $\frac{13}{2}$

( ) $\frac{15}{2}$

( ) $-\frac{15}{2}$

( ) $-\frac{13}{2}$

( ) $-\frac{2}{13}$

25. Solve the equation: $p - \frac{5}{11} = \frac{1}{3}$

Answers

1. $\frac{4}{13}$

2. $\frac{6}{x^3}$

3. $\frac{1}{8}$

4. $\frac{c^3}{63}$

5. 5, 15, 45

6. $-\frac{25}{3}$

7. $\frac{6t^4}{65s^4}$

8. 3687

9. $4c$

10. $\frac{1}{z}$

11. true

12. false

13. 1

14. $-\frac{7}{5}$

15. $\frac{25}{4}$

16. $\frac{153}{16}$

17. $14\frac{43}{55}$

18. $5\frac{1}{6}$

19. true

20. $\frac{30}{54}$

21. $\frac{3}{10}$

22. $\frac{17}{7}$

23. $\frac{424}{64}$

24. $-\frac{13}{2}$

25. $\frac{26}{33}$

1. Simplify this fraction to its lowest terms. Select the correct answer.

$\frac{16}{40}$

( ) $\frac{2}{4}$

( ) $\frac{2}{5}$

( ) $\frac{4}{10}$

( ) $\frac{8}{20}$

2. True or False?

The result of simplifying the fraction $\frac{117k^2}{13k^5}$ to its lowest terms is $\frac{9k^2}{k^5}$.

( ) True
( ) False

3. This illustration shows the party affiliation of the governors of the 50 states.

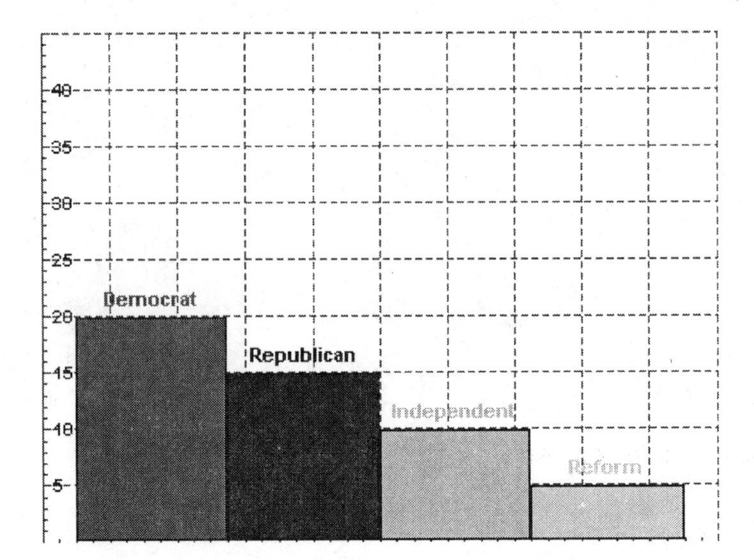

Which fraction is correct for Democrats?

( ) $\frac{15}{50}$

( ) $\frac{10}{50}$

( ) $\frac{20}{50}$

( ) $\frac{5}{50}$

4. Multiply. Reduce your answer to lowest terms and select the correct answer.

$$\left(-\frac{19}{12}\right) \times \left(-\frac{4}{38}\right).$$

( ) $\frac{4}{24}$

( ) $\frac{19}{114}$

( ) $\frac{1}{6}$

5. Multiply. Reduce your answer to lowest terms, and select the correct answer.

$$\frac{7y^4}{30} \times \left(\frac{5y}{56y^2}\right).$$

( ) $\frac{y^3}{48}$

( ) $\frac{y^2}{2688}$

( ) $\frac{30y^2}{48}$

6. A tennis ball is dropped from a height of*H*inches. Each time it hits the ground, it bounces one-third of the height of its previous bounce. See the illustration and find the missing bounce height*A*, if*H*= 162.

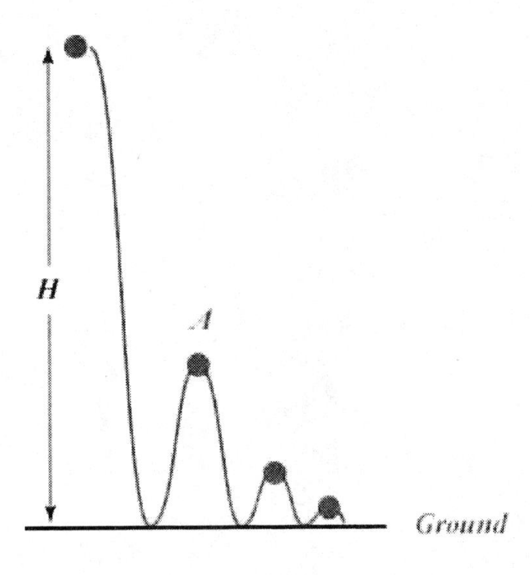

( ) 54
( ) 18
( ) 6

7. Find the quotient and select the correct answer.

$\frac{13}{3} \div \left(-\frac{7}{5}\right)$.

( ) $-\frac{61}{24}$

( ) $-\frac{64}{17}$

( ) $-\frac{65}{21}$

( ) $\frac{68}{19}$

( ) $-\frac{63}{26}$

( ) $-\frac{70}{20}$

8. Find the quotient and select the correct answer.

$$\frac{7u^3}{11n^4} \div \frac{11u}{2n}.$$

( ) $\dfrac{19n^4}{118u^5}$

( ) $\dfrac{17u^3}{126n^4}$

( ) $\dfrac{14u^2}{121n^3}$

( ) $\dfrac{11u^4}{125n^5}$

( ) $\dfrac{18n^2}{116u^3}$

( ) $\dfrac{9n^3}{124u^4}$

9. FURNITURE

A production process applies several layers of a clear acrylic coat to outdoor furniture to help protect it from the weather. If each protective coat is $\frac{5}{18}$ inch thick, how many applications will be needed to build up $\frac{5}{2}$ inch of clear finish? Select the correct answer.

( ) 11
( ) 21
( ) 5
( ) 9
( ) 4
( ) 22

10. Consider the fraction $\frac{11}{13}$. By what should we multiply the numerator and denominator of this fraction to express it as an equivalent fraction with a denominator of $39x$? Check your answer below.

( ) 39
( ) 39x
( ) x
( ) 3x
( ) 3

11. What is the result of the operation $\frac{4}{x} - \frac{2}{x}$?

( ) $\frac{6}{x}$
( ) $\frac{2}{x}$
( ) 2

12. True or False?

$$-4 + \frac{1}{5} = \frac{19}{5}$$

( ) True
( ) False

13. The illustration below shows the length of each section of a three-part hike. What is the longest section, if

$a = \frac{1}{2}$ $b = \frac{3}{5}$ $c = \frac{1}{4}$

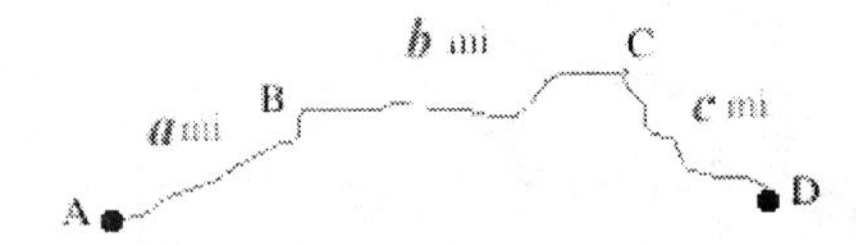

Select the correct answer.

( ) $\frac{1}{4}$

( )

$\frac{1}{2}$

( ) $\frac{3}{5}$

14. In the illustration below the divisions on the face of the meter represent fractions. If the arrow moves up 7 marks, what value will it register? Check your answer in the table at the bottom of the window.

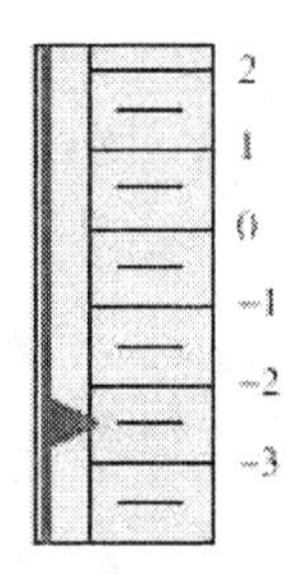

( ) 1

( ) $1\frac{1}{2}$

( ) $2\frac{1}{2}$

15. Write the following mixed number as an improper fraction.

$-10\frac{3}{5}$

Select the correct answer.

( ) $-\frac{53}{5}$

( ) $\frac{50}{5}$

( ) $-\frac{13}{5}$

16. Evaluate the power and write your answer as an improper fraction.

$$\left(1\frac{1}{2}\right)^2$$

Select the correct answer.

( ) $\frac{9}{4}$

( ) $\frac{4}{4}$

( ) $\frac{4}{4}$

17. Find the sum.

$$4\frac{2}{11} + 9\frac{3}{5}$$

Select the correct answer.

( ) $13\frac{43}{55}$

( ) $4\frac{43}{55}$

( ) $5\frac{43}{55}$

18. Find the difference.

$14\frac{3}{11} - 5$

Select the correct answer.

( ) $9\frac{8}{11}$

( ) $9\frac{3}{11}$

( ) $9\frac{3}{55}$

19. AIR TRAVEL

A businesswoman's flight leaves Montgomery at 4 P.M. and arrives in Boston at 8:15 P.M. Express the duration of the flight as a mixed number. Check your answer below.

( ) $4\frac{1}{4}$

( ) $5\frac{1}{4}$

( ) $12\frac{1}{4}$

( ) $4\frac{3}{4}$

20. True or False? $\frac{2}{3}\left(-\frac{1}{7}\right) + \frac{1}{3} = \frac{5}{21}$

( ) True
( ) False

21. Evaluate the following algebraic expression for $b = \frac{1}{5}$ and $c = \frac{2}{7}$

$$\frac{1}{4}b^2 + c$$

Select the correct answer.

( ) $\frac{217}{700}$

( ) $\frac{205}{700}$

( ) $\frac{208}{710}$

( ) $\frac{210}{707}$

( ) $\frac{207}{705}$

( ) $\frac{207}{700}$

22. Simplify the following complex fraction: $\dfrac{\frac{1}{3}}{\frac{4}{5}}$

( ) $\frac{5}{12}$

( ) $\frac{12}{5}$

( ) $\frac{15}{4}$

( ) $\frac{4}{15}$

( ) $\frac{3}{20}$

23. Evaluate the expression: $\dfrac{\frac{3}{5}+\frac{1}{2}}{\frac{3}{5}-\frac{1}{2}}$

( ) $\frac{13}{1}$

( ) $\frac{1}{13}$

( ) $\frac{1}{11}$

( ) $\frac{11}{1}$

( ) $\frac{11}{6}$

24. Solve the equation: $\frac{3}{8}x = 9$

( ) -1
( ) 55
( ) 3
( ) -8
( ) -5
( ) 24

25. Of those invited to a wedding, $\frac{1}{8}$ were friends of the bride. The friends of the groom numbered 70. How many people were invited to the wedding?

( ) 77
( ) 82
( ) 139
( ) 32
( ) 80
( ) 171

Answers

1. $\frac{2}{5}$

2. true

3. $\frac{20}{50}$

4. $\frac{1}{6}$

5. $\frac{y^3}{48}$

6. 54

7. $-\frac{65}{21}$

8. $\frac{14u^2}{121n^3}$

9. 9

10. $3x$

11. $\frac{2}{x}$

12. true

13. $\frac{3}{5}$

14. 1

15. $-\frac{53}{5}$

16. $\frac{9}{4}$

17. $13\frac{43}{55}$

18. $9\frac{3}{11}$

19. $4\frac{1}{4}$

20. true

21. $\frac{207}{700}$

22. $\frac{5}{12}$

23. $\frac{11}{1}$

24. 24

25. 80

1. Simplify this fraction to its lowest terms. Select the correct answer.

$\frac{48}{60}$

( ) $\frac{16}{20}$
( ) $\frac{12}{15}$
( ) $\frac{4}{5}$
( ) $\frac{4}{4}$

2. True or False?

The result of simplifying the fraction $\frac{21y^3}{3y^7}$ to its lowest terms is $\frac{7y^3}{y^7}$.

( ) True
( ) False

3. To complete the job, Bob will have to work for 8 hours. If Bob works on the job for only 5 hours, what amount of the job will be completed? Select the correct answer.

( ) $\frac{5}{8}$
( ) $\frac{8}{5}$

4. Multiply. Reduce your answer to lowest terms and select the correct answer.

$$\left(-\frac{3}{24}\right) \times \left(-\frac{6}{18}\right) .$$

( ) $\frac{1}{24}$

( ) $\frac{6}{144}$

( ) $\frac{3}{72}$

5. Multiply. Reduce your answer to lowest terms, and select the correct answer.

$$\frac{3a^{10}}{14} \times \left(\frac{2a}{9a^{4}}\right) .$$

( ) $\frac{14a^{6}}{21}$

( ) $\frac{a^{6}}{189}$

( ) $\frac{a^{7}}{21}$

6. A tennis ball is dropped from a height of*H*inches. Each time it hits the ground, it bounces one-third of the height of its previous bounce. See the illustration and find the missing bounce height*A*, if*H*= 108.

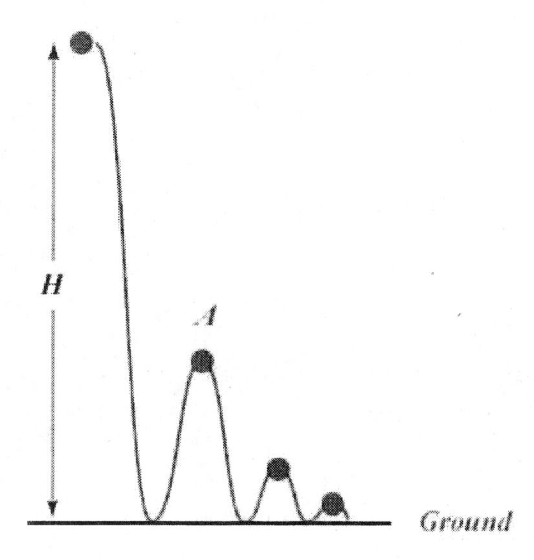

( ) 12
( ) 4
( ) 36

7. Find the quotient and select the correct answer.

$\frac{3}{2} \div \left(-\frac{2}{3}\right)$.

( ) $-\frac{7}{8}$

( ) $-\frac{11}{2}$

( ) $-\frac{9}{4}$

( ) $\frac{13}{7}$

( ) $-\frac{12}{-1}$

( ) $-\frac{4}{6}$

8. Find the quotient and select the correct answer.

$$\frac{5a^5}{2s^4} \div \frac{7a}{11s}.$$

( ) $\frac{55a^4}{14s^3}$

( ) $\frac{54a^6}{15s^5}$

( ) $\frac{53a^5}{16s^4}$

( ) $\frac{56s^4}{17a^3}$

( ) $\frac{58s^5}{12a^4}$

( ) $\frac{57s^6}{13a^5}$

9. UNDERGROUND CABLE

If we take Route 1 we will require fewer days to install underground TV cable from the broadcasting station to the subdivision. True or False?

Proposal	Amount of cable installed per day	Cable required
Route 1	$\frac{10}{4}$ of a mile	140 miles
Route 2	$\frac{2}{4}$ of a mile	30 miles

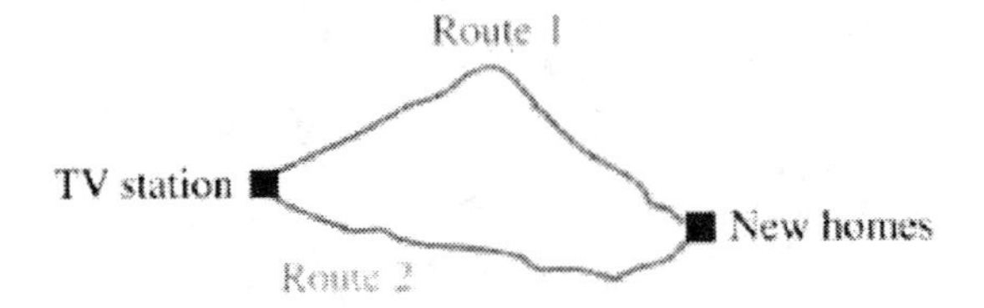

( ) True
( ) False

10. Consider the fraction $\frac{3}{13}$. By what should we multiply the numerator and denominator of this fraction to express it as an equivalent fraction with a denominator of $39z$? Check your answer below.

( ) z
( ) $3z$
( ) $39z$
( ) 3
( ) 39

11. What is the result of the operation $\frac{5}{b} - \frac{3}{b}$?

( ) $\frac{2}{b}$
( ) 2
( ) $\frac{8}{b}$

12. True or False?

$-10 + \frac{3}{5} = \frac{47}{5}$

( ) True
( ) False

13. The illustration below shows the length of each section of a three-part hike. What is the longest section, if

$a = \frac{3}{4}$ $b = \frac{13}{17}$ $c = \frac{5}{8}$

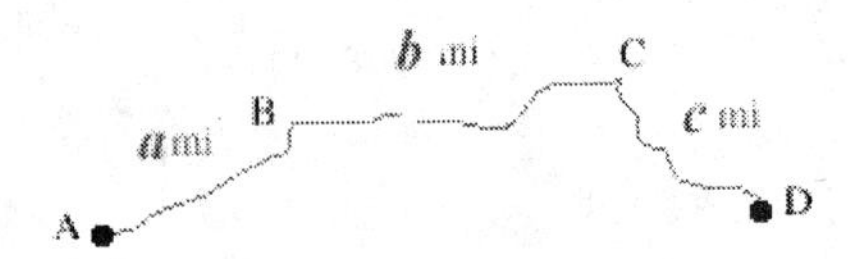

Select the correct answer.

( ) $\frac{5}{8}$

( ) $\frac{13}{17}$

( )

$\frac{3}{4}$

14. In the illustration below the divisions on the face of the meter represent fractions. If the arrow moves up 7 marks, what value will it register? Check your answer in the table at the bottom of the window.

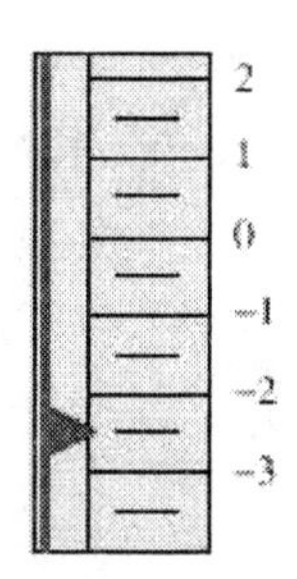

( ) $1\frac{1}{2}$

( ) 1

( ) $2\frac{1}{2}$

15. Write the following mixed number as an improper fraction.

$-4\frac{4}{5}$

Select the correct answer.

( ) $-\frac{8}{5}$

( ) $\frac{20}{5}$

( ) $-\frac{24}{5}$

16. Evaluate the power and write your answer as an improper fraction.

$$\left(3\frac{1}{3}\right)^2$$

Select the correct answer.

( ) $\frac{16}{9}$

( ) $\frac{81}{9}$

( ) $\frac{100}{9}$

17. Find the sum.

$$5\frac{1}{11} + 7\frac{3}{5}$$

Select the correct answer.

( ) $2\frac{38}{55}$

( ) $5\frac{38}{55}$

( ) $12\frac{38}{55}$

18. Find the difference.

$19\frac{3}{8} - 2$

Select the correct answer.

( ) $17\frac{3}{16}$

( ) $17\frac{3}{8}$

( ) $17\frac{5}{8}$

19. AIR TRAVEL

A businesswoman's flight leaves Miami at 2 P.M. and arrives in New York at 10:15 P.M. Express the duration of the flight as a mixed number. Check your answer below.

( ) $9\frac{1}{4}$

( ) $8\frac{1}{4}$

( ) $8\frac{3}{4}$

( ) $12\frac{1}{4}$

20. True or False? $\frac{2}{7}\left(-\frac{4}{5}\right) + \frac{2}{7} = \frac{2}{35}$

( ) True
( ) False

21. Evaluate the following algebraic expression for $b = \frac{1}{3}$ and $c = \frac{2}{7}$

$\frac{1}{4}b^2 + c$

Select the correct answer.

( ) $\frac{80}{262}$

( ) $\frac{79}{257}$

( ) $\frac{82}{259}$

( ) $\frac{89}{252}$

( ) $\frac{79}{252}$

( ) $\frac{77}{252}$

22. Simplify the following complex fraction: $\dfrac{\frac{1}{7}}{\frac{2}{5}}$

( ) $\frac{14}{5}$

( ) $\frac{5}{14}$

( ) $\frac{35}{2}$

( ) $\frac{2}{35}$

( ) $\frac{7}{10}$

23. Evaluate the expression: $\dfrac{\frac{1}{5}+\frac{3}{4}}{\frac{1}{5}-\frac{3}{4}}$

( ) $\frac{-11}{21}$

( ) $\frac{21}{-11}$

( ) $\frac{19}{-6}$

( ) $\frac{-11}{19}$

( ) $\frac{19}{-11}$

24. To improve reading skills, elementary school children read silently at the end of the school day for $\frac{3}{4}$ of an hour on Mondays and for $\frac{5}{8}$ of an hour on Fridays. For the month of January, how many hours did the children read silently in class? Use the following calendar for help.

S	M	T	W	T	F	S
	1	2	3	4	5	6
7	8	9	10	11	12	13
14	15	16	17	18	19	20
21	22	23	24	25	26	27
28	29	30	31			

( ) $12\frac{1}{2}$ hours

( ) $60\frac{1}{4}$ hours

( ) $6\frac{1}{8}$ hours

( ) $16\frac{1}{8}$ hours

( ) $6\frac{1}{4}$ hours

25. Solve the equation: $11u = 3u - 13$

( ) $\frac{13}{11}$

( ) $-\frac{13}{8}$

( ) $\frac{8}{13}$

( ) $\frac{13}{14}$

( ) $-\frac{8}{13}$

( ) $-\frac{13}{14}$

Answers

1. $\frac{4}{5}$

2. true

3. $\frac{5}{8}$

4. $\frac{1}{24}$

5. $\frac{a^7}{21}$

6. 36

7. $-\frac{9}{4}$

8. $\frac{55a^4}{14s^3}$

9. true

10. $3z$

11. $\frac{2}{b}$

12. true

13. $\frac{13}{17}$

14. 1

15. $-\frac{24}{5}$

16. $\frac{100}{9}$

17. $12\frac{38}{55}$

18. $17\frac{3}{8}$

19. $8\frac{1}{4}$

20. true

21. $\frac{79}{252}$

22. $\frac{5}{14}$

23. $\frac{19}{-11}$

24. $6\frac{1}{4}$ hours

25. $-\frac{13}{8}$

1. A design for a yearbook is shown in the illustration. The page is divided into 12 parts. The parts that are shaded will contain pictures, and the remainder of the squares will contain copy. If the pictures are to cover an area of 100 square inches, how many square inches are there on the page?

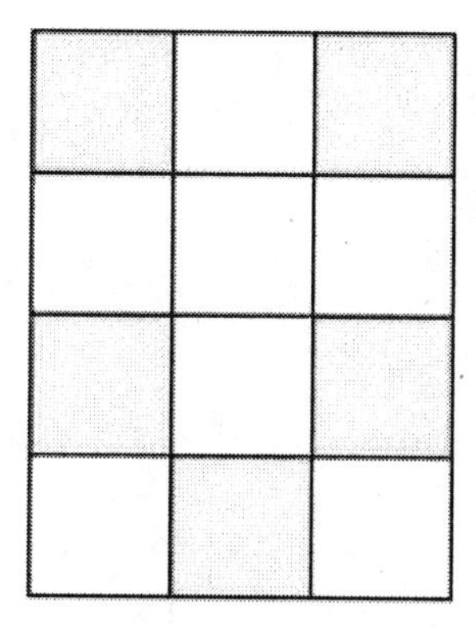

( ) 253
( ) 240
( ) 477
( ) 579
( ) 57
( ) 314

2. What is the difference in power between a $\frac{1}{3}$-hp and a $\frac{1}{4}$-hp garage door opener?

3. The denominators of two fractions are given below. Find the lowest common denominator.

6 and 36

4. Solve the equation: $-3 - 25 + \frac{7}{7}t = 0$

( ) 38
( ) 63
( ) 35
( ) 22
( ) 28
( ) 58

5. By what are the numerator and the denominator of the following fraction being multiplied?

$$\frac{11 \cdot a}{13 \cdot a}$$

( ) 11
( ) *a*
( ) 13

6. Complete the operation and simplify if necessary.

$$\frac{3}{5} - \frac{3x}{13}$$

Select the correct answer.

( ) $\frac{39 + 15x}{65}$
( ) $\frac{39 - 15x}{65}$
( ) $\frac{39 - 15x}{13}$

7. To complete the job, Bob will have to work for 8 hours. If Bob works on the job for only 5 hours, what amount of the job will be completed? Select the correct answer.

( ) $\frac{8}{5}$
( ) $\frac{5}{8}$

8. In developing taillights for an automobile, designers must be aware of a safety standard that requires an area of 70 square inches to be visible from behind the vehicle. If the designers want the taillights to be $a = 3\frac{1}{2}$ inches high, how wide must they be to meet safety standards? (See illustration.)

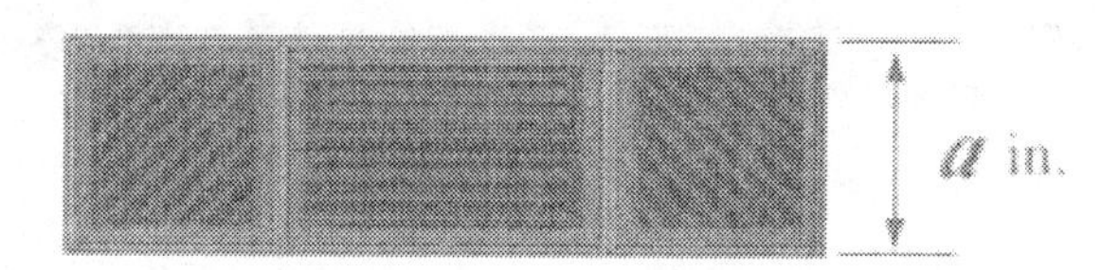

9. True or False?

The following expressions are equivalent.

$-4y$ and $\frac{-24y}{6}$

( ) True
( ) False

10. True or False?

$$-2 + \frac{9}{13} = \frac{17}{13}$$

( ) True
( ) False

11. Complete the operation below.

$$\frac{10}{c} + \frac{5}{c}$$

12. Simplify this fraction to its lowest terms. Select the correct answer.

$$\frac{20m^5c^4}{110m^4c^5}$$

( ) $\frac{2m^5c^4}{11m^4c^5}$

( ) $\frac{20m}{110c}$

( ) $\frac{2m}{11c}$

13. Multiply and select the correct answer.

$\frac{a}{m} \times \frac{n}{h}$.

( ) $\frac{ah}{mn}$

( ) $\frac{mn}{ah}$

( ) $\frac{an}{mh}$

14. How many people can be served $\frac{1}{2}$-pound hamburgers if a caterer purchases 450 pounds of ground beef?

15. Consider the fraction $\frac{3}{7}$. By what should we multiply the numerator and denominator of this fraction to express it as an equivalent fraction with a denominator of $28c$?

16. Evaluate the expression: $\dfrac{\frac{1}{5}+\frac{3}{4}}{\frac{1}{5}-\frac{3}{4}}$

( ) $\dfrac{-11}{19}$

( ) $\dfrac{19}{-11}$

( ) $\dfrac{-11}{21}$

( ) $\dfrac{19}{-6}$

( ) $\dfrac{21}{-11}$

17. Solve the equation: $4x - \dfrac{11}{5} = \dfrac{1}{7}$

( ) $-\dfrac{46}{140}$

( ) $\dfrac{82}{140}$

( ) $-\dfrac{82}{140}$

( ) $\dfrac{62}{35}$

( ) $\dfrac{75}{35}$

( ) $\dfrac{46}{140}$

18. Complete the operation below and simplify if necessary.

$$\frac{18}{c} - \frac{3}{c}$$

19. Find the quotient and select the correct answer.

$$\frac{5f^5}{3s^4} \div \frac{11f}{2s}.$$

( ) $\frac{6f^6}{38s^5}$

( ) $\frac{15s^4}{28f^3}$

( ) $\frac{10f^4}{33s^3}$

( ) $\frac{7f^5}{31s^4}$

( ) $\frac{5s^5}{30f^4}$

( ) $\frac{8s^6}{29f^5}$

20. Find the area of the license plate in the illustration below if

$a = 4\frac{1}{4}$ and $b = 6\frac{1}{4}$

Select the correct answer.

( ) $\frac{25}{16}$

( ) $\frac{425}{16}$

( ) $\frac{384}{16}$

21. Evaluate the expression and simplify if necessary.

$$\frac{2}{7}\left(-\frac{4}{5}\right) + \frac{2}{5}$$

22. Find the quotient. $8 \div \frac{1}{9}$.

23. The fire escape stairway in an office building is shown in the illustration below. Each riser is $7\frac{1}{2}$ inches high. If each floor is 195 inches high and the building is 60 stories tall, how many steps are there in the stairway?

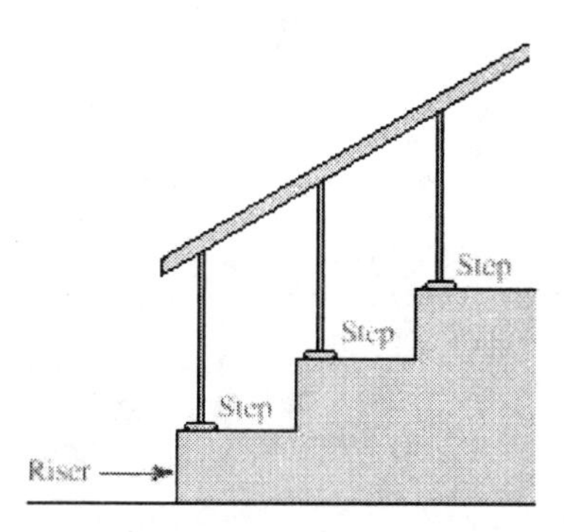

Select the correct answer.

( ) 390
( ) 780
( ) 1560

24. A telephone book has white pages and yellow pages. $\frac{6}{7}$ of the book consists of the white pages; the yellow pages number 130. What is the total number of pages in the telephone book?

25. MARATHON

Each lap around a stadium track is $\frac{1}{4}$ mile. How many laps would a runner have to complete to get a 49-mile workout? Find your answer below.

( ) 408
( ) 446
( ) 177
( ) 196
( ) 394
( ) 375

Answers

1. 240

2. $\frac{1}{12}$

3. 36

4. 28

5. a

6. $\frac{39 - 15x}{65}$

7. $\frac{5}{8}$

8. 20

9. true

10. true

11. $\frac{15}{c}$

12. $\frac{2m}{11c}$

13. $\frac{an}{mh}$

14. 900

15. $4c$

16. $\frac{19}{-11}$

17. $\frac{82}{140}$

18. $\frac{15}{c}$

19. $\frac{10t^4}{33s^3}$

20. $\frac{425}{16}$

21. $\frac{2}{35}$

22. 72

23. 1560

24. 910

25. 196

1. The operator of a machine is to turn the dial shown below counter clockwise from setting 2 to setting B. Describe this action as a fraction of one complete revolution.

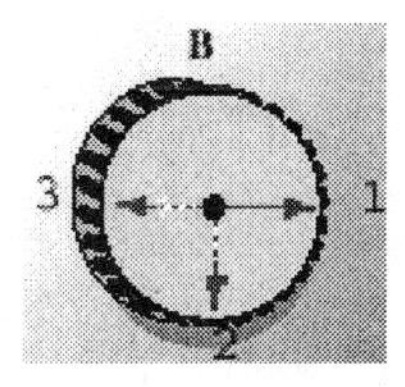

2. Write the following mixed number as an improper fraction:

$-6\frac{6}{7}$

3. Find $10 \div \frac{2}{4}$. Choose your answer below.

( ) 20
( ) 40
( ) 1.25
( ) 20
( ) 30

4. Find the quotient.

$\frac{1}{5t} \div \left(-\frac{13}{3}\right)$.

5. A hardware chain purchases large amounts of nails and packages them in $\frac{5}{3}$ pound bags for sale. How many of these bags of nails can be obtained from 9735 pounds of nails?

( ) 2917
( ) 2137
( ) 5841
( ) 10149
( ) 137
( ) 1275

6. Multiply these fractions and write your answer as an improper fraction.

$$\left(-4\frac{1}{3}\right) \cdot \left(-3\frac{1}{5}\right)$$

7. Divide.

$$5 \div 5\frac{1}{3}$$

Select the correct answer.

( ) $\frac{15}{15}$
( ) $\frac{15}{16}$
( ) $\frac{5}{16}$

8. Write the following mixed number as an improper fraction.

$-6\frac{1}{7}$

Select the correct answer.

( ) $-\frac{43}{7}$

( ) $\frac{42}{7}$

( ) $-\frac{7}{7}$

9. Solve the equation: $m - \frac{3}{11} = \frac{1}{11}$

10. How much molding will be needed to make the square picture frame in this illustration if $a = 2\frac{1}{28}$?

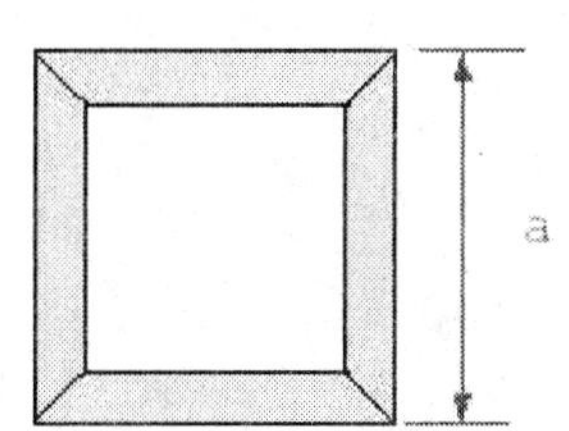

11. Complete the operation and simplify if necessary.

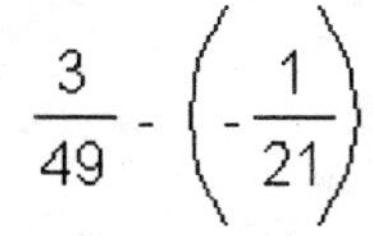

$$\frac{3}{49} - \left(-\frac{1}{21}\right)$$

12. A set of forestry maps divides the 2654 acres of an old-growth forest into $\frac{2}{3}$ acre sections. How many sections do the maps contain?

( ) 3981
( ) 627
( ) 188
( ) 6428
( ) 8297
( ) 6940

13. A design for a bathroom tile is shown in the illustration below, where$A$=B= 3. Find the area of the tile that is blue.

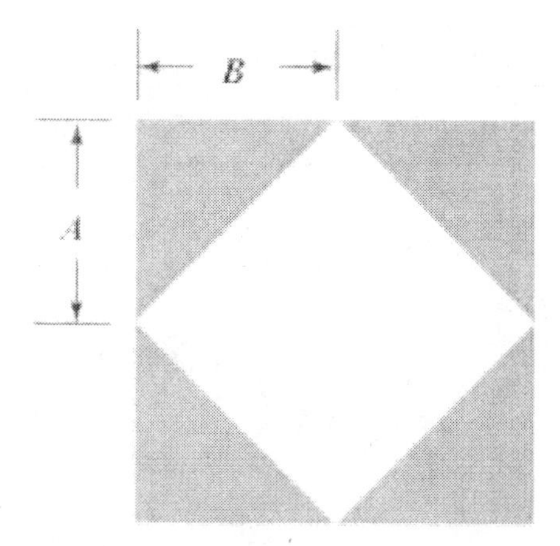

( ) 9
( ) 18
( ) 36

14. COOKING

A recipe calls for $\frac{7}{2}$ cup of flour, and the only measuring container you have holds $\frac{1}{8}$ cup. How many $\frac{1}{8}$ cups of flour would you need to add to follow the recipe? Select the correct answer.

( ) 21
( ) 25
( ) 4
( ) 31
( ) 12
( ) 28

15. COOKING

A recipe calls for $\frac{5}{3}$ cup of flour, and the only measuring container you have holds $\frac{1}{9}$ cup. How many $\frac{1}{9}$ cups of flour would you need to add to follow the recipe?

16. Find the sum.

$4\frac{3}{13} + 8\frac{2}{13}$

Select the correct answer.

( ) $12\frac{5}{78}$

( ) $12\frac{5}{13}$

( ) $4\frac{5}{13}$

17. To complete the job, Bob will have to work for 4 hours. If Bob works on the job for only 3 hours, what amount of the job will be completed? Select the correct answer.

( ) $\frac{3}{4}$

( ) $\frac{4}{3}$

18. Evaluate the following algebraic expression for $x = \frac{4}{3}$ and $y = \frac{2}{5}$

$$\left|\frac{2x}{y - x}\right|$$

Simplify your answer and express it as a mixed number if possible.

19. Find the perimeter of the following triangle, where $a = 1\frac{6}{7}$ and $b = \frac{3}{4}$

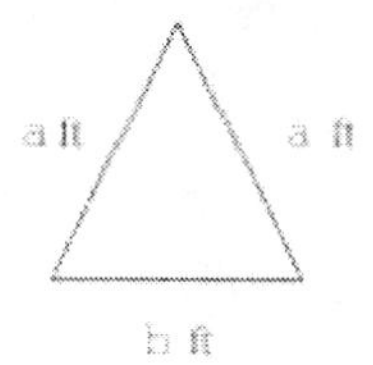

20. Solve the equation: $13m = 7m - 11$

( ) $-\frac{11}{20}$

( ) $\frac{11}{13}$

( ) $\frac{6}{11}$

( ) $-\frac{6}{11}$

( ) $-\frac{11}{6}$

( ) $\frac{11}{20}$

21. Simplify the following fraction and check your answer below.

$15\frac{19}{13}$

( ) $15\frac{6}{13}$

( ) $16\frac{6}{13}$

( ) $16\frac{19}{13}$

22. Select all of the following expressions that correctly express the product of this multiplication problem.

$\frac{55}{9} \cdot y$.

[ ] $\frac{55}{9}y$

[ ] $\frac{55y}{9}$

[ ] $\frac{55}{9y}$

23. Find the difference and simplify if necessary.

$225\frac{3}{6} - 105\frac{3}{36}$

24. During a checkup, a pediatrician found that only $\frac{5}{7}$ of a child's baby teeth had emerged. The mother counted 10 teeth in the child's mouth. How many baby teeth will the child eventually have?

( ) 6
( ) 14
( ) 32
( ) 1
( ) 20
( ) 34

25. Place a < or > symbol between the fractions to make a true statement.

$\frac{3}{4} \quad \frac{1}{2}$

Answers

1. $\frac{2}{4}$

2. $-\frac{48}{7}$

3. 20

4. $-\frac{3}{65t}$

5. 5841

6. $\frac{208}{15}$

7. $\frac{15}{16}$

8. $-\frac{43}{7}$

9. $\frac{44}{121}$

10. $8\frac{1}{7}$

11. $\frac{16}{147}$

12. 3981

13. 18

14. 28

15. 15

16. $12\frac{5}{13}$

17. $\frac{3}{4}$

18. $\frac{120}{42}$

19. $\frac{125}{28}$

20. $-\frac{11}{6}$

21. $16\frac{6}{13}$

22. $\frac{55}{9}y$ I $\frac{55y}{9}$

23. $120\frac{5}{12}$

24. 14

25. $\frac{1}{2} < \frac{3}{4}$

1. Simplify this fraction to its lowest terms. Select the correct answer.

$\frac{48}{60}$

( ) $\frac{16}{20}$

( ) $\frac{4}{4}$

( ) $\frac{4}{5}$

( ) $\frac{12}{15}$

2. True or False?

The result of simplifying the fraction $\frac{20a^2}{2a^5}$ to its lowest terms is $\frac{10a^2}{a^5}$.

( ) True
( ) False

3. This illustration shows the party affiliation of the governors of the 50 states.

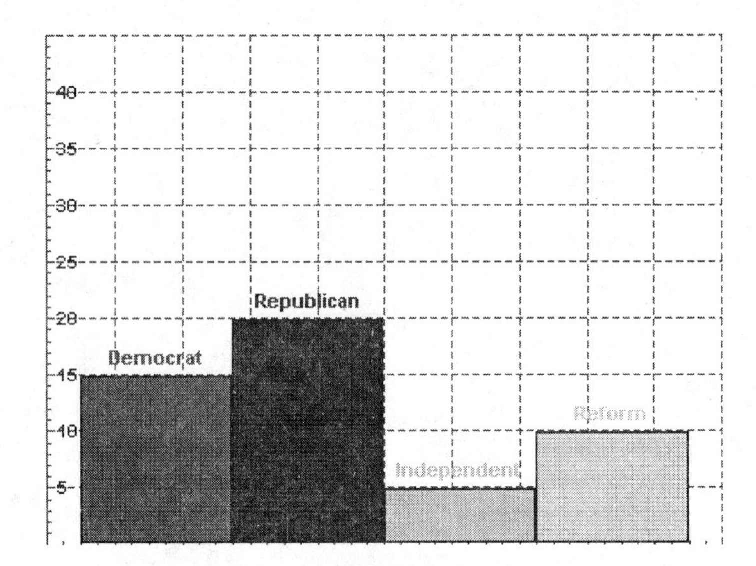

Which fraction is correct for Democrats?

( ) $\frac{15}{50}$

( ) $\frac{20}{50}$

( ) $\frac{5}{50}$

( ) $\frac{10}{50}$

4. To complete the job, Bob will have to work for 8 hours. If Bob works on the job for only 7 hours, what amount of the job will be completed? Select the correct answer.

( ) $\frac{7}{8}$

( ) $\frac{8}{7}$

5. Multiply. Reduce your answer to lowest terms and select the correct answer.

$$\left(-\frac{7}{20}\right) \times \left(-\frac{10}{28}\right).$$

( ) $\frac{7}{56}$

( ) $\frac{10}{80}$

( ) $\frac{1}{8}$

6. Multiply. Reduce your answer to lowest terms, and select the correct answer.

$$\frac{2b^8}{8} \times \left(\frac{4b}{18b^3}\right).$$

( ) $\frac{b^6}{18}$

( ) $\frac{b^5}{324}$

( ) $\frac{8b^5}{18}$

7. A tennis ball is dropped from a height of *H* inches. Each time it hits the ground, it bounces one-third of the height of its previous bounce. See the illustration and find the missing bounce height *A*, if *H* = 135.

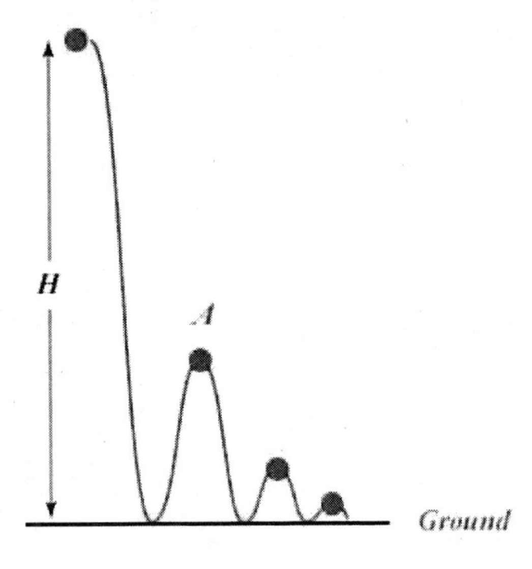

( ) 5
( ) 15
( ) 45

8. Find the quotient and select the correct answer.

$\frac{5}{11} \div \left(-\frac{2}{13}\right).$

( ) $-\frac{65}{22}$

( ) $-\frac{69}{19}$

( ) $\frac{62}{17}$

( ) $-\frac{63}{24}$

( ) $-\frac{60}{20}$

( ) $-\frac{67}{26}$

9. Find the quotient and select the correct answer.

$$\frac{3u^5}{11s^5} \div \frac{11u}{2s}.$$

( ) $\frac{8s^5}{120u^5}$

( ) $\frac{7s^4}{123u^4}$

( ) $\frac{5u^5}{116s^5}$

( ) $\frac{6u^4}{121s^4}$

( ) $\frac{11u^6}{122s^6}$

( ) $\frac{1s^6}{126u^6}$

10. FURNITURE

A production process applies several layers of a clear acrylic coat to outdoor furniture to help protect it from the weather. If each protective coat is $\frac{3}{20}$ inch thick, how many applications will be needed to build up $\frac{3}{2}$ inch of clear finish? Select the correct answer.

( ) 3
( ) 10
( ) 21
( ) 12
( ) 5
( ) 19

11. A hardware chain purchases large amounts of nails and packages them in $\frac{5}{3}$ pound bags for sale. How many of these bags of nails can be obtained from 9720 pounds of nails?

( ) 2285
( ) 7561
( ) 13494
( ) 5832
( ) 3095
( ) 12204

12. Consider the fraction $\frac{3}{13}$. By what should we multiply the numerator and denominator of this fraction to express it as an equivalent fraction with a denominator of $117b$?

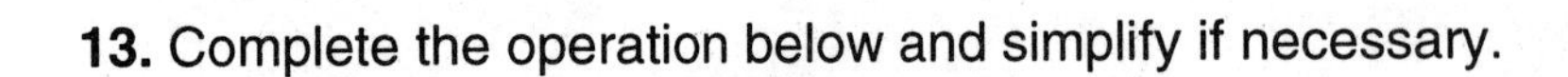

13. Complete the operation below and simplify if necessary.

$$\frac{12}{c} - \frac{1}{c}$$

14. Complete the operation and simplify if necessary.

$$-7 + \frac{2}{3}$$

15. The illustration below shows the length of each part of a three-part hike. Match the lengths from longest to shortest in the table at the bottom of the window, if

$a = \frac{1}{2}$ $b = \frac{6}{11}$ $c = \frac{1}{4}$

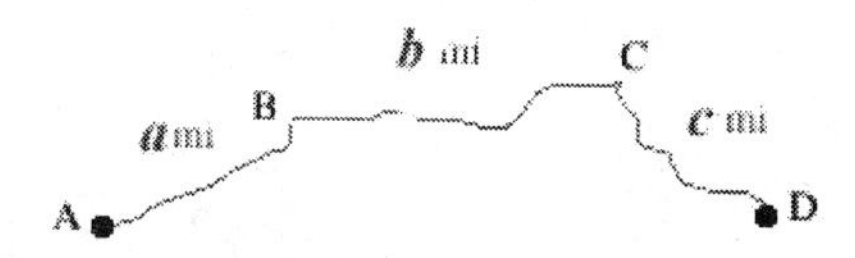

$\frac{1}{4}$	longest
$\frac{1}{2}$	shortest
$\frac{6}{11}$	middle length

16. In the illustration below the divisions on the face of the meter represent fractions. If the arrow moves up 3 marks, what value will it register?

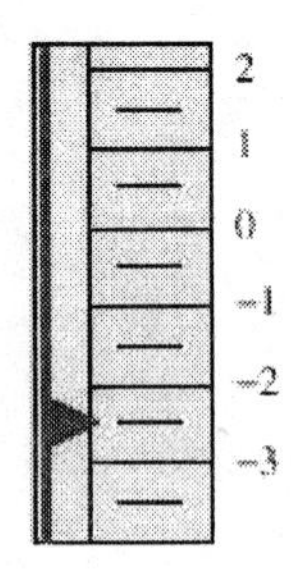

17. Write the following mixed number as an improper fraction:

$-6\frac{1}{5}$

18. Evaluate the power and write your answer as an improper fraction.

$\left(1\frac{5}{7}\right)^2$

19. Find the sum and simplify if necessary.

$12\frac{2}{11} + 9\frac{1}{5}$

20. Find the difference.

$20\frac{7}{8} - 8$

21. AIR TRAVEL

A businesswoman's flight leaves Miami at 3 P.M. and arrives in New York at 8:15 P.M. Express the duration of the flight as a mixed number.

22. Evaluate the expression and simplify if necessary.

$\frac{1}{5}\left(-\frac{4}{7}\right) + \frac{4}{11}$

23. Evaluate the following algebraic expression for $b = \frac{1}{5}$ and $c = \frac{2}{7}$

$$\frac{1}{2}b^2 + c$$

Select the correct answer.

( ) $\frac{107}{350}$

( ) $\frac{110}{357}$

( ) $\frac{107}{355}$

( ) $\frac{117}{350}$

( ) $\frac{108}{360}$

( ) $\frac{105}{350}$

24. Simplify the following complex fraction: $\dfrac{\frac{1}{5}}{\frac{4}{3}}$

( ) $\frac{5}{12}$

( ) $\frac{4}{15}$

( ) $\frac{15}{4}$

( ) $\frac{20}{3}$

( ) $\frac{3}{20}$

25. To improve reading skills, elementary school children read silently at the end of the school day for $\frac{3}{8}$ of an hour on Mondays and for $\frac{1}{4}$ of an hour on Fridays. For the month of January, how many hours did the children read silently in class? Use the following calendar for help.

S	M	T	W	T	F	S
	1	2	3	4	5	6
7	8	9	10	11	12	13
14	15	16	17	18	19	20
21	22	23	24	25	26	27
28	29	30	31			

Answers

1. $\frac{4}{5}$

2. true

3. $\frac{15}{50}$

4. $\frac{7}{8}$

5. $\frac{1}{8}$

6. $\frac{b^6}{18}$

7. 45

8. $-\frac{65}{22}$

9. $\frac{6u^4}{121s^4}$

10. 10

11. 5832

12. $9b$

13. $\frac{11}{c}$

14. $\frac{-19}{3}$

15. 1/4 -> shortest, 6/11 -> longest, 1/2 -> middle length

16. -1

17. $-\frac{31}{5}$

18. $\frac{144}{49}$

19. $21\frac{21}{55}$

20. $12\frac{7}{8}$

21. $5\frac{1}{4}$

22. $\frac{24}{35}$

23. $\frac{107}{350}$

24. $\frac{3}{20}$

25. $\frac{92}{32}$

1. Write the following fraction as a decimal: $\frac{9}{10}$

2. Round the following decimal to the nearest tenth:

798.67

3. As of January 2000, Janet Evans held the world record in swimming. Her time is given below in minutes and seconds. Round the seconds to the nearest tenth of a second.

Janet Evans, 400-meter freestyle, 4:04.81

4. The table below shows the cities with the highest one-hour concentrations of ozone (in parts per million) during the summer of 1999.

Crestline, California	0.168
Galveston, Texas	0.122
Houston, Texas	0.137
Texas City, Texas	0.186
Westport, Connecticut	0.15
White Plains, New York	0.107

Which reading is highest?

5. Add the following numbers: $41 + 7.83 + 4.7 + 5.34$

6. Subtract: $36 - 20.553$

7. Evaluate the following expression: $29.5 - 20.8 + 38.1$

8. The following table shows a patient's health chart. A nurse failed to fill in certain portions. (98.6° Fahrenheit is considered normal.) Complete the chart.

Patient's Temperature	How much above normal
100.6	
	1.1
98.7	
99.5	
	2.3

9. Multiply $\frac{17}{100}$ and $\frac{3}{10}$. Write the answer first as a fraction and then as a decimal.

10. Evaluate the following expression:

$-6.1 \cdot |-7.5| - 0.3 \cdot |-4.9|$

11. The barbell illustrated below is evenly loaded with weights. If A= 64.5 pounds, B= 22.7 pounds and C= 20.3 pounds, how much weight is loaded on the barbell?

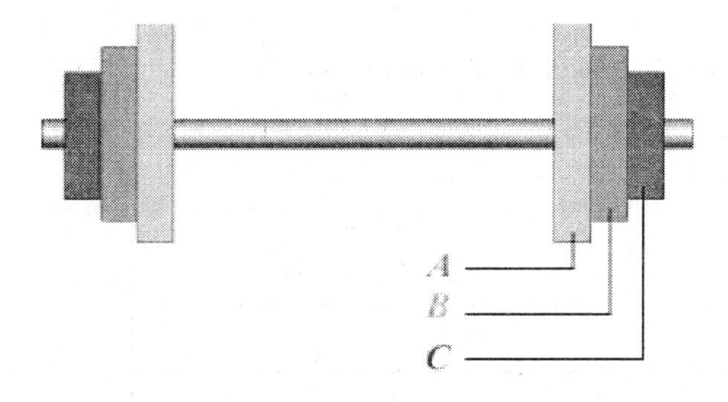

12. Divide: $35.8 \div 0.04$

13. Evaluate the following expression. If the answer is not exact, round it to the nearest hundredth.

$$\frac{9.3 - x^2 + 3.9}{x^3} \text{ for } x=0.5$$

14. The following table shows the first row of the starting grid for the 1998 Indianapolis 500 automobile race. The drivers were ranked in this order based on the speed driven in a qualifying run. What was the mean qualifying speed for the drivers in the first row? (Round the result to the nearest thousandth if necessary.)

Billy Boat	Greg Ray	Kenny Brack
223.171mph	221.511mph	220.321mph

15. Write the following fraction in decimal form:

$-\frac{6}{200}$

16. Evaluate the following expression. Express your answer as a fraction in lowest terms.

$\frac{1}{9} + 0.5$

17. Write the following fraction in decimal form.

$\frac{5}{999}$

18. A geologist weighed a rock sample at the site where it was discovered and found it to weigh $15\frac{3}{8}$ lb. Later, a more accurate digital scale in the laboratory gave the weight as 15.171 lb. What is the difference between the two measurements?

19. In what order should the operations be undone to isolate the variable in the following equation?

$\frac{a}{5} - 2.5 = 2.2$

20. Solve the following equation:

$\frac{d}{6} = -21.5$

21. What is the value of a in the following equation?

$-3.3a - 5.5 + 4.1a = -1.9$

22. Midway through a telethon, the donations had reached $22.9 million. How much more was donated in the second half of the program if the final total pledged was $38.4 million?

$ ___ million more was donated.

23. Without evaluating the square roots, write the largest of the following three numbers.

$-\sqrt{29}$, $-\sqrt{15}$, $-\sqrt{19}$

24. What is the whole number whose square lies between 140 and 149?

25. Simplify the following expression without using a calculator:

$\sqrt{49}$

Answers

1. 0.9

2. 798.67

3. 4.81

4. 0.186

5. 58.87

6. 15.447

7. 46.8

8. 100.6, 2, 99.7, 1.1, 98.7, 0.1, 99.5, 0.9, 100.9, 2.3

9. $\frac{51}{1000}$, 0.051

10. -47.22

11. 215

12. 895

13. 103.6

14. 221.667667

15. -0.03

16. $\frac{55}{90}$

17. 0.005005...

18. 0.204

19.

20. -129

21. 4.5

22. 15.5

23. $-\sqrt{15}$

24. 12

25. 7

1. Write the following fraction as a decimal: $\frac{6}{10}$

2. Round the following decimal to the nearest hundredth:

54.4599

3. We use a decimal point when working with dollars, but the decimal point is not necessary when working with cents. For each dollar amount give the equivalent amount expressed as cents.

Dollars	Cents
\$0.12	
\$0.41	
\$2.62	

4. The table below shows the cities with the highest one-hour concentrations of ozone (in parts per million) during the summer of 1999.

Crestline, California	0.14
Galveston, Texas	0.161
Houston, Texas	0.169
Texas City, Texas	0.183
Westport, Connecticut	0.151
White Plains, New York	0.169

Which reading is highest?

5. Add the following numbers: $47 + 6.48 + 2.3 + 3.28$

6. Evaluate the following expression: $(-20.8 - 43.31) - (-30)$

7. Certain dimensions of a compact car are shown below, where A=182, $a1$=44.2 and $a2$=39.3. What is the wheelbase of the car?

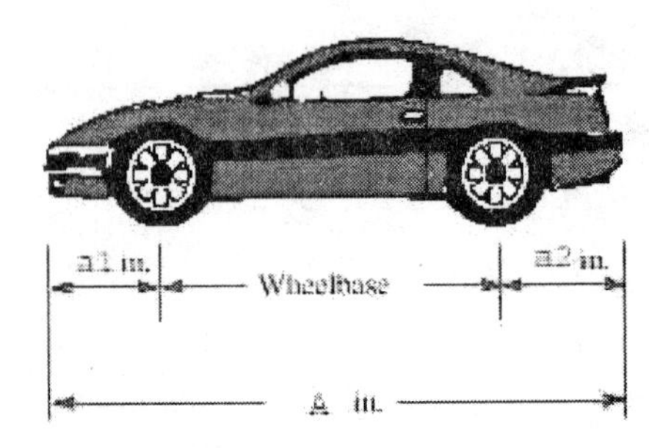

8. Multiply $\frac{13}{100}$ and $\frac{3}{1000}$. Write the answer first as a fraction and then as a decimal.

9. Evaluate the following expression:

$-6.3 \cdot |-5.6| - 1.7 \cdot |-7.9|$

10. In the city map illustrated below, the streets form a grid. Each street is 0.34 miles apart. Find the distance of a trip from the airport to city hall.

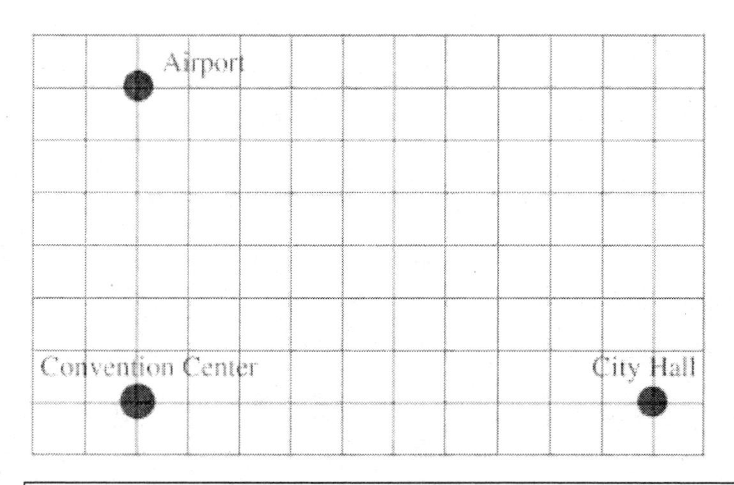

11. Divide: $47.8 \div 0.04$

12. Evaluate the following expression and round the result to the nearest hundredth:

$$\frac{(0.1)^2 - (0.6)^2}{0.485 + 0.9}$$

13. Evaluate the following expression. If the answer is not exact, round it to the nearest hundredth.

$$\frac{1.9 - x^2 + 7.5}{x^3} \text{ for } x = 0.3$$

14. A volume control is shown in the illustration below. If the distance between the low and high settings is 14.28 cm, how far apart are the equally spaced volume settings?

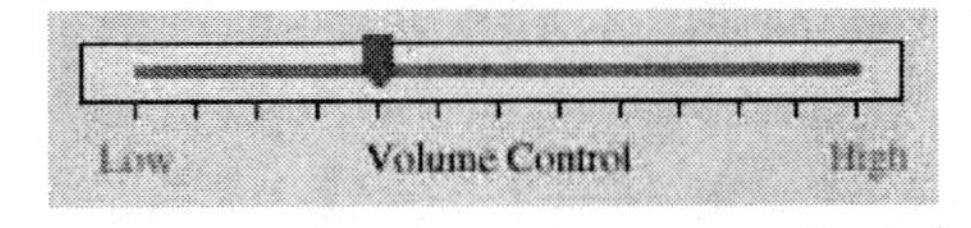

15. Write the following fraction in decimal form:

$$-\frac{9}{100}$$

16. Fill in the correct symbol (> or <) to make a true statement:

$$\frac{7}{16} \_\_\_\_ 0.4575$$

17. Write the following fraction in decimal form.

$$\frac{5}{999}$$

18. In what order should the operations be undone to isolate the variable in the following equation?

$$\frac{a}{17.8} - 1.1 = 4.6$$

19. Solve the following equation:

$$\frac{d}{20} = 27.7$$

20. What is the value of a in the following equation?

$5.7a - 2.1 + 7.3a = 124$

21. Without evaluating the square roots, write the largest of the following three numbers.

$-\sqrt{21}\ ,\ -\sqrt{15}\ ,\ -\sqrt{28}$

22. What is the whole number whose square lies between 165 and 174?

23. Simplify the following expression without using a calculator:

$-\sqrt{0.81}$

24. Use a calculator to evaluate: $2846.845 + 5564.2877$

25. Use the imaginary triangles set up by a surveyor in the illustration below to find the length of the lake.

$L = \sqrt{454276}$ meters

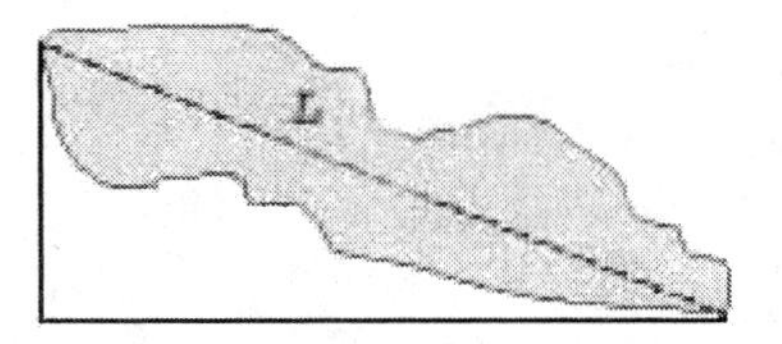

Answers

1. 0.6

2. 54.4599

3. 0.12, 12, 0.41, 41, 2.62, 262

4. 0.183

5. 59.06

6. -34.11

7. 98.5

8. $\frac{39}{100000}$, 0.00039

9. -48.71

10. 5.44

11. 1195

12. -0.252708

13. 344.814815

14. 1.19

15. -0.09

16. $0.4575 > \frac{7}{16}$

17. 0.005005...

18.

19. 554

20. 9.7

21. $-\sqrt{15}$

22. 13

23. -0.9

24. 8411.1327

25. 674

1. Write the following fraction as a decimal: $\frac{3}{10}$

2. Round the following decimal to the nearest thousandth: 680.4813

Select the correct answer:

( ) 680.481
( ) 680.410
( ) 680.482
( ) 680.4814

3. We use a decimal point when working with dollars, but the decimal point is not necessary when working with cents. For each dollar amount give the equivalent amount expressed as cents.

Dollars	Cents
$0.07	
$0.66	
$1.12	

4. The table below shows the cities with the highest one-hour concentrations of ozone (in parts per million) during the summer of 1999.

Crestline, California	0.182
Galveston, Texas	0.104
Houston, Texas	0.186
Texas City, Texas	0.199
Westport, Connecticut	0.135
White Plains, New York	0.187

Which city has the highest reading?

( ) Galveston, TX
( ) Houston, TX
( ) Texas City, TX
( ) Crestline, CA
( ) Westport, CT
( ) White Plains, NY

5. Add the following numbers: $10 + 9.32 + 7.8 + 2.58$

6. Subtract: $63 - 43.799$

( ) 19.199
( ) 19.201
( ) 20.201
( ) 19.326
( ) 19.211
( ) 19.101

7. Evaluate the following expression: $38.5 - 34.9 + 38.7$

8. The following bar chart shows the six most-watched television shows of all time: "Mash," "Dallas," "Cheers," "The Day After," "Roots," and "Seinfeld." What was the combined total audience of all six shows?

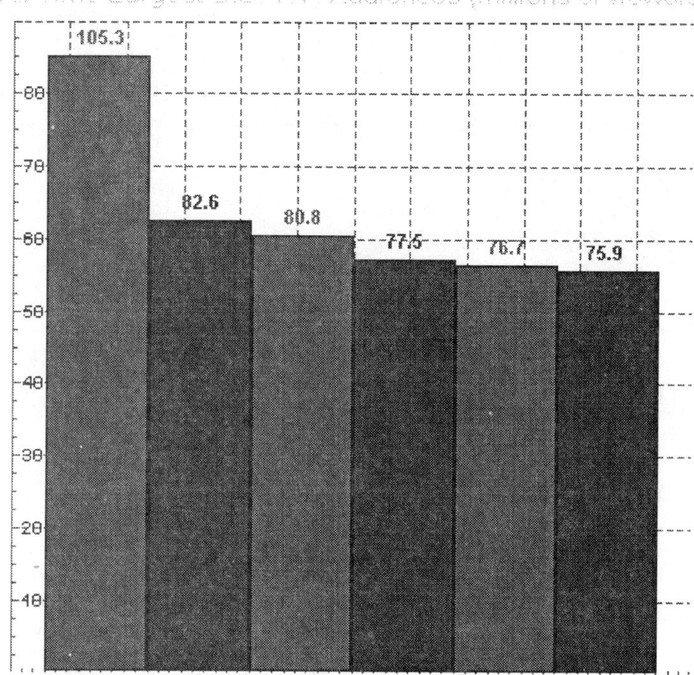

Select the correct answer:

( ) 487.7 million
( ) 488.8 million
( ) 500.8 million
( ) 498.8 million
( ) 498.9 million

9. Multiply $\frac{7}{10}$ and $\frac{9}{100}$. Write the answer first as a fraction and then as a decimal.

10. Evaluate the following expression:

$-9.5 \cdot |-6.3| - 1.1 \cdot |-2.5|$

11. Long bricks, called coping, can be used to outline the edge of a swimming pool. How many meters of coping will be needed in the construction of the swimming pool shown in the illustration? A= 39.9 meters, B= 95.7 meters.

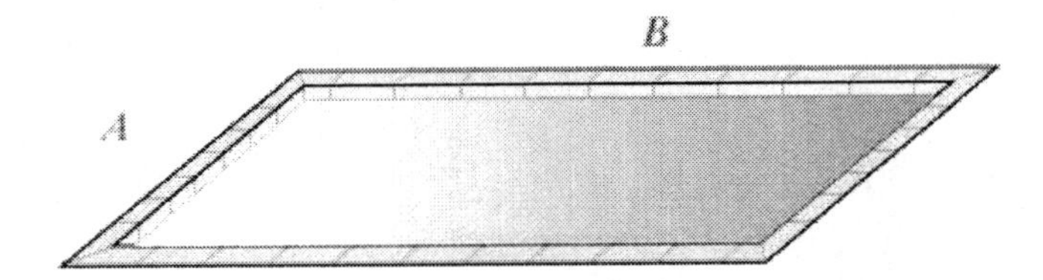

Select the correct answer:

( ) 3818.43 meters
( ) 135.6 meters
( ) 271.2 meters

12. Divide: $34.4 \div 0.08$

13. Evaluate the following expression. If the answer is not exact, round it to the nearest hundredth.

$$\frac{3.1 - x^2 + 1.1}{x^3} \text{ for } x=0.7$$

14. A volume control is shown in the illustration below. If the distance between the low and high settings is 21 cm, how far apart are the equally spaced volume settings?

Select the correct answer:

( ) 1.75 cm
( ) 2.85 cm
( ) 2.75 cm
( ) 2.05 cm
( ) 1.65 cm

15. Write the following fraction in decimal form:

$-\frac{9}{200}$

16. Write the following fraction in decimal form.

$\frac{7}{999}$

17. Evaluate the following expression.

$$\frac{4}{5} + 0.9$$

Select the correct answer:

( ) $\frac{17}{10}$
( ) none of these
( ) $\frac{13}{15}$
( ) $\frac{36}{50}$

18. While doing a tuneup, a mechanic checks the gap on the spark plugs of a car to be sure they are firing correctly. The owner's manual states that the gap should be $\frac{3}{145}$ of an inch. The gauge the mechanic uses to check the gap registers 0.022 inch, in decimal form. Is the spark plug gap too large or too small?

Select the correct answer:

( ) too small
( ) too large

19. In what order should the operations be undone to isolate the variable in the following equation?

$$\frac{b}{15.6} - 1.7 = 5.4$$

20. Solve the following equation:

$$\frac{d}{13} = -29.5$$

Select the correct answer:

( ) d= -383.5
( ) d= 86.9
( ) d= -2.269231
( ) d= -296.6

21. What is the value of x in the following equation?

$8.3x - 9.9 + 1.5x = 51.84$

22. One 5-ounce serving of broiled ground beef has 11.2 grams of saturated fat. This is 28 times the amount of saturated fat in 1 cup of cooked crab meat. How many grams of saturated fat are in 1 cup of cooked crab meat?

Select the correct answer:

( ) 2
( ) 2.5
( ) 5.4
( ) 0.4

23. Without evaluating the square roots, write the largest of the following three numbers.

$-\sqrt{26}$, $-\sqrt{22}$, $-\sqrt{24}$

24. What is the whole number whose square lies between 32 and 41?

Select the correct answer:

( ) 11
( ) 6
( ) 5
( ) 8

25. Simplify the following expression without using a calculator:

$\sqrt{196}$

Answers

1. 0.3

2. 680.481

3. 0.07, 7, 0.66, 66, 1.12, 112

4. Texas City, TX

5. 29.7

6. 19.201

7. 42.3

8. 498.8 million

9. $\frac{63}{1000}$, 0.063

10. -62.6

11. 271.2 meters

12. 430

13. 10.816327

14. 1.75 cm

15. -0.045

16. 0.007007...

17. $\frac{17}{10}$

18. too large

19.

20. d= -383.5

21. 6.3

22. 0.4

23. $-\sqrt{22}$

24. 6

25. 14

1. Write the following fraction in decimal form: $\frac{4}{6}$

( ) 0.666667
( ) 0.066667
( ) 0.6
( ) 0.4

2. Round the following decimal to the nearest tenth:

558.33

Select the correct answer:

( ) 558.34
( ) 558.3
( ) 558.5
( ) 558.4

3. As of January 2000, Janet Evans held the world record in swimming. Her time is given below in minutes and seconds. Round it to the nearest tenth of a second.

Janet Evans, 400-meter freestyle, 4:01.03

Select the correct answer:

( ) 4:01.13
( ) 4:01.1
( ) 4:01.2
( ) 4:01.0

4. The table below shows the cities with the highest one-hour concentrations of ozone (in parts per million) during the summer of 1999.

Crestline, California	0.129
Galveston, Texas	0.137
Houston, Texas	0.118
Texas City, Texas	0.197
Westport, Connecticut	0.1
White Plains, New York	0.145

Which city has the highest reading?

( ) White Plains, NY
( ) Houston, TX
( ) Crestline, CA
( ) Westport, CT
( ) Texas City, TX
( ) Galveston, TX

5. Add the following numbers: $27 + 7.43 + 4.4 + 9.52$

Select the correct answer:

( ) 49.35
( ) 48.25
( ) 48.3
( ) 48.35
( ) 48.55
( ) 48.36

6. Subtract: $49 - 28.209$

( ) 20.691
( ) 20.791
( ) 21.791
( ) 20.789
( ) 20.916
( ) 20.801

7. Evaluate the following expression: $27.3 - 41.9 + 24.5$

Select the correct answer.

( ) 10
( ) 9.7
( ) 11
( ) 9.9
( ) 10.9
( ) 5.9

8. The patient's temperature is 1.7° above normal. (98.6° Fahrenheit is considered normal.) What is his temperature?

Select the correct answer:

( ) 100.3°

( ) 101.4°

( ) 100.2°

( ) 101.3°

( ) 96.9°

( ) 100.1°

9. Multiply $\frac{13}{1000}$ and $\frac{7}{10}$

Select all correct answers:

[ ] 0.002
[ ] $\frac{91}{10000}$
[ ] $\frac{20}{1000}$
[ ] 0.0091

10. Evaluate the following expression:

$-5.3 \cdot |10| - 9.3 \cdot |-4.3|$

Select the correct answer:

( ) -92.99
( ) 13.01
( ) -13.01

11. The barbell illustrated below is evenly loaded with weights. If A= 57.9 pounds, B= 56.3 pounds and C= 8.3 pounds, how much weight is loaded on the barbell?

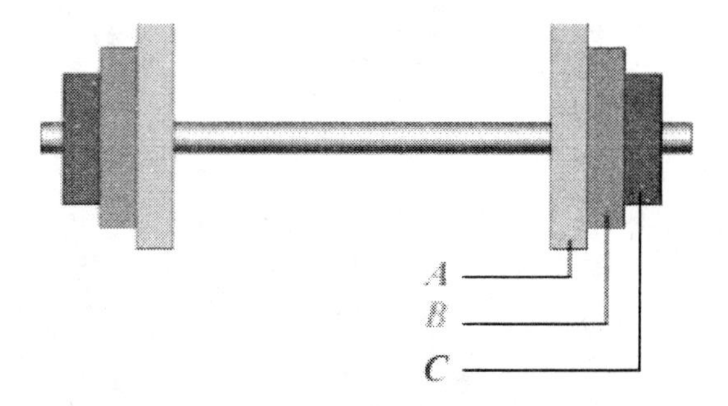

Select the correct answer:

( ) 19.8 pounds
( ) 245 pounds
( ) 122.5 pounds

12. Divide: $32.4 \div 0.02$

Select the correct answer:

( ) 1620
( ) 1619.9
( ) 1619.95
( ) 1620.5
( ) 1621
( ) 1621.11

13. Evaluate the following expression. If the answer is not exact, round it to the nearest hundredth.

$$\frac{5.7 - x^2 + 4.9}{x^3} \quad x=0.9$$

Select the correct answer:

( ) 13.32
( ) 13.45
( ) 13.43
( ) 13.58
( ) 13.28
( ) 13.94

14. The following table shows the first row of the starting grid for the 1998 Indianapolis 500 automobile race. The drivers were ranked in this order based on the speed driven in a qualifying run. What was the mean qualifying speed for the drivers in the first row? Round your answer to the nearest thousandth, if necessary.

Billy Boat	Greg Ray	Kenny Brack
223.899mph	221.379mph	220.021mph

Select the correct answer:

( ) 222.276 mph
( ) 222.866 mph
( ) 221.666 mph
( ) 221.768 mph
( ) 221.656 mph
( ) 221.766 mph

15. Write the following fraction in decimal form:

$$-\frac{2}{100}$$

Select the correct answer:

( ) 0.02
( ) 200
( ) -0.0002
( ) none of these
( ) -0.2
( ) - 0.02
( ) 0.0002

16. Evaluate the following expression.

$$\frac{1}{3}+0.3$$

Select the correct answer:

( ) $\frac{3}{30}$
( ) none of these
( ) $\frac{19}{30}$
( ) $\frac{4}{13}$

17. Write the fraction in decimal form. Use an overbar: $\frac{1}{9}$

Select the correct answer:

( ) $1.1\overline{1}$
( ) $0.\overline{1}$
( ) $0.\overline{3}$
( ) $0.0\overline{1}$
( ) none of these

18. A geologist weighed a rock sample at the site where it was discovered and found it to weigh $16\frac{5}{8}$ lb. Later, a more accurate digital scale in the laboratory gave the weight as 16.615 lb. What is the difference between the two measurements?

Select the correct answer:

( ) 0.01 lb
( ) 1.24 lb
( ) 0.007 lb
( ) 4.385 lb
( ) 0.014 lb
( ) none of these

19. What operations are performed on the variable in the following expression?

$$\frac{c}{14.4} - 13.7 = 8.8 .$$

Select all correct answers:

[ ] subtraction
[ ] division
[ ] addition
[ ] multiplication

20. Solve the following equation:

$$\frac{y}{10} = 16.7$$

Select the correct answer:

( ) y= 194.1
( ) y= 167
( ) y= 1.67
( ) y= 27.1

21. Solve the following equation:

$5.3b - 7.5 + 5.7b = 11.2$

Select the correct answer:

( ) b= -1.7
( ) b= 1.7
( ) b= 0.7

22. Midway through a telethon, the donations had reached $22.9 million. How much more was donated in the second half of the program if the final total pledged was $40.2 million?

Select the correct answer:

( ) $63.1 million
( ) $35.2 million
( ) $17.3 million

23. Which is the largest of the following three numbers?:

$-\sqrt{26}$, $-\sqrt{18}$, $-\sqrt{28}$

Select the correct answer:

( ) $-\sqrt{28}$
( ) $-\sqrt{18}$
( ) $-\sqrt{26}$

24. What is the whole number whose square lies between 12 and 21?

Select the correct answer:

( ) 9
( ) 6
( ) 4
( ) 3

25. Simplify the following expression without using a calculator:

$\sqrt{36}$

Select the correct answer:

( ) 8
( ) 5
( ) -5
( ) 6
( ) 11
( ) -6

Answers

1. 0.666667

2. 558.3

3. 4:01.0

4. Texas City, TX

5. 48.35

6. 20.791

7. 9.9

8. 100.3°

9. $\frac{91}{10000}$ I0.0091

10. -92.99

11. 245 pounds

12. 1620

13. 13.43

14. 221.766 mph

15. - 0.02

16. $\frac{19}{30}$

17. $0.\overline{1}$

18. 0.01 lb

19. subtractionIdivision

20. $y = 167$

21. $b = 1.7$

22. $17.3 million

23. $-\sqrt{18}$

24. 4

25. 6

1. Write the following fraction in decimal form: $\frac{1}{6}$

( ) 0.016667
( ) 0.166667
( ) 0.1
( ) 0.6

2. As of January 2000, Janet Evans held the world record in swimming. Her time is given below in minutes and seconds. Round it to the nearest tenth of a second.

Janet Evans, 400-meter freestyle, 4:04.81

Select the correct answer:

( ) 4:04.8
( ) 4:04.91
( ) 4:04.10
( ) 4:04.9

3. Represent the following situation using a signed number:

A river 6.05 feet below flood stage.

( ) 6.05 feet
( ) -60.5 feet
( ) -6.05 feet
( ) 605 feet

4. Arrange the decimals in order, from least to greatest:

155.37, 155.675, 155.423

Select the correct answer:

( ) 155.37, 155.423, 155.675
( ) 155.37, 155.675, 155.423
( ) 155.423, 155.37, 155.675

5. Add the following numbers: $\begin{array}{r} 47.1 \\ +28.7 \\ \hline \end{array}$

Select the correct answer.

( ) 71.8
( ) 75.6
( ) 76.8
( ) 75.8
( ) 75.9

6. Add: $-31.2 + 39.3$

Select the correct answer:

( ) 8.1
( ) 7.9
( ) -8
( ) -7.1
( ) 9.6

7. Evaluate the following expression: $(-35.7 + 40.3) - (-23.2 - 46)$

Select the correct answer:

( ) 74.9
( ) 74.8
( ) 70.7
( ) 73.6
( ) 73.8
( ) 73.9

8. A deposit slip for a savings account is shown below. First calculate the subtotal and then find the total deposit.

Cash	249.09
Checks (properly endorsed)	113.21
	47.51
Total from reverse side	354.37
Subtotal	
Less cash	24.77
Total deposit	

Select the correct amount of the total deposit:

( ) $788.95
( ) $790.05
( ) $738.41
( ) $739.41
( ) $738.31

9. Multiply $\frac{13}{100}$ and $\frac{1}{10}$

Select all correct answers:

[ ] 0.013
[ ] 0.014
[ ] $\frac{13}{1000}$
[ ] $\frac{14}{100}$

10. Evaluate the following expression:

$(7.1 + 1.5)(-1.9 - 1.5)$

Select the correct answer:

( ) -3.44
( ) -292.4
( ) -29.24
( ) -19.04

11. In May, the water level of a reservoir reached its high mark for the year. During the summer months, as water usage increased, the level dropped. In the months of May and June, the water level fell 4.1 feet each month. In August, because of high temperatures, it fell another 4.3 feet. By September, how far below the year's high mark had the water level fallen?

Select the correct answer:

( ) 12.7 feet
( ) 5.12 feet
( ) 12.5 feet

12. DNA is found in cells. It is referred to as the genetic "blueprint". In humans, it determines such traits as eye color, hair color, and height. A model of DNA appears in the illustration. If*a*= 0.001 inch and*c*= 10.1 inches, determine the dimension shown in the illustration.

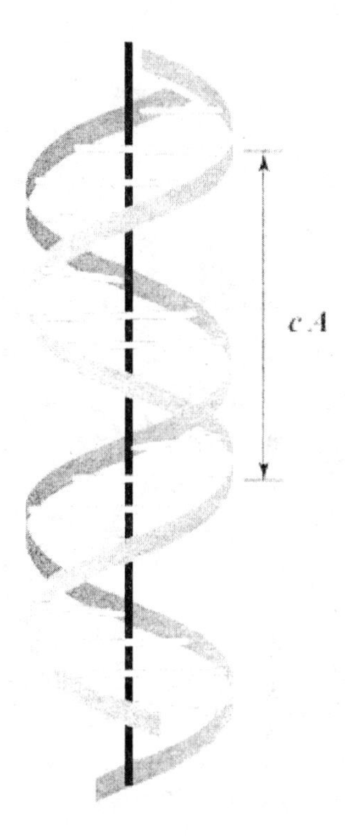

Select the correct answer:

( ) 0.0101
( ) 0.00101
( ) 0.101

13. Divide: $-27 \div 2$

Select the correct answer:

( ) -13
( ) -13.6
( ) -13.55
( ) -12.5
( ) -13.5

14. Do the following division mentally:

$-6.749 \div 1000$

Select the correct answer:

( ) -0.6749
( ) 67.49
( ) 6749
( ) -0.06749
( ) -0.006749
( ) 674.9

15. Evaluate the following expression. If the answer is not exact, round it to the nearest hundredth.

$$\frac{9.7 - x^2 + 8.3}{x^3} \quad x=0.9$$

Select the correct answer:

( ) 23.58
( ) 24.09
( ) 23.61
( ) 23.47
( ) 23.43
( ) 23.73

16. Write the following fraction in decimal form:

$$\frac{2}{5}$$

Select the correct answer:

( ) 10
( ) 0.2
( ) 0.4
( ) none of these
( ) 0.04

17. Write the following amount of money in dollars: 96 cents.

Select the correct answer:

( ) $9600.00
( ) $0.96
( ) $9.60

18. Evaluate the following expression.

$$\frac{2}{3}+0.3$$

Select the correct answer:

( ) $\frac{6}{30}$
( ) none of these
( ) $\frac{5}{13}$
( ) $\frac{29}{30}$

19. While doing a tuneup, a mechanic checks the gap on the spark plugs of a car to be sure they are firing correctly. The owner's manual states that the gap should be $\frac{3}{115}$ of an inch. The gauge the mechanic uses to check the gap registers 0.028 inch, in decimal form. Is the spark plug gap too large or too small?

Select the correct answer:

( ) too small
( ) too large

20. Find the value of *b* in the following equation:

$10.3\,(1.7 - b) + 8.3 = 18.6$

Select the correct answer:

( ) $b = 0.7$
( ) $b = 9.9$
( ) $b = -0.7$

21. One 5-ounce serving of broiled ground beef has 10.8 grams of saturated fat. This is 24 times the amount of saturated fat in 1 cup of cooked crab meat. How many grams of saturated fat are in 1 cup of cooked crab meat?

Select the correct answer:

( ) 2.25
( ) 5.45
( ) 2.222222
( ) 0.45

22. Simplify: $\sqrt{0}$

( ) 1
( ) 0
( ) undefined
( ) -1

23. Simplify the following expression without using a calculator:

$-5\sqrt{144} + 4\sqrt{81}$

Select the correct answer:

( ) -25
( ) -14
( ) -24
( ) -22
( ) -27

24. Use a calculator to find the following square root. Round the result to the nearest thousandth. $\sqrt{5}$

Select the correct answer:

( ) 2.237
( ) 2.336
( ) 2.246
( ) 2.235
( ) 2.236

25. The picture screen on a television set is measured diagonally, as shown in illustration below. If $a = \sqrt{1764}$ inches, find the size screen.

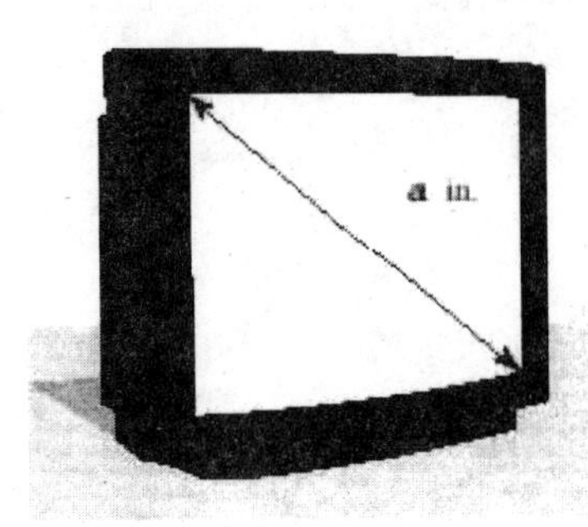

Select the correct answer:

( ) 52 inches
( ) 42 inches
( ) 38 inches
( ) 43 inches

Answers For

1. 0.166667

2. 4:04.8

3. -6.05 feet

4. 155.37, 155.423, 155.675

5. 75.8

6. 8.1

7. 73.8

8. $739.41

9. 0.013| $\frac{13}{1000}$

10. -29.24

11. 12.5 feet

12. 0.0101

13. -13.5

14. -0.006749

15. 23.58

16. 0.4

17. $0.96

18. $\frac{29}{30}$

19. too large

20. b= 0.7

21. 0.45

22. 0

23. -24

24. 2.236

25. 42 inches

1. Write the following fraction in decimal form: $\frac{1}{4}$

( ) 0.25
( ) 0.025
( ) 0.4
( ) 0.1

2. Round the following decimal to the nearest thousandth:

18.65645

3. We use a decimal point when working with dollars, but the decimal point is not necessary when working with cents. For each dollar amount give the equivalent amount expressed as cents:

$5.88, $0.51

Select the correct answer:

( ) 58.8, 51
( ) 588, 5.1
( ) 588, 51
( ) 588, 510

4. The table below shows the cities with the highest one-hour concentrations of ozone (in parts per million) during the summer of 1999.

Crestline, California	0.116
Galveston, Texas	0.166
Houston, Texas	0.137
Texas City, Texas	0.173
Westport, Connecticut	0.14
White Plains, New York	0.12

Which reading is highest?

5. Add the following numbers: 26 + 2.9 + 5.3 + 1.02

Select the correct answer:

( ) 36.22
( ) 35.22
( ) 35.23
( ) 35.17
( ) 35.42
( ) 35.12

6. Subtract: 45 - 27.535

7. Evaluate the following expression: $27.5 - 42.6 + 22.5$

Select the correct answer.

( ) 3.4
( ) 7.5
( ) 8.5
( ) 7.4
( ) 8.4
( ) 7.2

8. The following bar chart shows the six most-watched television shows of all time: "Mash," "Dallas," "Cheers," "The Day After," "Roots," and "Seinfeld." How many millions of viewers watched all six shows?

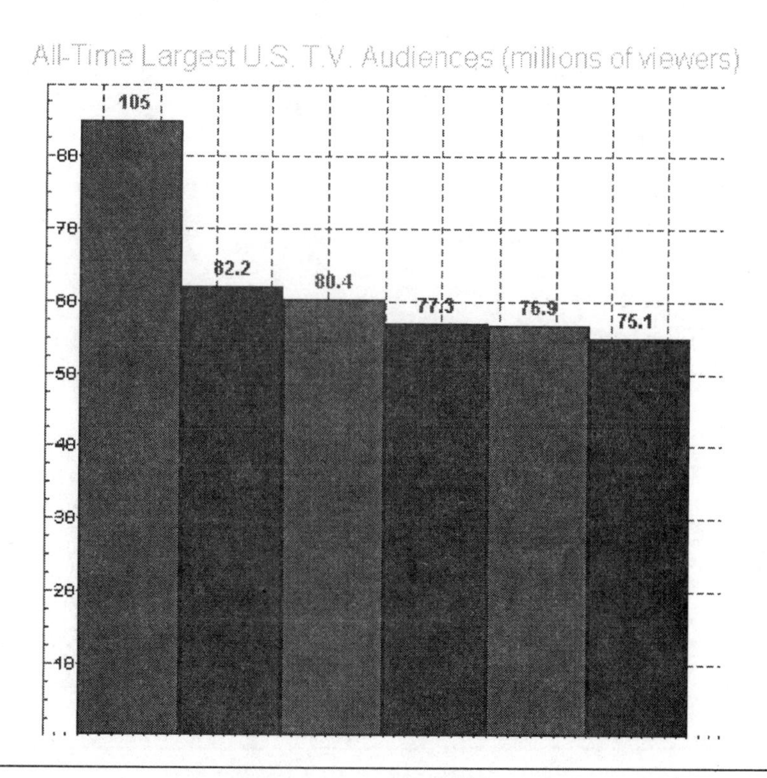

9. Multiply $\frac{11}{100}$ and $\frac{17}{1000}$

Select all correct answers:

[ ] 0.00028
[ ] $\frac{187}{100000}$
[ ] 0.00187
[ ] $\frac{28}{10000}$

10. Evaluate the following expression:

$-8.7 \cdot |6.4| - 5.3 \cdot |1.1|$

Select the correct answer:

( ) -49.85
( ) -61.51
( ) 49.85

11. Long bricks, called coping, can be used to outline the edge of a swimming pool. How many meters of coping will be needed in the construction of the swimming pool shown in the illustration? *A*= 34.5 meters, *B*= 46.7 meters.

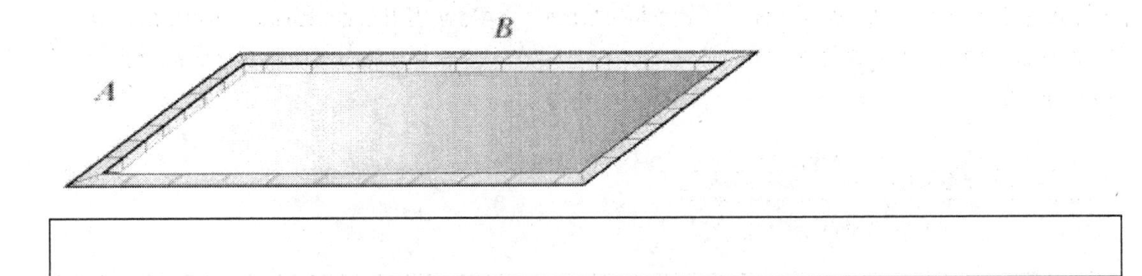

12. Divide: $30.6 \div 0.02$

Select the correct answer:

( ) 1530
( ) 1529.9
( ) 1531
( ) 1531.11
( ) 1530.5
( ) 1529.95

13. Evaluate the following expression. If the answer is not exact, round it to the nearest hundredth.

$$\frac{3.9 - x^2 + 8.7}{x^3} \quad x=0.5$$

Select the correct answer:

( ) 98.69
( ) 99.31
( ) 98.80
( ) 98.95
( ) 98.83
( ) 98.65

14. A volume control is shown in the illustration below. If the distance between the low and high settings is 13.32 cm, how far apart are the equally spaced volume settings?

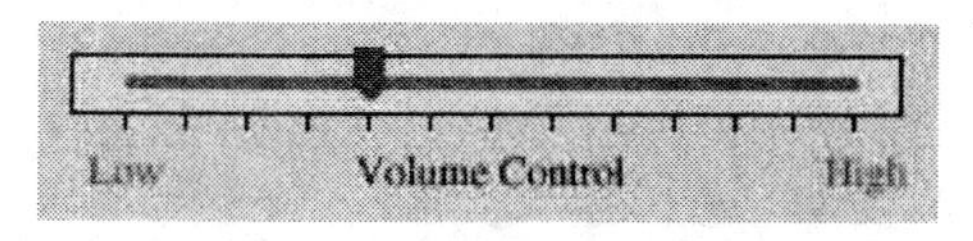

15. Write the following fraction in decimal form:

$$-\frac{7}{200}$$

Select the correct answer:

( ) none of these
( ) 1400
( ) 0.00035
( ) -0.7
( ) -0.00035
( ) - 0.035
( ) 0.035

16. Write the fraction in decimal form. Use an overbar: $\frac{5}{9}$

Select the correct answer:

( ) $0.\overline{4}$
( ) $0.\overline{5}$
( ) $5.5\overline{5}$
( ) $0.0\overline{5}$
( ) none of these

17. Evaluate the following expression. Express your answer as a fraction in lowest terms.

$$\frac{1}{2}+0.4$$

18. While doing a tuneup, a mechanic checks the gap on the spark plugs of a car to be sure they are firing correctly. The owner's manual states that the gap should be $\frac{3}{115}$ of an inch. The gauge the mechanic uses to check the gap registers 0.028 inch, in decimal form.
Which of the two numbers is larger? Does that mean that the spark plug gap is too large or too small?

19. What operations are performed on the variable in the following expression?

$$\frac{y}{13.5} - 9.5 = 16.7 \ .$$

Select all correct answers:

[ ] addition
[ ] subtraction
[ ] division
[ ] multiplication

20. Solve the following equation:

$$\frac{y}{18} = -2.9$$

21. Solve the following equation:

$-4.1a - 5.9 + 8.9a = 31.06$

Select the correct answer:

( ) $a = 9.9$
( ) $a = 7.7$
( ) $a = -7.7$

22. One 5-ounce serving of broiled ground beef has 9.9 grams of saturated fat. This is 22 times the amount of saturated fat in 1 cup of cooked crab meat. How many grams of saturated fat are in 1 cup of cooked crab meat?

23. Which is the largest of the following three numbers?:

$-\sqrt{17}$, $-\sqrt{15}$, $-\sqrt{18}$

Select the correct answer:

( ) $-\sqrt{18}$
( ) $-\sqrt{15}$
( ) $-\sqrt{17}$

24. What is the whole number whose square lies between 221 and 230?

25. Simplify the following expression without using a calculator:

$\sqrt{25}$

Select the correct answer:

( ) 7
( ) 10
( ) -5
( ) 4
( ) -4
( ) 5

Answers

1. 0.25

2. 18.65645

3. 588, 51

4. 0.173

5. 35.22

6. 17.465

7. 7.4

8. 496.9

9. $\frac{187}{100000}$ I0.00187

10. -61.51

11. 162.4

12. 1530

13. 98.80

14. 1.11

15. - 0.035

16. $0.\overline{5}$

17. $\frac{18}{20}$

18.

19. subtractionIdivision

20. -52.2

21. $a = 7.7$

22. 0.45

23. $-\sqrt{15}$

24. 15

25. 5

1. Write the following fraction in decimal form: $\frac{2}{4}$

( ) 0.5
( ) 0.2
( ) 0.05
( ) 0.4

2. Round the following decimal to the nearest tenth:

711.27

3. As of January 2000, Janet Evans held the world record in swimming. Her time is given below in minutes and seconds. Round it to the nearest tenth of a second.

Janet Evans, 400-meter freestyle, 4:04.21

Select the correct answer:

( ) 4:04.31
( ) 4:04.2
( ) 4:04.4
( ) 4:04.3

4. The table below shows the cities with the highest one-hour concentrations of ozone (in parts per million) during the summer of 1999.

Crestline, California	0.142
Galveston, Texas	0.108
Houston, Texas	0.119
Texas City, Texas	0.165
Westport, Connecticut	0.105
White Plains, New York	0.125

Which reading is highest?

5. Add the following numbers: 40 + 1.44 + 3.9 + 9.14

Select the correct answer:

( ) 54.43
( ) 54.68
( ) 54.48
( ) 54.38
( ) 54.49
( ) 55.48

6. Subtract: 62 - 44.675

7. Evaluate the following expression: $28.7 - 45.1 + 23.7$

Select the correct answer.

( ) 7.4
( ) 3.3
( ) 7.3
( ) 8.3
( ) 8.4
( ) 7.1

8. The following table shows a patient's health chart. A nurse failed to fill in certain portions. (98.6° Fahrenheit is considered normal.) Complete the chart.

Patient's Temperature	How much above normal
100.8	
	2.2
99.9	
98.8	
	1.7

9. Multiply $\frac{13}{100}$ and $\frac{3}{10}$

Select all correct answers:

[ ] $\frac{39}{1000}$
[ ] 0.039
[ ] 0.016
[ ] $\frac{16}{100}$

10. Evaluate the following expression:

$5.3 \cdot |-9.6| - 2.7 \cdot |-8.5|$

11. The barbell illustrated below is evenly loaded with weights. If A = 88.3 pounds, B = 45.9 pounds and C = 26.5 pounds, how much weight is loaded on the barbell?

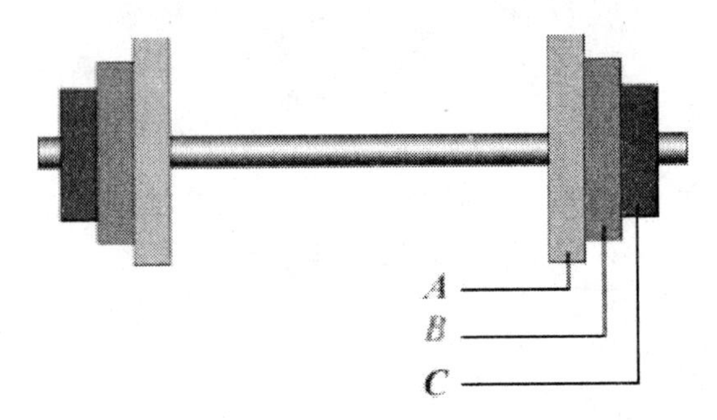

Select the correct answer:

( ) 137.8 pounds
( ) 160.7 pounds
( ) 321.4 pounds

12. Divide: $30.2 \div 0.04$

13. Evaluate the following expression. If the answer is not exact, round it to the nearest hundredth.

$$\frac{8.3 - x^2 + 7.1}{x^3} \quad x=0.1$$

Select the correct answer:

( ) 15390.00
( ) 15390.51
( ) 15389.85
( ) 15390.03
( ) 15389.89
( ) 15390.15

14. The following table shows the first row of the starting grid for the 1998 Indianapolis 500 automobile race. The drivers were ranked in this order based on the speed driven in a qualifying run. What was the mean qualifying speed for the drivers in the first row? (Round the result to the nearest thousandth if necessary.)

Billy Boat	Greg Ray	Kenny Brack
222.035mph	221.427mph	220.553mph

15. Write the following fraction in decimal form:

$$-\frac{4}{200}$$

Select the correct answer:

( ) -0.0002
( ) 800
( ) - 0.02
( ) -0.4
( ) 0.0002
( ) 0.02
( ) none of these

16. Evaluate the following expression. Express your answer as a fraction in lowest terms.

$$\frac{6}{7}+0.2$$

17. Write the fraction in decimal form. Use an overbar: $\frac{8}{9}$

Select the correct answer:

( ) $0.\overline{8}$
( ) $8.8\overline{8}$
( ) none of these
( ) $0.0\overline{8}$
( ) $0.\overline{4}$

18. A geologist weighed a rock sample at the site where it was discovered and found it to weigh $13\frac{7}{8}$ lb. Later, a more accurate digital scale in the laboratory gave the weight as 13.627 lb. What is the difference between the two measurements?

19. What operations are performed on the variable in the following expression?

$$\frac{y}{14.2} - 13.3 = 0.8 \ .$$

Select all correct answers:

[ ] subtraction
[ ] division
[ ] addition
[ ] multiplication

20. Solve the following equation:

$$\frac{y}{16} = 45.1$$

21. Solve the following equation:

$3.5a - 7.9 + 1.3a = 25.22$

Select the correct answer:

( ) $a = -6.9$
( ) $a = 6.1$
( ) $a = 6.9$

22. Without evaluating the square roots, write the largest of the following three numbers.

$-\sqrt{28}$, $-\sqrt{13}$, $-\sqrt{22}$

23. What is the whole number whose square lies between 140 and 149?

Select the correct answer:

( ) 12
( ) 11
( ) 17
( ) 14

24. Simplify the following expression without using a calculator:

$\sqrt{81}$

25. Find the length of the slanted side of the following roof truss, c, where a= 3, b= 4 and $c = \sqrt{49}$.

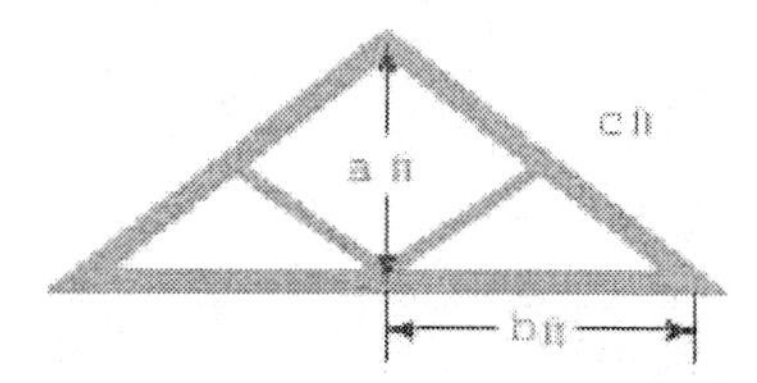

Select the correct answer:

( ) 4 ft
( ) 14 ft
( ) 3 ft
( ) 7 ft

Answers

1. 0.5

2. 711.27

3. 4:04.2

4. 0.165

5. 54.48

6. 17.325

7. 7.3

8. 100.8, 2.2, 100.8, 2.2, 99.9, 1.3, 98.8, 0.2, 100.3, 1.7

9. $\frac{39}{1000}$ l0.039

10. 27.93

11. 321.4 pounds

12. 755

13. 15390.00

14. 221.338333

15. - 0.02

16. $\frac{74}{70}$

17. $0.\overline{8}$

18. 0.248

19. subtractionldivision

20. 721.6

21. a= 6.9

22. $-\sqrt{13}$

23. 12

24. 9

25. 7 ft

1. Write the following fraction as a decimal: $\frac{7}{10}$

2. Round the following decimal to the nearest hundredth:

713.782

Select the correct answer:

( ) 713.9
( ) 713.78
( ) 713.79
( ) 713.783

3. We use a decimal point when working with dollars, but the decimal point is not necessary when working with cents. For each dollar amount give the equivalent amount expressed as cents.

Dollars	Cents
$0.38	
$0.67	
$2.96	

4. The table below shows the cities with the highest one-hour concentrations of ozone (in parts per million) during the summer of 1999.

Crestline, California	0.135
Galveston, Texas	0.148
Houston, Texas	0.146
Texas City, Texas	0.149
Westport, Connecticut	0.115
White Plains, New York	0.144

Which city has the highest reading?

( ) Houston, TX
( ) Westport, CT
( ) Galveston, TX
( ) White Plains, NY
( ) Texas City, TX
( ) Crestline, CA

5. Add the following numbers: $22 + 6.71 + 8.1 + 3.4$

6. Evaluate the following expression: $\left(-26.6 - 36.57\right) - \left(-38\right)$

Select the correct answer:

( ) -25.16
( ) -25.17
( ) -28.67
( ) -24.06
( ) -24.07
( ) -25.37

7. Certain dimensions of a compact car are shown below, where A=185.2,$a1$=42.4 and$a2$=40.3. What is the wheelbase of the car?

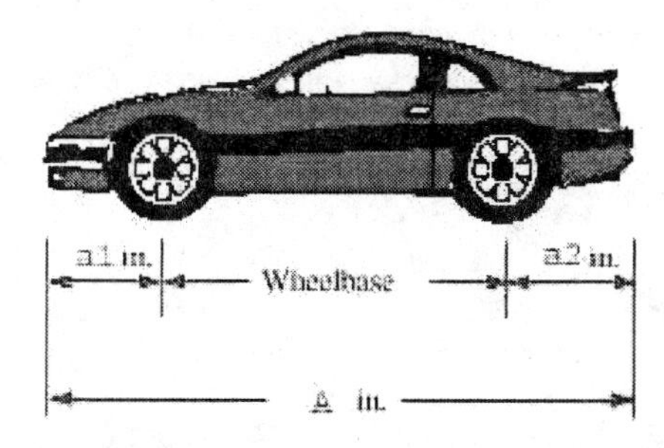

8. Multiply $\frac{13}{100}$ and $\frac{7}{10}$

Select all correct answers:

[ ] $\frac{91}{1000}$
[ ] 0.02
[ ] $\frac{20}{100}$
[ ] 0.091

9. Evaluate the following expression:

$4.3 \cdot |0.7| - 4.7 \cdot |-1.1|$

10. In the city map illustrated below, the streets form a grid. Each street is 0.29 miles apart. Find the distance of a trip from the airport to city hall.

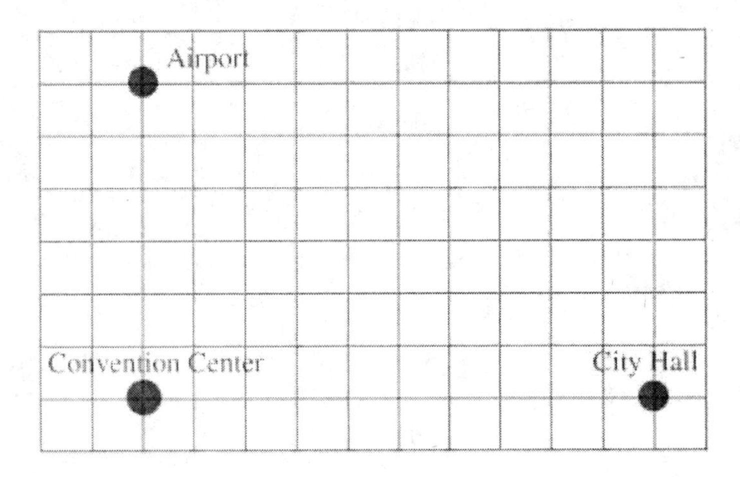

Select the correct answer:

( ) 46.4 miles
( ) 4.06 miles
( ) 4.64 miles

11. Divide: $48.8 \div 0.08$

12. Evaluate the following expression and round the result to the nearest hundredth:

$$\frac{(0.6)^2 - (0.2)^2}{0.705 + 0.6}$$

Select the correct answer:

( ) 0.25
( ) 0.10
( ) 0.76
( ) 0.40
( ) 0.25
( ) 0.14

13. Evaluate the following expression. If the answer is not exact, round it to the nearest hundredth.

$$\frac{1.7 - x^2 + 8.1}{x^3} \text{ for} x\text{=0.7}$$

14. A volume control is shown in the illustration below. If the distance between the low and high settings is 21.96 cm, how far apart are the equally spaced volume settings?

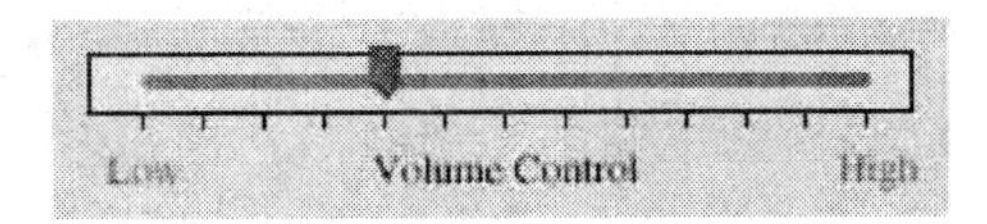

Select the correct answer:

( ) 1.73 cm
( ) 1.83 cm
( ) 2.83 cm
( ) 2.93 cm
( ) 2.13 cm

15. Write the following fraction in decimal form:

$$-\frac{3}{200}$$

16. Fill in the correct symbol (> or <) to make a true statement.

$\frac{9}{16}$ ____ 0.5825

Select the correct answer:

( ) <
( ) >

17. Write the following fraction in decimal form.

$$\frac{7}{999}$$

18. Use a calculator to evaluate: $2969.261 + 5508.7235$

19. What operations are performed on the variable in the following expression?

$$\frac{x}{15} - 17.5 = 15.6 \ .$$

Select all correct answers:

[ ] addition
[ ] subtraction
[ ] division
[ ] multiplication

20. Solve the following equation:

$$\frac{a}{18} = -50.5$$

21. Solve the following equation:

$7.3b - 2.5 + 8.9b = 15.32$

Select the correct answer:

( ) $b = 1.1$
( ) $b = -1.1$
( ) $b = 2.3$

22. Without evaluating the square roots, write the largest of the following three numbers.

$-\sqrt{29}\ ,\ -\sqrt{18}\ ,\ -\sqrt{22}$

23. What is the whole number whose square lies between 221 and 230?

Select the correct answer:

( ) 14
( ) 20
( ) 15
( ) 17

24. Simplify the following expression without using a calculator:

$-\sqrt{0.25}$

25. Use the imaginary triangles set up by a surveyor, illustrated below, to find the length of the lake

$L = \sqrt{606841}$ meters

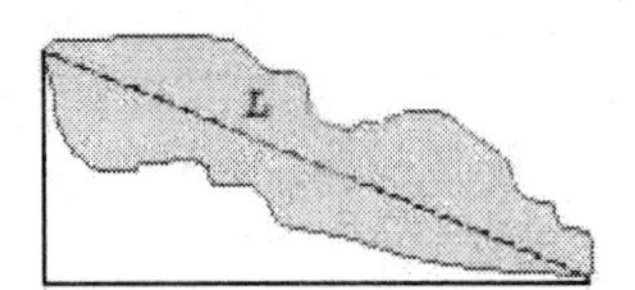

Select the correct answer:

( ) 779 meters
( ) 774 meters
( ) 780 meters
( ) 789 meters

Answers

1. 0.7

2. 713.78

3. 0.38, 38, 0.67, 67, 2.96, 296

4. Texas City, TX

5. 40.21

6. -25.17

7. 102.5

8. $\frac{91}{1000}$ l0.091

9. -2.16

10. 4.64 miles

11. 610

12. 0.25

13. 27.142857

14. 1.83 cm

15. -0.015

16. <

17. 0.007007...

18. 8477.9845

19. subtractionldivision

20. -909

21. $b = 1.1$

22. $-\sqrt{18}$

23. 15

24. -0.5

25. 779 meters

1. Consider the ordered pair $(2, 1)$.

Match the following.

the x-coordinate	1
the y-coordinate	2

2. Subtract the polynomials:

$8c^3 - 6c^3$.

3. Complete the table so that the points given are solutions of the equation $5x + y = 0$.

x	y
0	
	0
	15

4. Which one of the points below is on the*x*-axis?

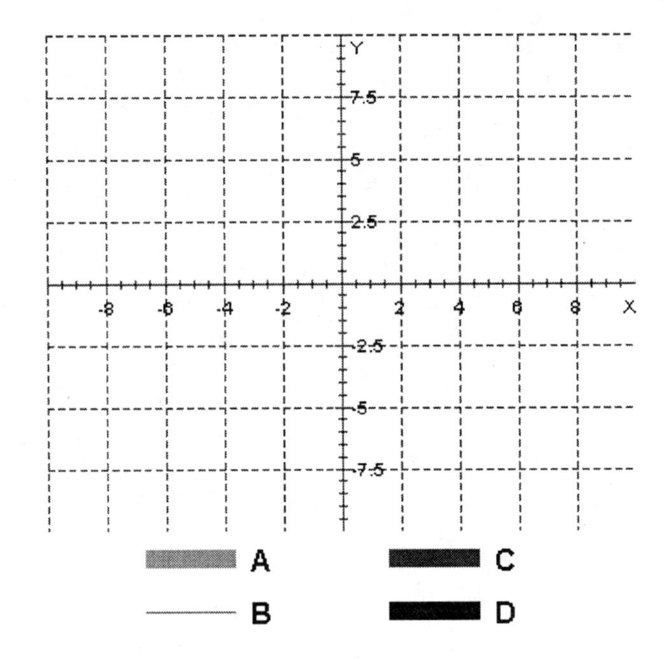

5. Complete the table.

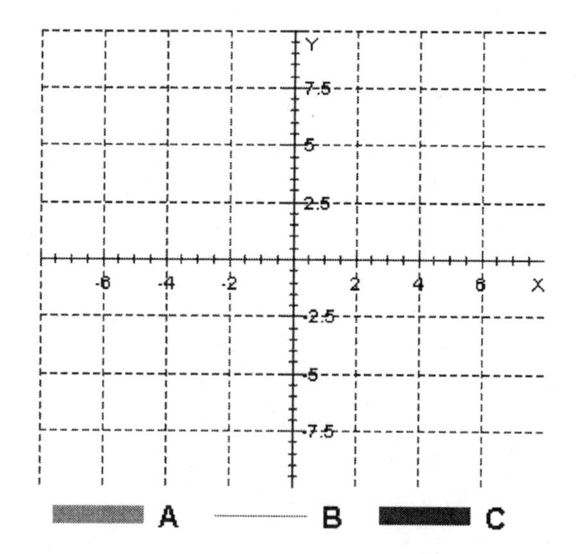

Point	x	y
A		
B		
C		

6. What is the x-intercept of the line represented in the following graph?

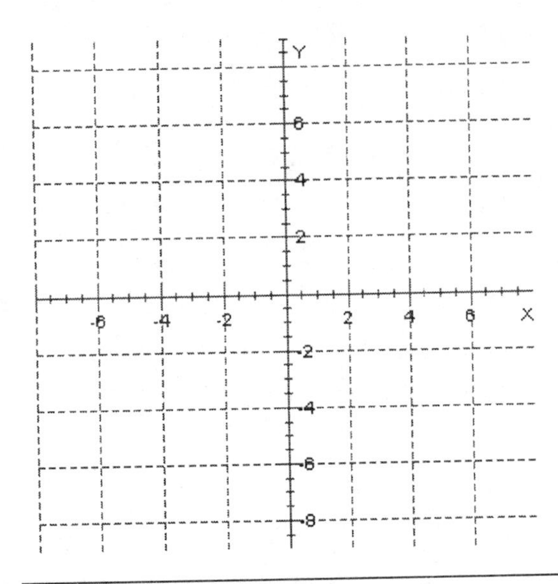

7. The graph of the equation $y = bx + -2$ is given. Find b.

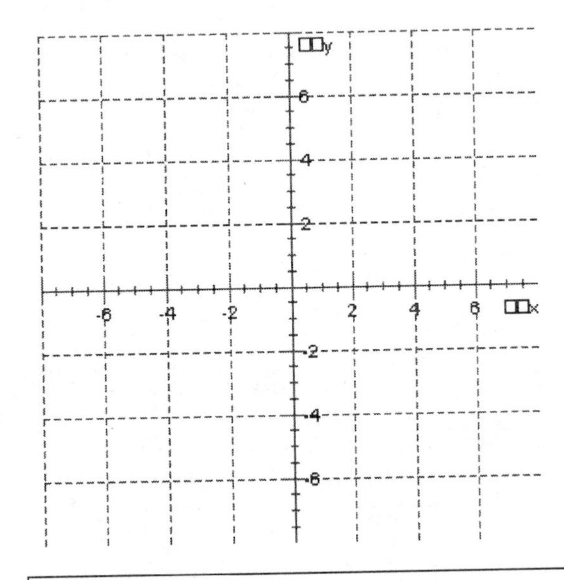

8. Complete the table and graph the equation $y = 5x$.

x	y
-10	
-7	
8	
10	

9. The following graph shows the value y (in thousands of dollars) of a car that is x years old. Estimate the value of the car for the given values of x and complete the table.

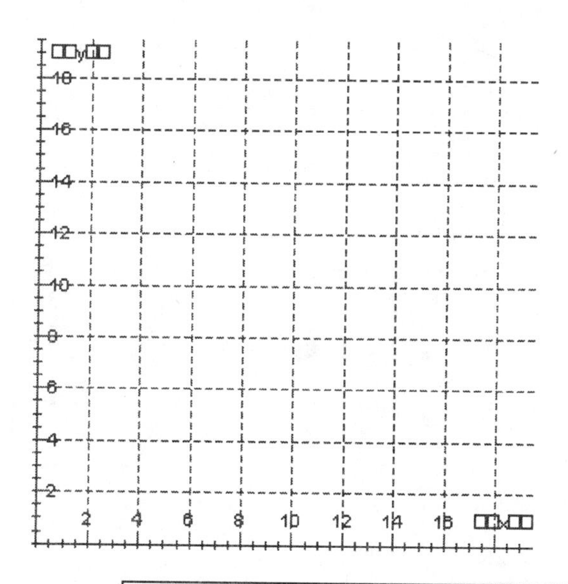

x	y
3	
2	
9	

10. Evaluate the exponential expression x^{n+m} for $x = 1, n = 1, m = 2$.

11. Rewrite the following expression using only one exponent:

$c^9 \cdot c^9$

12. Simplify the product:

$-2y^8(4y^8)$

13. Simplify the product:

$2s^4c^4 \cdot 2c^4s^4$

14. Simplify the expression:

$(9x^8x^4)^2$

15. What is the degree of the polynomial $6d^6 - 7d^5 - 8$?

16. What is the degree of the following polynomial?

$2d^7$.

17. Given the polynomial $-10a^2 - 4a + 9$, match the values of a on the left with the corresponding solution on the right.

-9	9
9	-765
8	-663
0	-837

18. The height h (in feet) of a ball shot straight up with an initial velocity of 64 feet per second is given by the equation $h = -16t^2 + 64t$. Find the height of the ball after t = 1.5 seconds.

19. Combine the like terms:
$9b$ and $4b$.

20. Add the polynomials:
$(-4c^2+5)+(7c^2-5)$.

21. A young couple bought two cars, one for $9200 and the other for $9300. The first car is expected to depreciate $600 per year and the second car $1100 per year.

Write a single equation that will give the value y of both cars after x years.

22. Find the product:

$5(c + 9)$.

23. Find the product:

$7(2a^5 - a)a$.

24. Square the binomial:

$(8a + 9)^2$.

25. Express the area of the rectangle in the illustration if $x = 10$.

(x + 2) ft

(x − 2) ft

Answers

1. the*x*- coordinate -> 2, the*y*- coordinate -> 1

2. $2c^{3}$

3. 0, 0, 0, 0, -3, 15

4. C

5. A, 2, -6, B, -6, 8, C, -4, -2

6. (-4,0)

7. -1

8. -10, -50, -7, -35, 8, 40, 10, 50

9.

10. 1

11. c^{18}

12. $-8y^{16}$

13. $4s^{8}c^{8}$

14. $81x^{24}$

15. 6

16. 7

17. 0 -> 9, 8 -> -663, 9 -> -837, -9 -> -765

18. 60

19. $13b$

20. $3c^2$

21. $y = 18500 - 1700x$

22. $5c + 45$

23. $14a^6 - 7a^2$

24. $64a^2 + 144a + 81$

25. 96

1. Use the information from the graph below to complete the Table for 2, 4, 6 and 8 servings of instant mashed potatoes.

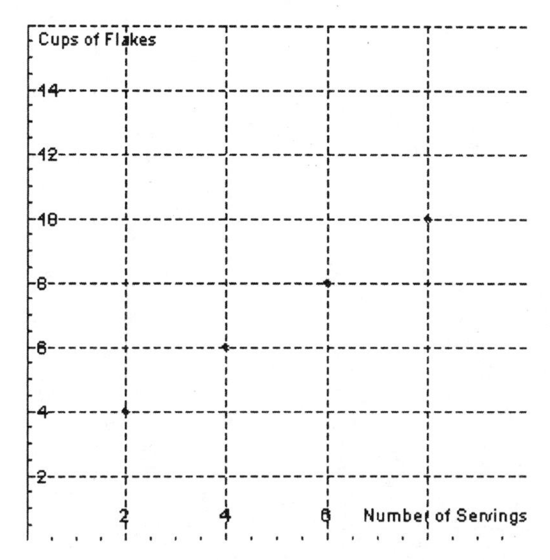

Number of servings	Flakes (cups)
2	
4	
6	
8	

2. Complete the table of solutions below for $x - 7y = -58$.

x	y
	-4
	-8
-2	

3. What is thex-coordinate of the point on the graph?

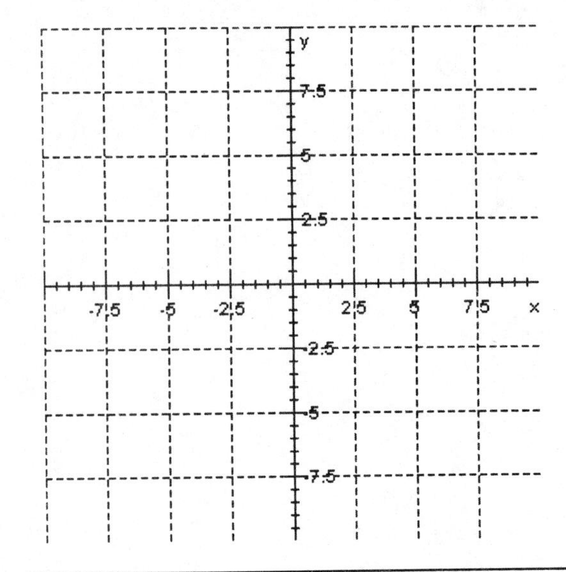

4. The map in the illustration below shows the areas where damage was caused by an earthquake.

Match the points with their coordinantes.

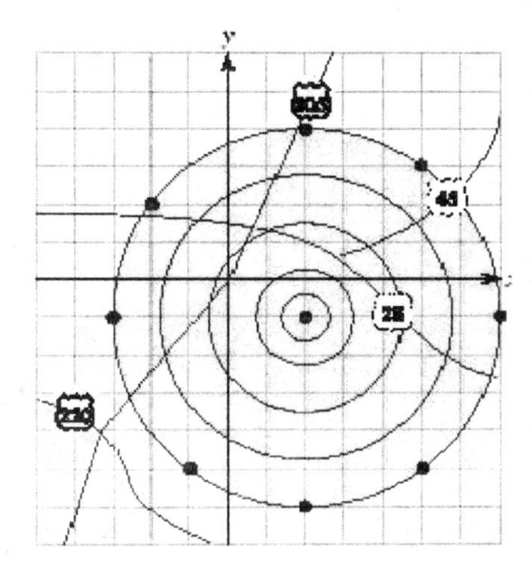

A	(5, -5)
B	(-2, 2)
D	(5, 3)
C	(-3, -1)

5. What is the*x*-intercept of the line represented in the following graph?

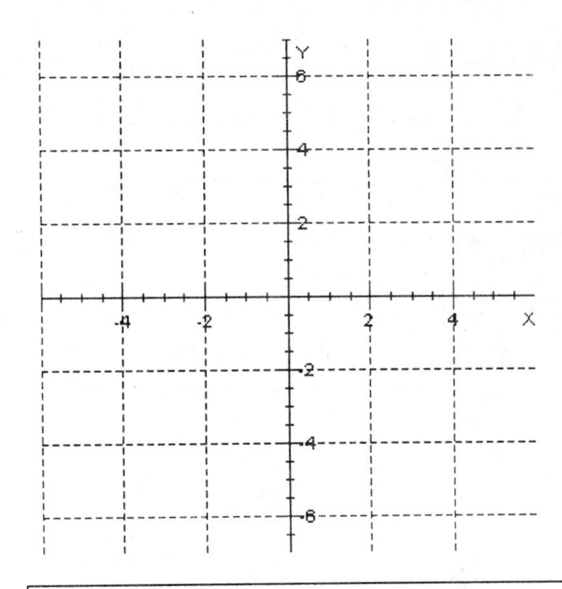

6. Complete the table and graph the equation 10*y*+ 7*x*= 0.

x	y
-10	
-8	
	-2.8
7	
	-7

7. Complete the table and graph the equation$y$= 2x.

x	y
-10	
-6	
4	
10	

8. The following graph shows the value$y$(in thousands of dollars) of a car that is$x$ years old. Estimate the value of the car for the given values of$x$and complete the table.

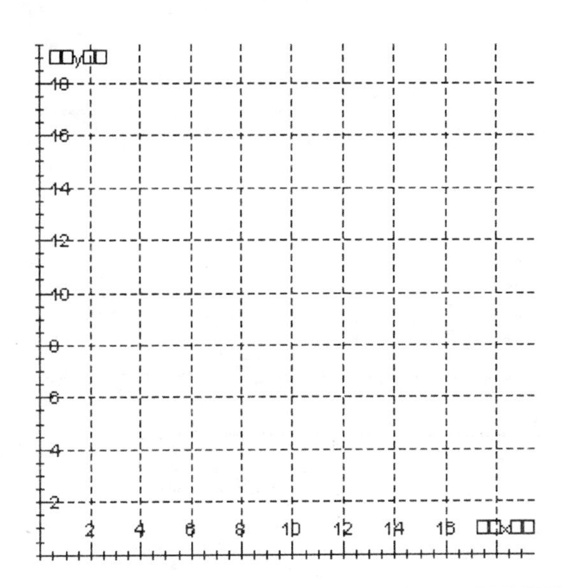

x	y
2	
4	
10	

9. Rewrite the following expression using only one exponent:

$b^{10} \cdot b^{4}$

10. Simplify the product:

$-6s^{6}(2s^{6})$

11. Simplify the product:

$5s^{3}b^{4} \cdot 3b^{3}s^{4}$

12. Simplify the expression:

$(8y^{9}y^{4})^{4}$

13. Write the degree of the following polynomial:

$3d^{8} + 9d^{5} - 7$.

14. Evaluate the polynomial $6b^{3} + 7b - 13$ for each given value and complete the table.

b	$6b^{3}+7b-13$
-5	
5	
9	

15. Graph the following equation by first making a table of solutions:

$y = -\frac{1}{10}x^2 + 1$.

x	y
-4	
-2	
0	
2	
4	

16. The number of feet that a car travels before stopping depends on the driver's reaction time and the braking distance. (See illustration.) For one driver, the stopping distance*d*is given by the equation $d = 0.2w^2 + 0.6w$, where*w*is the velocity of the car. Find the stopping distance for each of the following speeds.

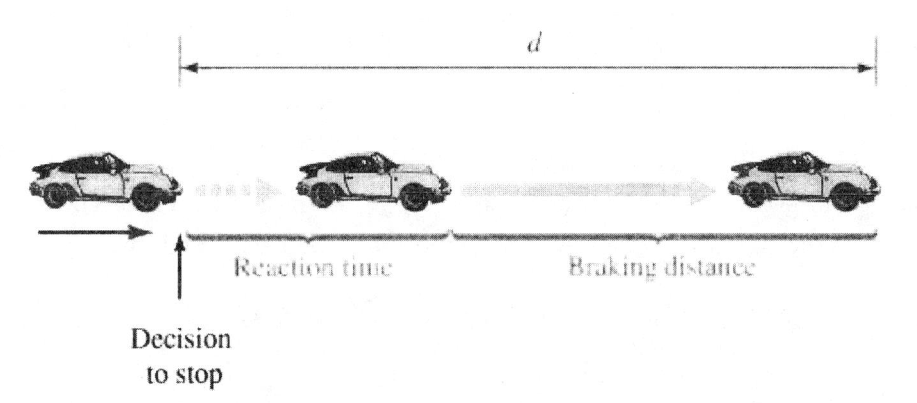

w	0
30	
60	
10	
70	

17. Combine the like terms:
$3c$and $2c$.

18. Add the polynomials:
$(2y^2+9y)+(5y^2-3y+5)$.

19. Add the polynomials:
$2a^2+9a+2$ and
$3a^2-7a+7$

20. Subtract the polynomials:
$6y^2+7y+9$
$-(-8y^2-4y+1)$

21. A young couple bought two cars, one for $6500 and the other for $9900. The first car is expected to depreciate $500 per year and the second car $1000 per year.

Write a single equation that will give the value*y*of both cars after*x*years.

22. Find the product:
$(-6s^3)(-2s^6)$.

23. Find the product:
$10y(9y^2-y+7)$.

24. Square the binomial:

$(9f + 3)^2$.

25. Multiply the polynomials on the left and connect with a correct answer on the right.

$(c+7)(c^2-3c-27)$	$c^3+4c^2-48c-189$
$(c-7)(c^2-3c+27)$	$c^3+4c^2+6c+189$
$(c+7)(c^2-3c+27)$	$c^3-10c^2+48c-189$

Answers

1. 2, 4, 4, 6, 6, 8, 8, 10

2. -86, -4, -114, -8, -2, 8

3. 4

4. A -> (-3,-1), B -> (5,3), C -> (5,-5), D -> (-2,2)

5. (-2,0)

6. -10, 7, -8, 5.6, 4, -2.8, 7, -4.9, 10, -7

7. -10, -20, -6, -12, 4, 8, 10, 20

8.

9. b^{14}

10. $-12s^{12}$

11. $15s^{7}b^{7}$

12. $4096y^{52}$

13. 8

14. -5, -798, 5, 772, 9, 4424

15. -4, -0.6, -2, 0.6, 0, 1, 2, 0.6, 4, -0.6

16. 30, 198, 60, 756, 10, 26, 70, 1022

17. $5c$

18. $7y^{2}+6y+5$

19. $5a^{2}+2a+9$

20. $14y^2 + 11y + 8$

21. $y = 16400 - 1500x$

22. $12s^9$

23. $90y^3 - 10y^2 + 70y$

24. $81t^2 + 54t + 9$

25. (c+7)*(c^2-3*c+27) -> c^3+4*c^2+6*c+189, (c-7)*(c^2-3*c+27) -> c^3
10*c^2+48*c-189, (c+7)*(c^2-3*c-27) -> c^3+4*c^2-48*c-189

1. Consider the ordered pair

$(-10, -5)$.

Match the following.

the y-coordinate	- 10
the x-coordinate	- 5

2. Match the points with their coordinates.

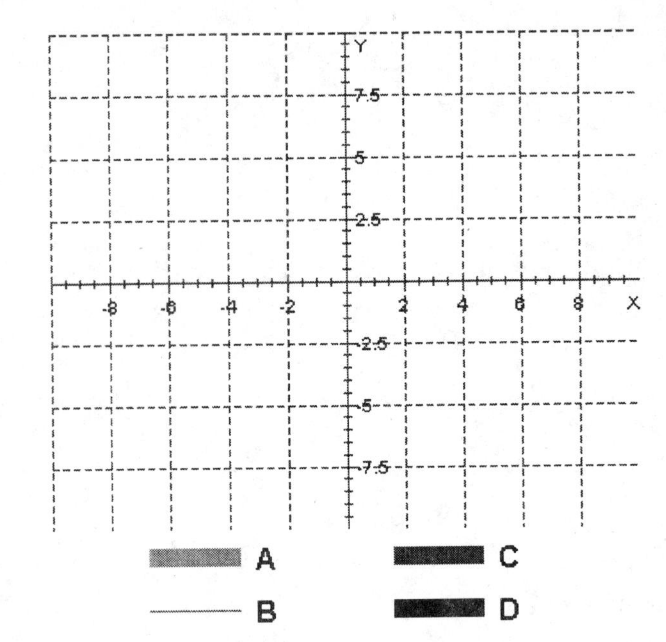

C	(-2, -4)
A	(4, 3)
B	(-6, -5)
D	(6, 1)

3. Which one of the points below is in Quadrant IV?

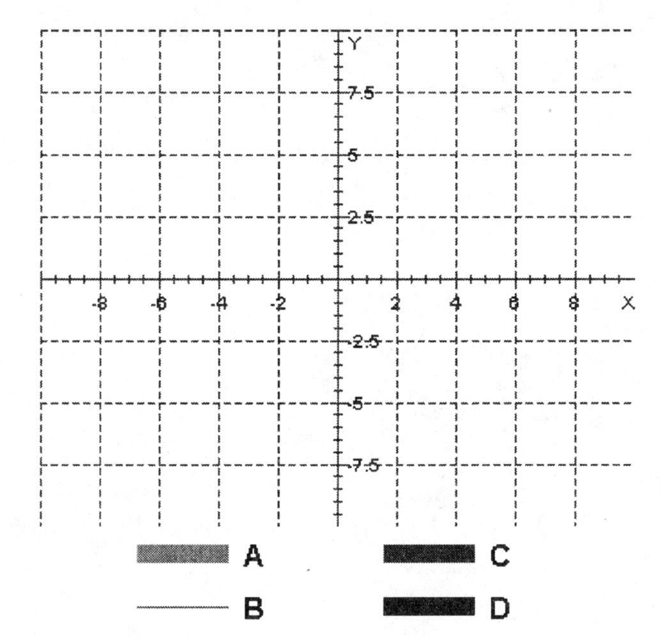

( ) A
( ) A
( ) C
( ) B

4. The map in the illustration below shows the areas where damage was caused by an earthquake.

Match the points with their coordinantes.

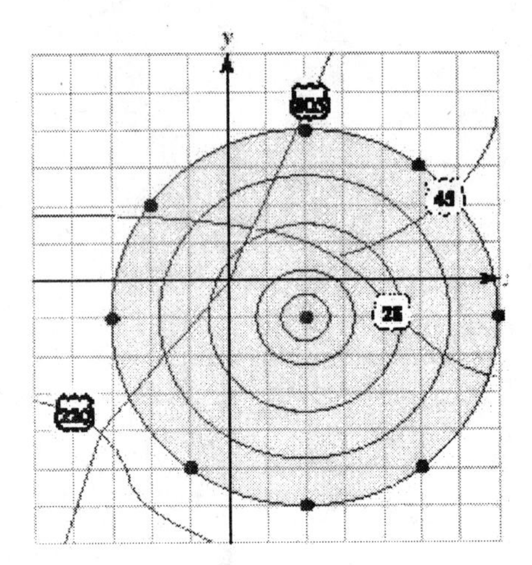

D	(5, 3)
B	(-3, -1)
C	(5, -5)
A	(-2, 2)

5. Select all the points that are either*x*-intercepts or*y*-intercepts of the line graphed below.

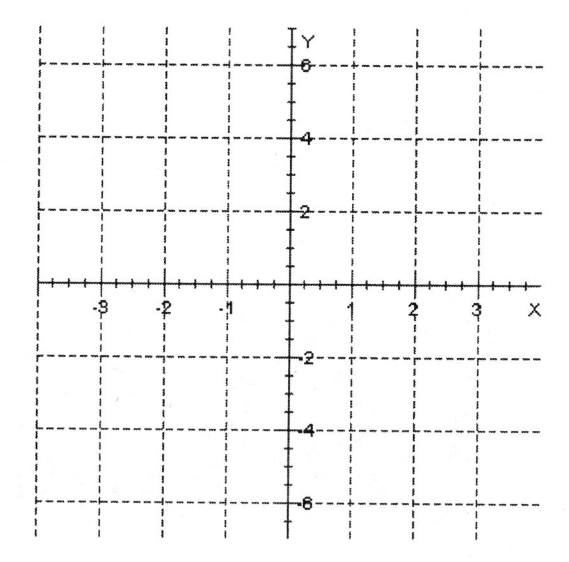

[ ] (0,2)
[ ] (4,0)
[ ] (2,0)
[ ] (0,4)

6. The graph of the equation $y = bx + 2$ is given. Find b.

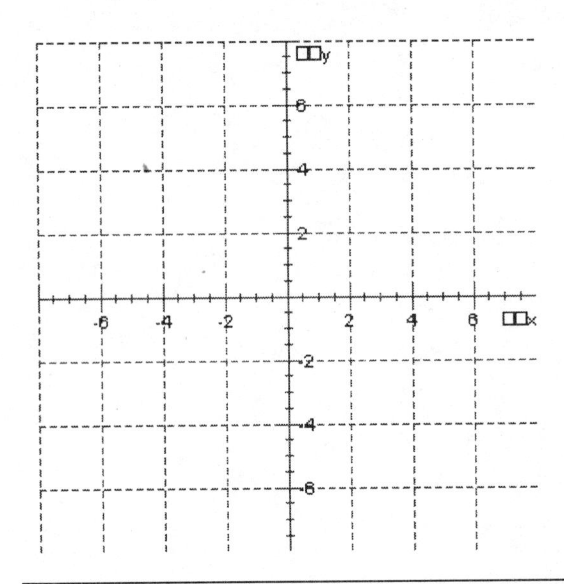

7. Which line in the following graph is the graph of equation $y = 5x$?

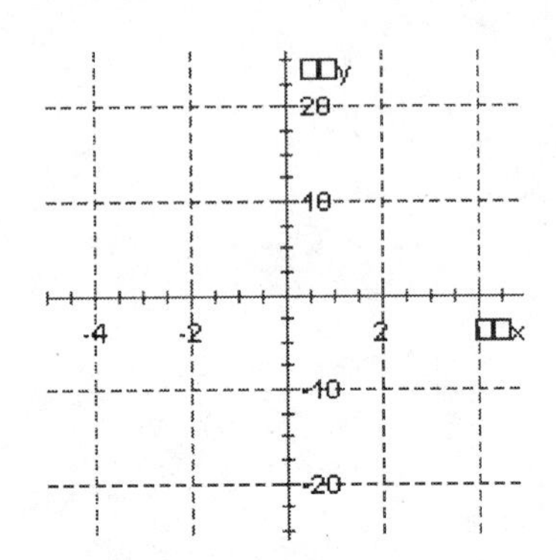

( ) Red
( ) Blue

8. The following graph shows the value y (in thousands of dollars) of a car that is x years old. Estimate the value of the car for the given values of x and complete the table.

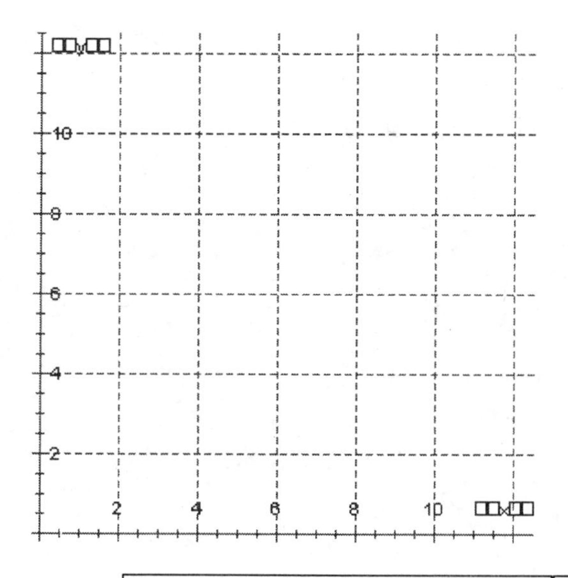

x	y
8	
1	
3	

9. If $74 is invested in a savings account paying 8% per year simple interest, the amount C in the account over a period time t is given by the formula $C = 8t + 74$. Find C, if $t = 2$.

( ) 130
( ) 90
( ) 82

10. Evaluate the exponential expression x^{n+m} for $x = 3, n = 3, m = 2$.

( ) 243
( ) 27
( ) 9
( ) 729

11. Simplify the product:

$-9t^{5}(2t^{4})$

12. Simplify the product:

$5y^{5}t^{5} \cdot 3t^{5}y^{5}$

( ) $15y^{5}t^{10}$
( ) $15y^{5}t^{10}$
( ) $15y^{10}t^{10}$

13. Simplify the expression:

$(10y^{10}y^{4})^{4}$

14. Match each polynomial on the left with the correct type of polynomial on the right.

$16a^9$	trinomial
$17 - 10a^{10} + 13b$	binomial
$-14b + a$	monomial

15. Choose the correct degree of the following polynomial:
$0b + 21$.

( ) 1
( ) 0
( ) 2
( ) 21

16. Graph the following equation by first making a table of solutions:
$y = -\frac{1}{2}x^2 + 8$.

x	y
-4	
-2	
0	
2	
4	

17. The cable of a suspension bridge hangs in the shape of a parabola. (See the illustration below.) Use the information in the illustration to find y, if x= 4.

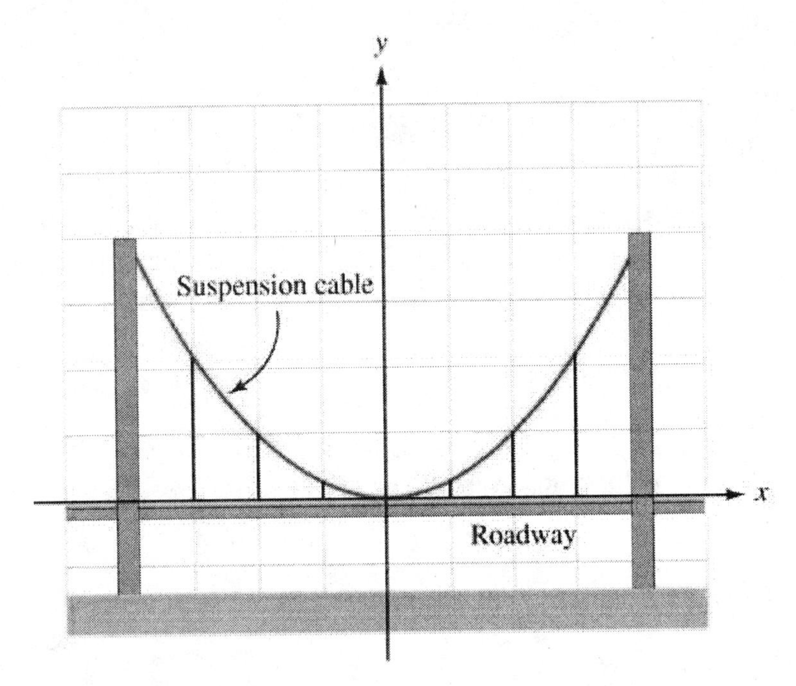

( ) -4
( ) 2
( ) 4
( ) -2
( ) 3
( ) -3

18. Choose the correct answer for combining the like terms:
9z and 8z.

( ) 17
( ) 16z
( ) 72z
( ) 17z

19. Add the polynomials:

$(7x^2+7x+7)+(5x^2-3x+4)$.

20. Choose the correct answer for subtracting the polynomials:

$7z^2+9z+3$

$-(-4z^2-6z+2)$

( ) $11z^2+3z$

( ) $11z^2+3z+5$

( ) $11z^2+15z+1$

( ) $11z^2+3z-5$

21. A young couple bought two cars, one for \$6900 and the other for \$10900. The first car is expected to depreciate \$800 per year and the second car \$1000 per year.

Write a single equation that will give the value *y* of both cars after *x* years.

22. Choose the correct product:

$(4t^6)(4t^9)$.

( ) $4t^{15}$

( ) $16t^{15}$

( ) $16t^{54}$

23. Find the product:

$(b + 8)(b + 5)$.

24. Choose the correct answer for the square of the binomial:

$(8a - 7)^2$.

( ) $64a^2 + 112a - 7$

( ) $64a^2 - 56a - 49$

( ) $64a^2 - 112a + 49$

25. Multiply the polynomials on the left and connect with a correct answer on the right.

$(b+5)(b^2-3b+16)$	b^3+2b^2+b+80
$(b+5)(b^2-3b-16)$	$b^3+2b^2-31b-80$
$(b-5)(b^2-3b+16)$	$b^3-8b^2+31b-80$

Answers

1. the*x*- coordinate -> -10, the*y*- coordinate -> -5

2. A -> (-6,-5), B -> (-2,-4), C -> (4,3), D -> (6,1)

3. C

4. A -> (-3,-1), B -> (5,3), C -> (5,-5), D -> (-2,2)

5. (2,0)I(0,4)

6. -2

7. Red

8.

9. 90

10. 243

11. $-18t^{9}$

12. $15y^{10}t^{10}$

13. $10000y^{56}$

14. 16a^9 -> monomial, -14b+a -> binomial, 17-10a^10+13b -> trinomial

15. 1

16. -4, 0, -2, 6, 0, 8, 2, 6, 4, 0

17. 4

18. 17*z*

19. $12x^{2}+4x+11$

20. $11z^2 + 15z + 1$

21. $y = 17800 - 1800x$

22. $16t^{15}$

23. $b^2 + 13b + 40$

24. $64a^2 - 112a + 49$

25. (b+5)*(b^2-3*b+16) -> b^3+2*b^2+1*b+80, (b-5)*(b^2-3*b+16) -> b^3 8*b^2+31*b-80, (b+5)*(b^2-3*b-16) -> b^3+2*b^2-31*b-80

1. Choose the correct answer for the area of the rectangle in the illustration if$x$= 6.

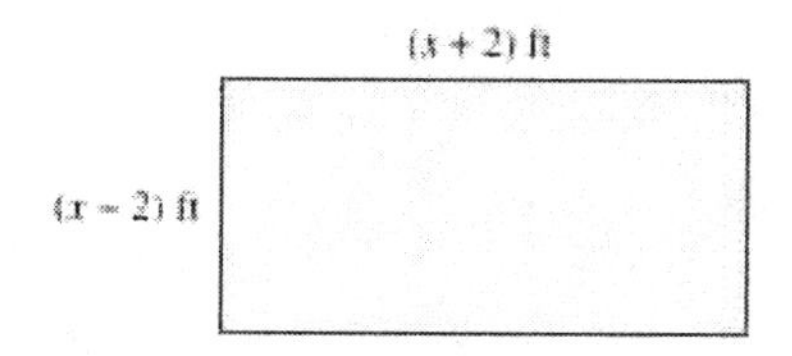

( ) 12
( ) 32
( ) 16

2. What is the$x$-coordinate of the ordered pair $(-7,-5)$?

( ) -5
( ) -7

3. Consider the equation $8x + y = 4$. Which of these points are the solutions of the equation?

[ ] $(2,0)$
[ ] $(2,-12)$
[ ] $(-2,-12)$
[ ] $(0,4)$

4. Which one of the points below is on the x-axis?

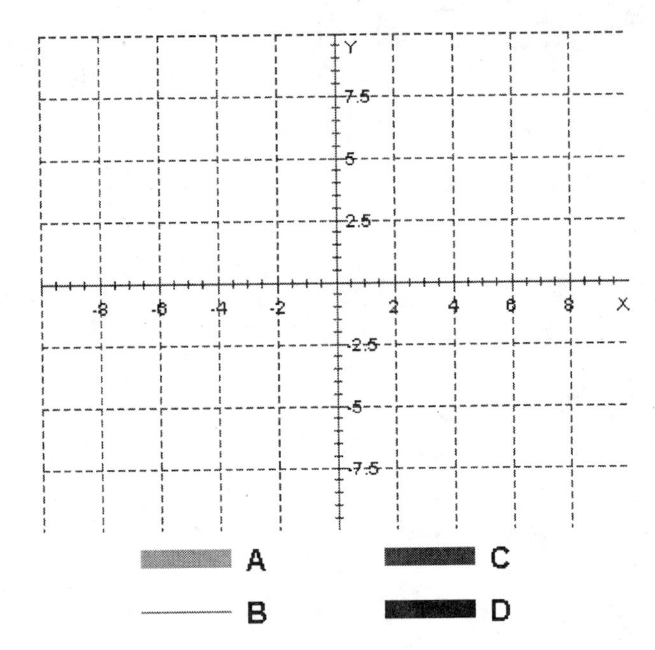

( ) A
( ) C
( ) D
( ) B

5. Which of the points below has the coordinates $(4,9)$?

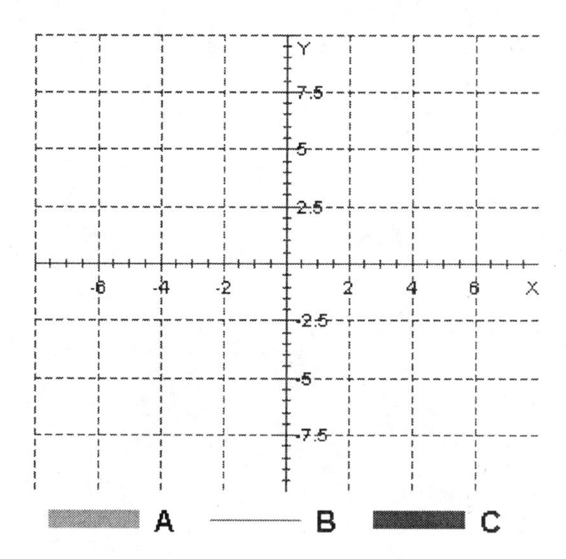

( ) A
( ) B
( ) C

6. Select all the points that are either$x$-intercepts or$y$-intercepts of the line graphed below.

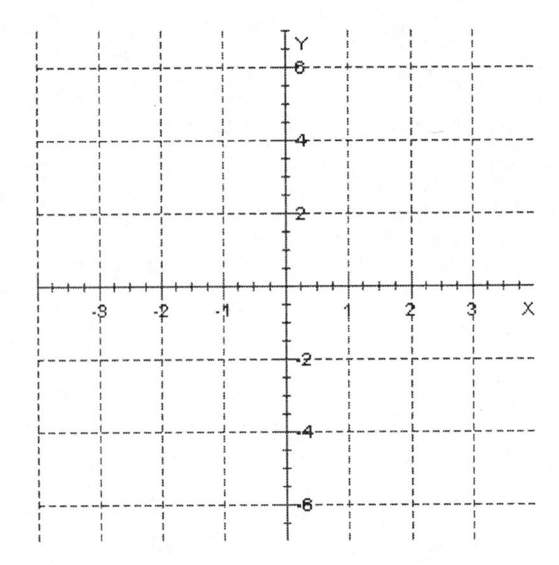

[ ] (0,4)
[ ] (0,-2)
[ ] (-2,0)
[ ] (4,0)

7. Which of the following points is the solution for the equation -4y+ 2x= 9?

[ ] (5, -6.25)
[ ] (5, 0.25)
[ ] (-8, -6.25)
[ ] (8, 1.75)

8. Which line in the following graph is the graph of equation $y = 5x$?

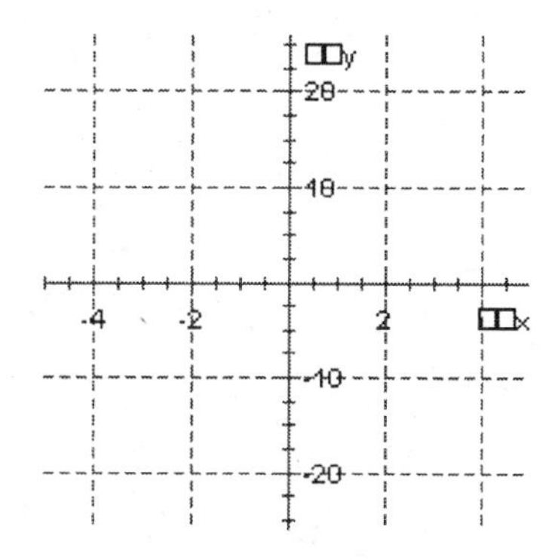

( ) Blue
( ) Red

9. The following graph shows the value y (in thousands of dollars) of a car that is x years old. Estimate x, if the value of the car equals 9.

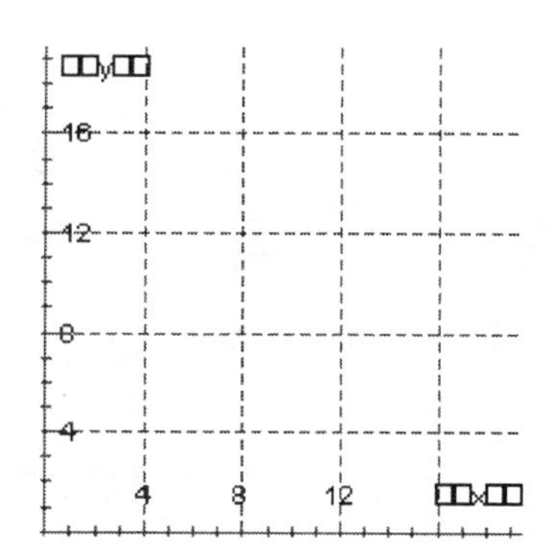

( ) 10
( ) 8
( ) 5

10. Evaluate the exponential expression x^{n+m} for $x = 3, n = 3, m = 2$.

( ) 9
( ) 27
( ) 729
( ) 243

11. What is $f^9 \cdot f^9$ rewritten using only one exponent?

( ) f^{81}
( ) f^{18}
( ) f^0

12. Simplify the product:

$-9s^8(7s)$

( ) $63s^8$
( ) $-63s^9$
( ) $9s^9$

13. Simplify the product:

$4s^3f^3 \cdot 2f^3s^3$

( ) $8s^3f^6$
( ) $8s^6f^6$
( ) $8s^3f^6$

14. Simplify the expression:

$(5s^3s^2)^2$

( ) $25s^{10}$

( ) $25s^7$

( ) $5s^{12}$

( ) $5s^{10}$

15. The degree of a polynomial is the same as

( ) the degree of its term with largest degree
( ) the number of variables
( ) the degree of its term with least degree

16. Choose the correct degree of the following polynomial:

$-4b^7$.

( ) 1
( ) -4
( ) 7

17. Evaluate the polynomial $4d^2 - 3d + 7$ for $d = 5$.

( ) 92
( ) 122
( ) 78

18. The height$h$(in feet) of a ball shot straight up with an initial velocity of 64 feet per second is given by the equation $h = -16t^2 + 64t$. What is the height of the ball after 3 seconds?

( ) 64
( ) 60
( ) 48

19. Choose the correct answer for combining the like terms:
9*b*and 6*b*.

( ) 54*b*
( ) 15
( ) 14*b*
( ) 15*b*

20. Choose the correct answer for adding the polynomials:
$(-5z^2+2)+(5z^2-2)$.

( ) $0z^2+4$
( ) $0z^4$
( ) $0z^2$
( ) $10z^2$

21. Choose the correct answer for subtracting the polynomials:
$7a^3-4a^3$.

( ) 3
( ) $4a^3$
( ) $28a^3$
( ) $3a^3$

22. A young couple bought two cars, one for $9300 and the other for $7600. The first car is expected to depreciate $700 per year and the second car $800 per year.

Choose the correct single equation that will give the value y of both cars after x years.

( ) $y = 16900 + 1500x$
( ) $y = 16900 - 1500x$
( ) $y = 10100 - 8300x$
( ) $y = 1500 - 16900x$

23. Choose the correct answer for the product:
$6(b + 5)$.

( ) $6b + 5$
( ) $6b + 30$
( ) $6b + 6$

24. Choose the correct answer for the product:
$3(3b^4 - b)b$.

( ) $3b^5 - 3b$
( ) $9b^5 - 3b^2$
( ) $3b^4 - 3b$

25. Choose the correct answer for the square of the binomial:
$(6b + 4)^2$.

( ) $36b^2 + 24b + 16$
( ) $36b^2 + 48b + 4$
( ) $36b^2 + 48b + 16$

Answers

1. 32

2. -7

3. $(2,-12) \text{I} (0,4)$

4. B

5. A

6. (0,4)I(-2,0)

7. (5, 0.25)I(-8, -6.25)I(8, 1.75)

8. Red

9. 10

10. 243

11. t^{18}

12. $-63s^9$

13. $8s^6t^6$

14. $25s^{10}$

15. the degree of its term with largest degree

16. 7

17. 92

18. 48

19. 15*b*

20. $0z^2$

21. $3a^3$

22. $y = 16900 - 1500x$

23. $6b + 30$

24. $9b^5 - 3b^2$

25. $36b^2 + 48b + 16$

1. The graph shows the number of shovels of sand that should be used for a given number of shovels of cement when mixing concrete for a walkway.

What number of shovels of sand should be used for a 2 shovels of cement ?

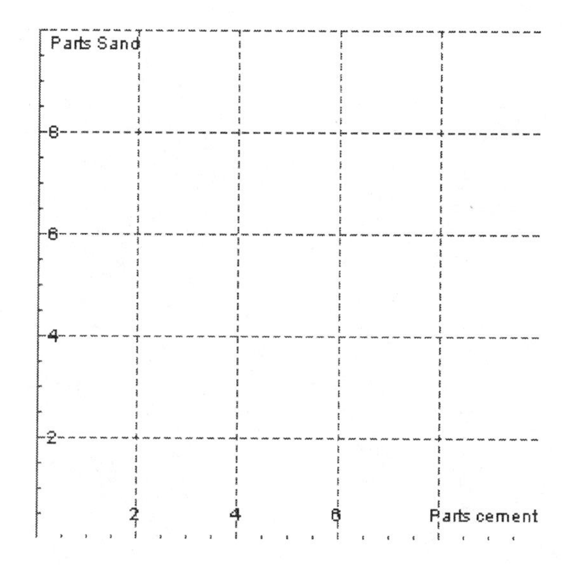

( ) 2
( ) 3
( ) 1

2. Which of the given equations has the solution $(-2, 6)$?

( ) $x + 9y = -56$
( ) $x - 9y = -56$
( ) $9x - y = -56$

3. What is the*x*-coordinate of the point on the graph?

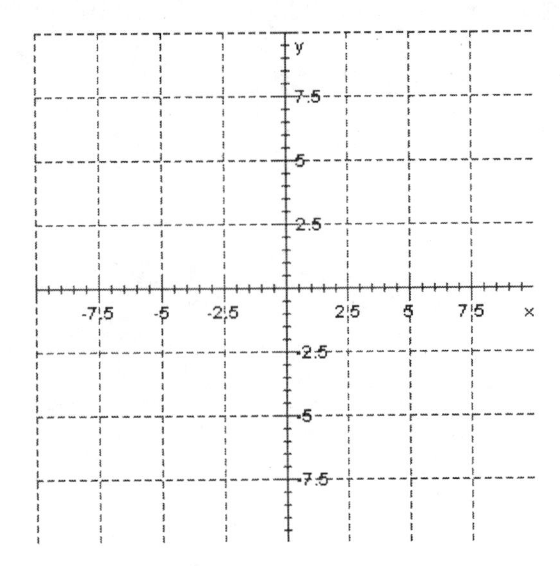

( ) 0
( ) 3
( ) -3
( ) 0

4. The map in the illustration below shows the areas where damage was caused by an earthquake.

At which points was damage done?

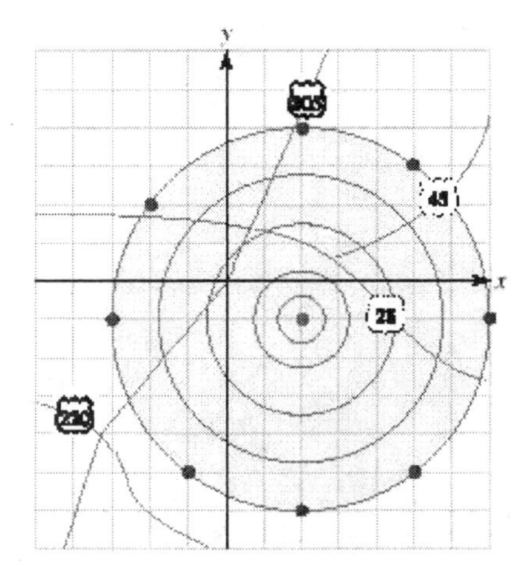

[] $\left(4, -4\right)$
[] $\left(6, -2\right)$
[] $\left(1, -6\right)$
[] $\left(-4, 6\right)$

5. Select all the points that are either x-intercepts or y-intercepts of the line graphed below.

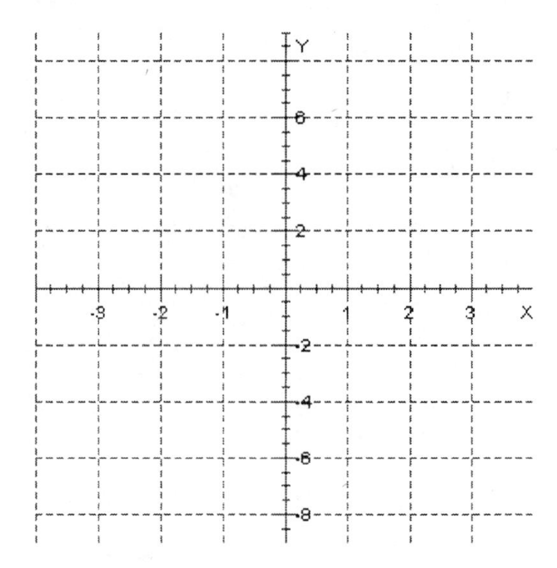

[ ] (2,0)
[ ] (0,-6)
[ ] (0,2)
[ ] (-6,0)

6. Which of the following points is the solution for the equation $10y + 6x = -10$?

[ ] (2, -2.2)
[ ] (6, -4.6)
[ ] (2, 3.2)
[ ] (-7, 3.2)

7. Which line in the following graph is the graph of equation $y = 5x$?

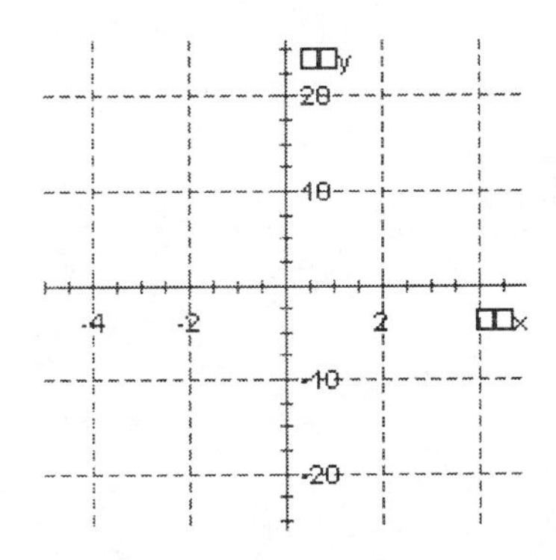

( ) Red
( ) Blue

8. The following graph shows the value y (in thousands of dollars) of a car that is x years old. Estimate x, if the value of the car equals 13.

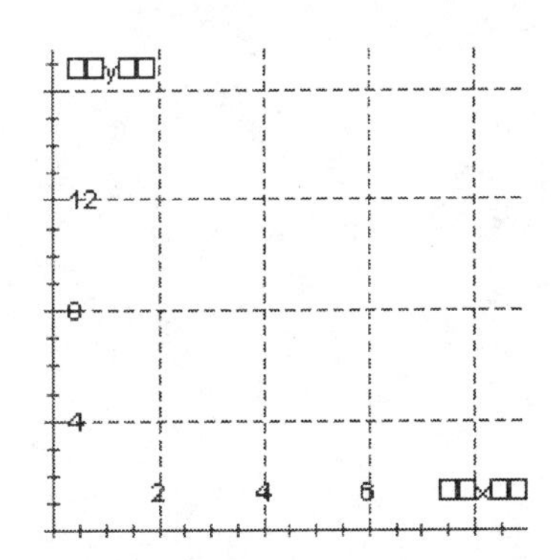

( ) 2
( ) 5
( ) 3

9. What is $c^7 \cdot c^8$ rewritten using only one exponent?

( ) c^{56}
( ) c^{-1}
( ) c^{15}

10. Simplify the product:

$-5s^{8}(6s)$

( ) $30s^{8}$

( ) $5s^{9}$

( ) $-30s^{9}$

11. Simplify the product:

$3y^{4}b^{4} \cdot 5b^{4}y^{4}$

( ) $15y^{4}b^{8}$

( ) $15y^{4}b^{8}$

( ) $15y^{8}b^{8}$

12. Simplify the expression:

$(4y^{6}y^{4})^{3}$

( ) $64y^{30}$

( ) $64y^{13}$

( ) $4y^{72}$

( ) $4y^{30}$

13. Choose the correct degree of the following polynomial:

$3b^{3} + 8b^{2} - 5$.

( ) 2

( ) 5

( ) 3

14. Evaluate the polynomial $10y^3 + 6y - 19$ for $y = -2$.

( ) -111
( ) -73
( ) -87

15. Which of the following graphs is the graph of equation $y = \frac{1}{2}x^2 - 2$?

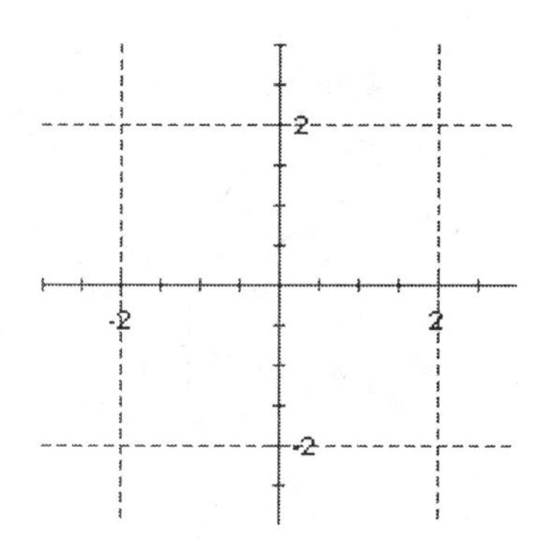

( ) Red
( ) Blue

16. The number of feet that a car travels before stopping depends on the driver's reaction time and the braking distance. (See illustration.) For one driver, the stopping distance *d* is given by the equation $d = 0.11u^2 + 0.7u$, where *u* is the velocity of the car. Find the stopping distance for speed *u* = 30 mph.

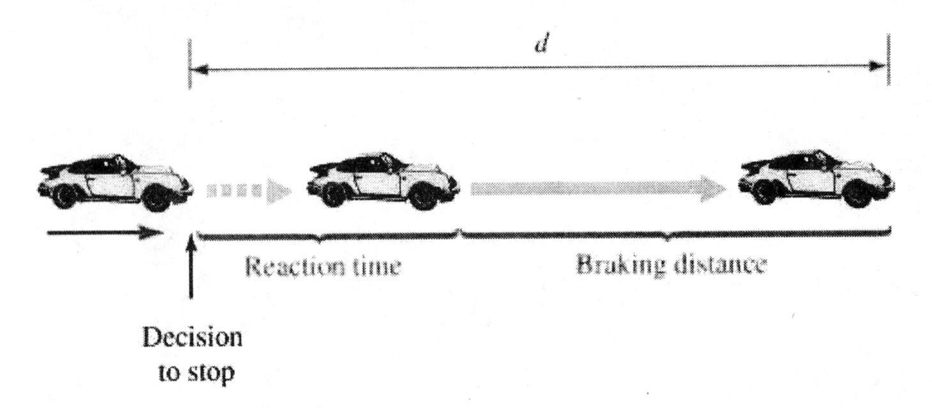

( ) 310 ft
( ) 954 ft
( ) 120 ft
( ) 18 ft

17. Choose the correct answer for combining the like terms:
8*x* and 9*x*.

( ) 17*x*
( ) 16*x*
( ) 17
( ) 72*x*

18. Choose the correct answers for adding the polynomials:
$(7y^2+8y)+(3y^2-6y+3)$.

( ) $10y^2+2y-3$
( ) $10y^2+2y+3$
( ) $10y^2+2y$
( ) $10y^2+14y+3$

19. Choose the correct answer for adding the polynomials:

$8y^2 + 9y + 5$ and

$5y^2 - 3y + 1$

( ) $13y^2 + 12y + 6$
( ) $13y^2 + 6y$
( ) $13y^2 + 6y - 6$
( ) $13y^2 + 6y + 6$

20. Choose the correct answer for subtracting the polynomials:

$7b^2 + 9b + 8$

$-(-6b^2 - 2b + 7)$

( ) $13b^2 + 7b + 15$
( ) $13b^2 + 7b - 15$
( ) $13b^2 + 7b$
( ) $13b^2 + 11b + 1$

21. A young couple bought two cars, one for $9400 and the other for $8600. The first car is expected to depreciate $500 per year and the second car $1000 per year.

Choose the correct single equation that will give the value y of both cars after x years.

( ) $y = 1500 - 18000x$
( ) $y = 18000 + 1500x$
( ) $y = 10400 - 9100x$
( ) $y = 18000 - 1500x$

22. Choose the correct product:

$(-3f^{9})(-5f^{5})$.

() $3f^{14}$

() $-15f^{45}$

() $15f^{14}$

23. Choose the correct answer for the product:

$8b(3b^{6} - b + 5)$.

() $3b^{6} - 8b^{2} - 8b$

() $24b^{7} - 8b^{2} + 40b$

() $8b^{7} - 8b^{2} + 5b$

24. Choose the correct answer for the square of the binomial:

$(7s + 7)^{2}$.

() $49s^{2} + 98s + 7$

() $49s^{2} + 49s + 49$

() $49s^{2} + 98s + 49$

25. Choose the correct answer for multiplying the polynomials:

$(s + 5)(s^{2} - 3s + 17)$.

() $s^{3} + 2s^{2} + 2s + 85$

() $s^{3} + 5s^{2} + 14s + 85$

() $s^{3} + 2s^{2} + 12s + 5$

Answers

1. 1

2. $x - 9y = -56$

3. 0

4. $(4, -4)$ | $(6, -2)$

5. (2,0)|(0,-6)

6. (2, -2.2)|(6, -4.6)|(-7, 3.2)

7. Red

8. 2

9. c^{15}

10. $-30s^{9}$

11. $15y^{8}b^{8}$

12. $64y^{30}$

13. 3

14. -111

15. Red

16. 120 ft

17. 17*x*

18. $10y^2 + 2y + 3$

19. $13y^2 + 6y + 6$

20. $13b^2 + 11b + 1$

21. $y = 18000 - 1500x$

22. $15t^{14}$

23. $24b^{7} - 8b^{2} + 40b$

24. $49s^{2} + 98s + 49$

25. $s^{3} + 2s^{2} + 2s + 85$

1. Choose the correct answer for the square of the binomial:

$(2t - 4)^2$.

( ) $4t^2 - 16t + 16$

( ) $4t^2 + 16t - 4$

( ) $4t^2 - 8t - 16$

2. Simplify the expression:

$(2x^7x^4)^4$

3. Which line in the following graph is the graph of equation $y = 4x$?

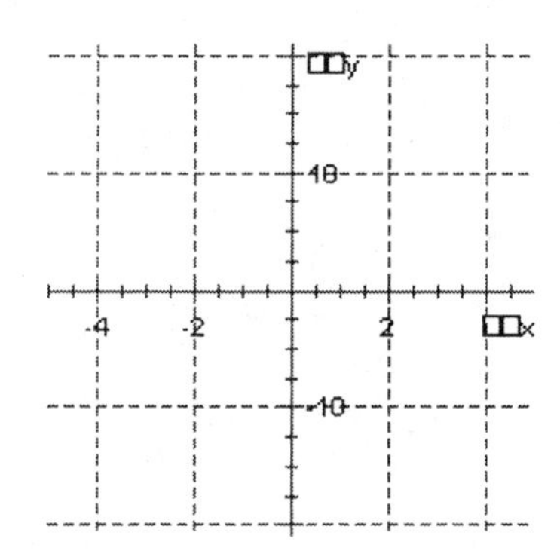

( ) Blue

( ) Red

4. The map in the illustration below shows the areas where damage was caused by an earthquake.

Match the points with their coordinantes.

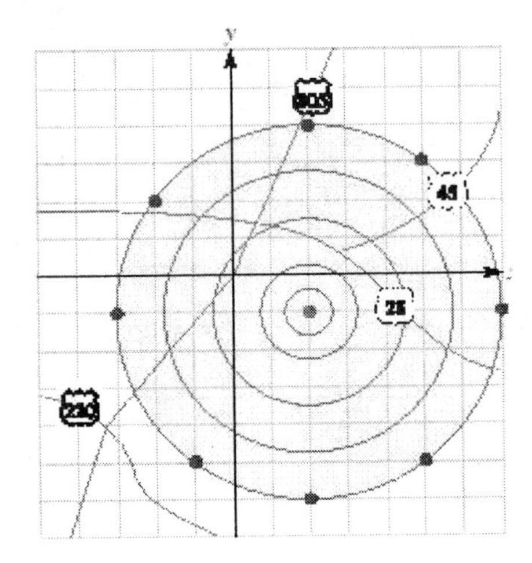

B	$(5, 3)$
C	$(5, -5)$
D	$(-2, 2)$
A	$(-3, -1)$

5. Choose the correct product:

$(10y^3)(2y^8)$.

( ) $20y^{24}$

( ) $10y^{11}$

( ) $20y^{11}$

6. Graph the following equation by first making a table of solutions:

$y = -\frac{1}{8}x^2 + 8$.

x	y
-4	
-2	
0	
2	
4	

7. Choose the correct answer for subtracting the polynomials:

$$\begin{array}{r} 4c^2+8c+8 \\ -(-7c^2-3c+4) \\ \hline \end{array}$$

( ) $11c^2+11c+4$

( ) $11c^2+5c$

( ) $11c^2+5c-12$

( ) $11c^2+5c+12$

8. The following graph shows the value y (in thousands of dollars) of a car that is x years old. Estimate the value of the car for the given values of x and complete the table.

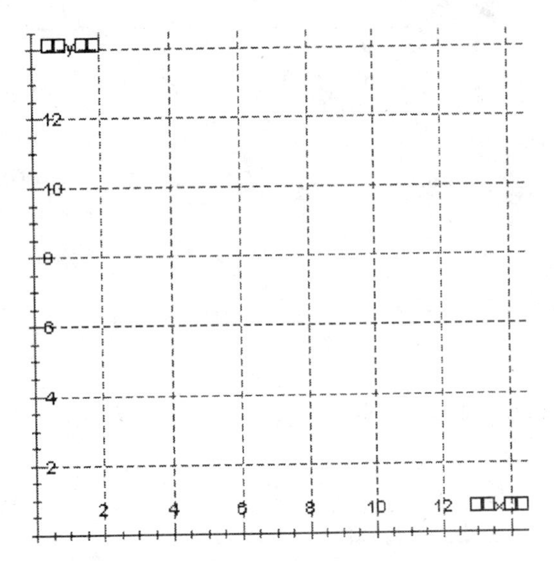

x	y
2	
1	
10	

9. Simplify the product:

$-9y^4(8y^7)$

10. Choose the correct answer for combining the like terms:

$6y$ and $2y$.

( ) $12y$
( ) 8
( ) $8y$
( ) $7y$

11. Add the polynomials:

$(6c^2+5c+7)+(9c^2-6c+2)$.

12. Simplify the product:

$5y^5b^2 \cdot 5b^5y^2$

( ) $25y^5b^7$

( ) $25y^2b^7$

( ) $25y^7b^7$

13. Multiply the polynomials on the left and connect with a correct answer on the right.

$(c+8)(c^2-2c-28)$	$c^3+6c^2+12c+224$
$(c-8)(c^2-2c+28)$	$c^3-10c^2+44c-224$
$(c+8)(c^2-2c+28)$	$c^3+6c^2-44c-224$

14. If $90 is invested in a savings account paying 3% per year simple interest, the amount C in the account over a period time t is given by the formula $C = 3t + 90$. Find C, if $t = 2$.

( ) 96
( ) 111
( ) 105

15. Which one of the points below is in Quadrant IV?

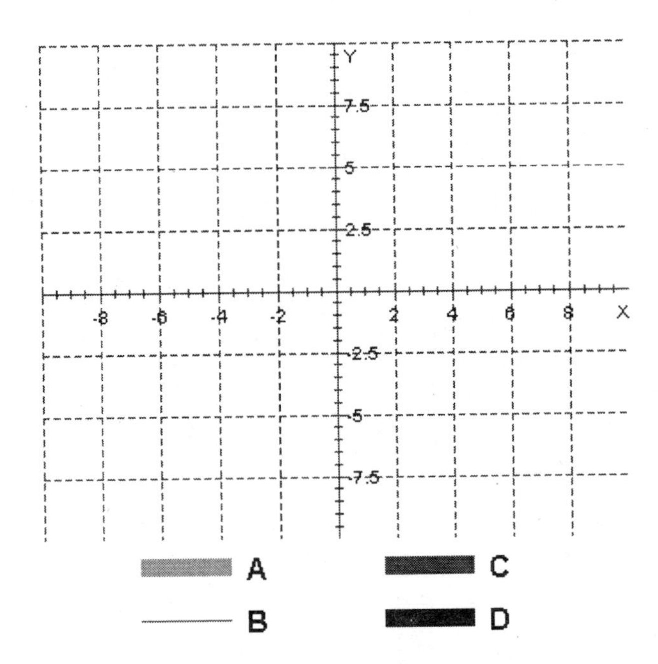

( ) C
( ) B
( ) A
( ) A

16. A young couple bought two cars, one for $8700 and the other for $8200. The first car is expected to depreciate $700 per year and the second car $900 per year.

Write a single equation that will give the value y of both cars after x years.

17. The cable of a suspension bridge hangs in the shape of a parabola. (See the illustration below.) Use the information in the illustration to find y, if $x = -4$.

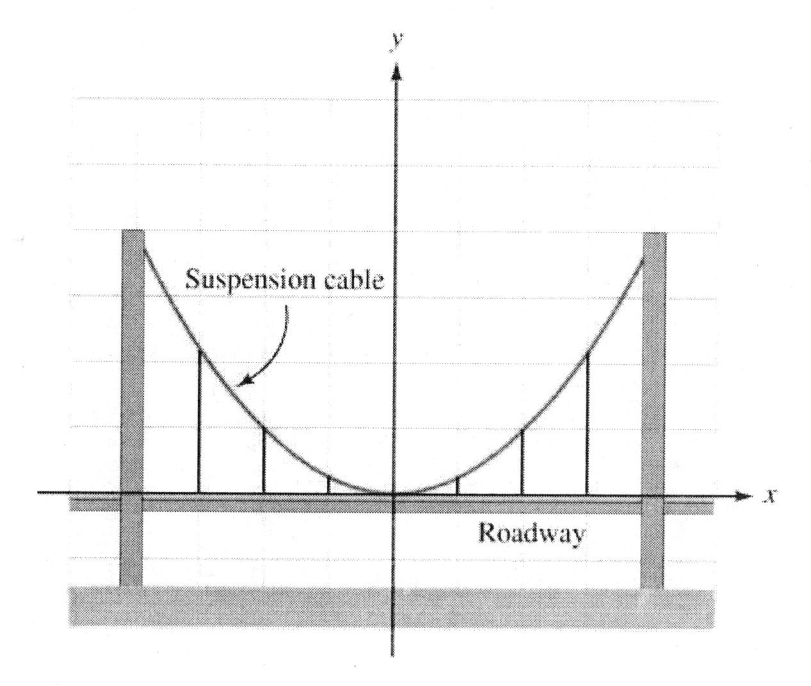

( ) -3
( ) -4
( ) -2
( ) 2
( ) 4
( ) 3

18. Consider the ordered pair

$(-8, 8)$.

Match the following.

the x-coordinate	-8
the y-coordinate	8

19. The graph of the equation $y = bx + -2$ is given. Find b.

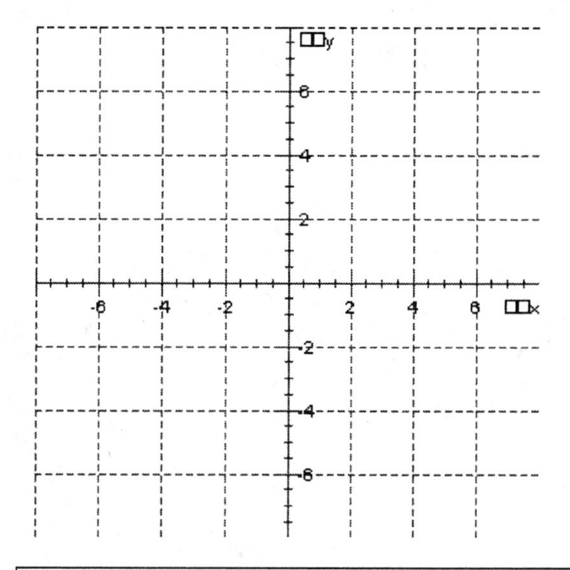

20. Choose the correct degree of the following polynomial:
$21d + 12$.

( ) 1
( ) 21
( ) 2
( ) 12

21. Match the points with their coordinates.

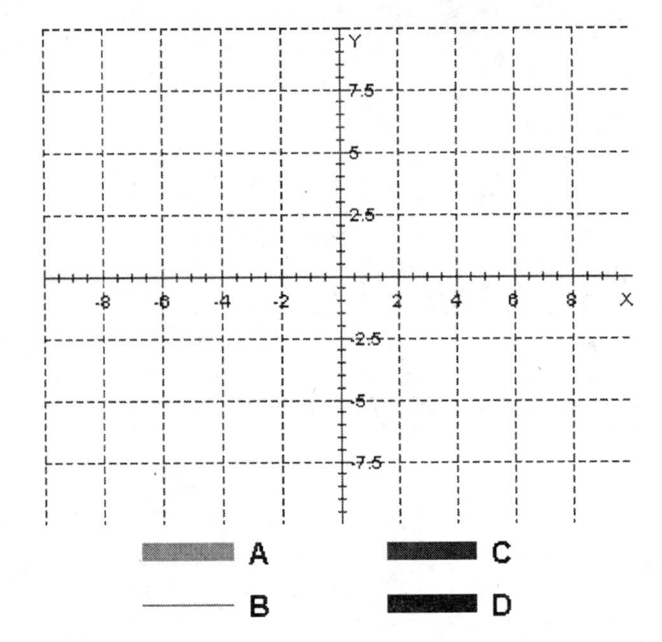

D	(2, -2)
B	(-2, 7)
A	(-6, -6)
C	(-8, 6)

22. Evaluate the exponential expression x^{n+m} for $x = 2, n = 3, m = 2$.

( ) 4
( ) 32
( ) 8
( ) 64

23. Find the product:
$(t + 3)(t + 5)$.

24. Select all the points that are either x-intercepts or y-intercepts of the line graphed below.

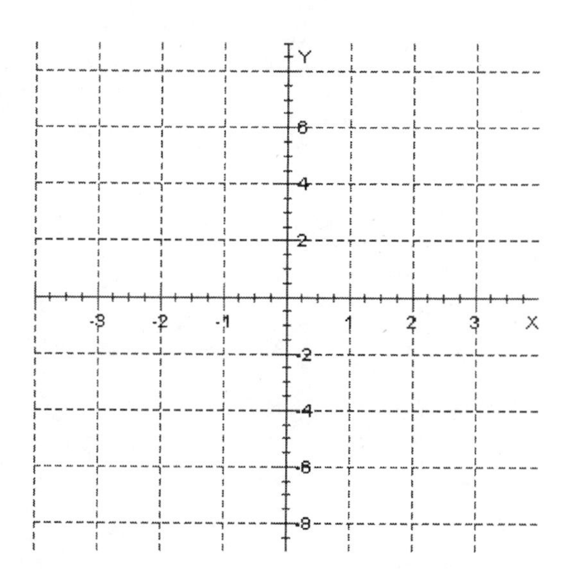

[ ] (-6,0)
[ ] (0,-2)
[ ] (0,-6)
[ ] (-2,0)

25. Match each polynomial on the left with the correct type of polynomial on the right.

$-9a^5$	binomial
$7 + 16a^3 - 19b$	trinomial
$18b - a$	monomial

Answers

1. $4f^2 - 16f + 16$

2. $16x^{44}$

3. Red

4. A -> (-3,-1), B -> (5,3), C -> (5,-5), D -> (-2,2)

5. $20y^{11}$

6. -4, 6, -2, 7.5, 0, 8, 2, 7.5, 4, 6

7. $11c^2 + 11c + 4$

8.

9. $-72y^{11}$

10. $8y$

11. $15c^2 + -c + 9$

12. $25y^7b^7$

13. (c+8)*(c^2-2*c+28) -> c^3+6*c^2+12*c+224, (c-8)*(c^2-2*c+28) -> c^3
10*c^2+44*c-224, (c+8)*(c^2-2*c-28) -> c^3+6*c^2-44*c-224

14. 96

15. C

16. $y = 16900 - 1600x$

17. 4

18. the*x*- coordinate -> -8, the*y*- coordinate -> 8

19. -1

20. 1

21. A -> (-8,6), B -> (-6,-6), C -> (-2,7), D -> (2,-2)

22. 32

23. $t^2 + 8t + 15$

24. (0,-6)l(-2,0)

25. -9a^5 -> monomial, 18b-a -> binomial, 7+16a^3-19b -> trinomial

1. The graph shows the number of shovels of sand that should be used for a given number of shovels of cement when mixing concrete for a walkway. Complete a table using this data.

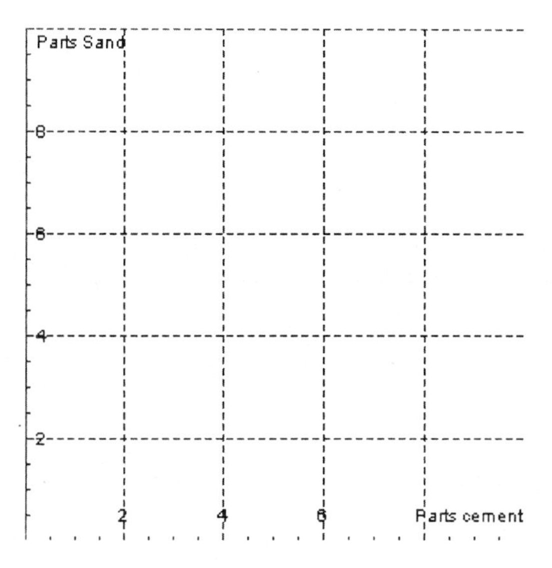

Parts Cement	Parts Sand

2. If $81 is invested in a savings account paying 6% per year simple interest, the amount *A* in the account over a period time *t* is given by the formula $A = 6t + 81$. Find *A*, if $t = 8$.

( ) 129
( ) 87
( ) 117

3. Consider the equation $6x + y = -40$. Which of these points are the solutions of the equation?

[] $(0,-40)$
[] $(8,-88)$
[] $(-8,-88)$
[] $(-5,0)$

4. Which one of the points below is in Quadrant III?

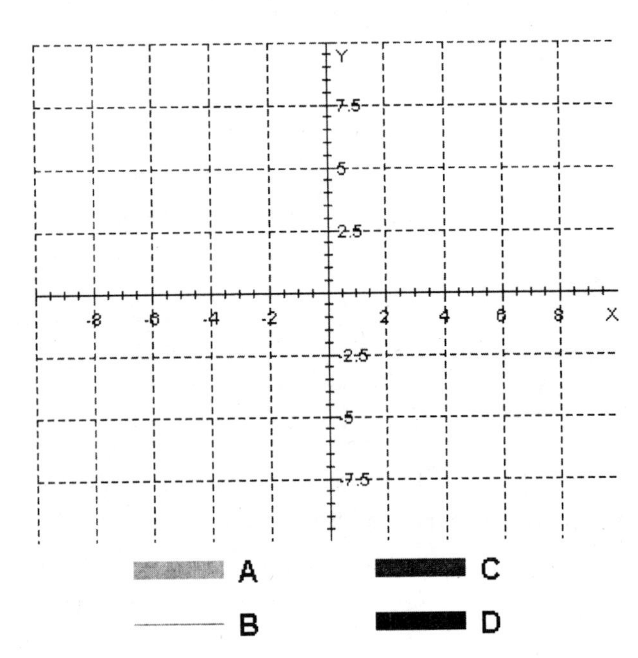

5. See the information from the graph below for 2, 4, 6 and 8 servings of instant mashed potatoes.

How many cups of flakes will we need for 2 servings of instant mashed potatoes?

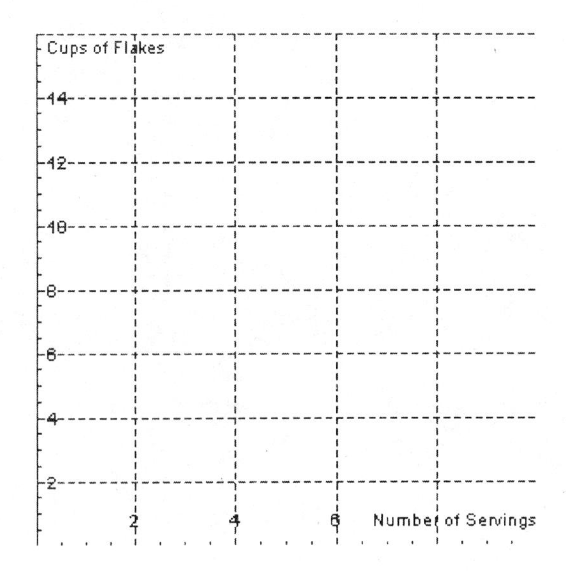

( ) 10
( ) 6
( ) 8
( ) 4

6. In the equation $g = 17x - 6$, which variable is the dependent variable?

7. The graph of a linear equation is shown below. What three points were apparently plotted to obtain the graph? (All of the coordinates are integers.)

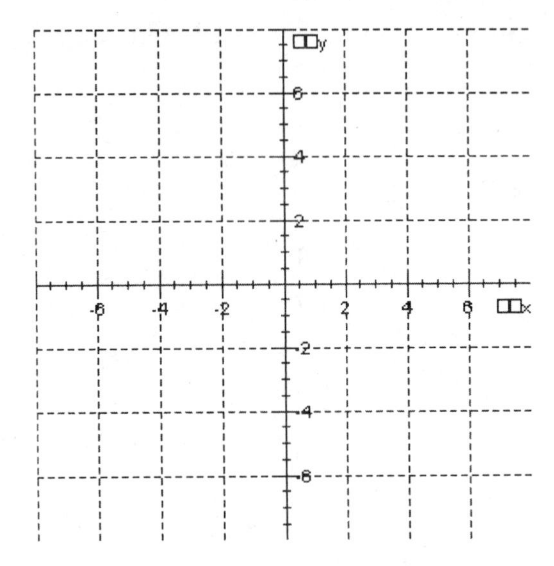

[ ] (-6, -5)
[ ] (-6, 5)
[ ] (4, 5)
[ ] (-2, 0)
[ ] (4, -5)
[ ] (-2, -1)

8. The graph of the equation $y = kx + 2$ is given. Find k.

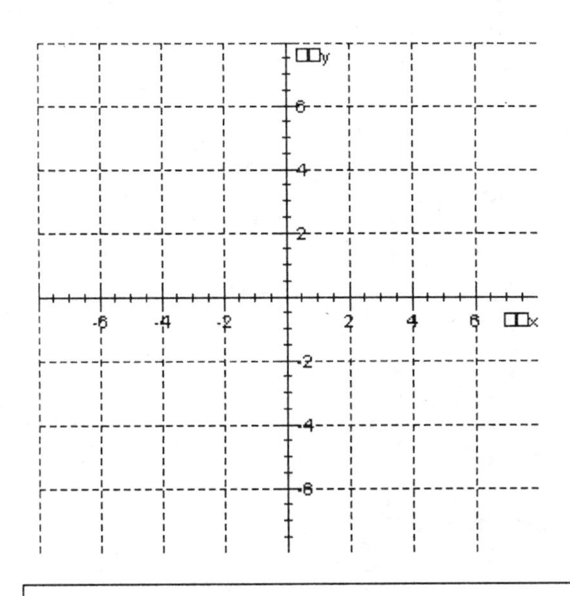

9. Evaluate the exponential expression $(x^m)^n$ for $x = 2, n = 3, m = 2$.

10. What is $4^{10}(4^{10})$ rewritten using only one exponent?

( ) 4^{100}
( ) 4^{10}
( ) 4^{20}

11. Simplify the product:

$s^5 \cdot b^5 s^2$

12. Simplify the expression:

$(3x^5x^3)^4$

( ) $81x^{32}$
( ) $81x^{12}$
( ) $3x^{60}$
( ) $3x^{32}$

13. What is the degree of the polynomial $3x^7 + 5x^2 + 6$?

14. Choose the correct degree of the following polynomial:
21c+ 12.

( ) 21
( ) 1
( ) 2
( ) 12

15. Graph the following equation by first making a table of solutions: $y = \frac{1}{8}x^2$.

x	y
-4	
-2	
0	
2	
4	

16. The cable of a suspension bridge hangs in the shape of a parabola. (See the illustration below.) Use the information in the illustration to find *y*, if *x* = -4.

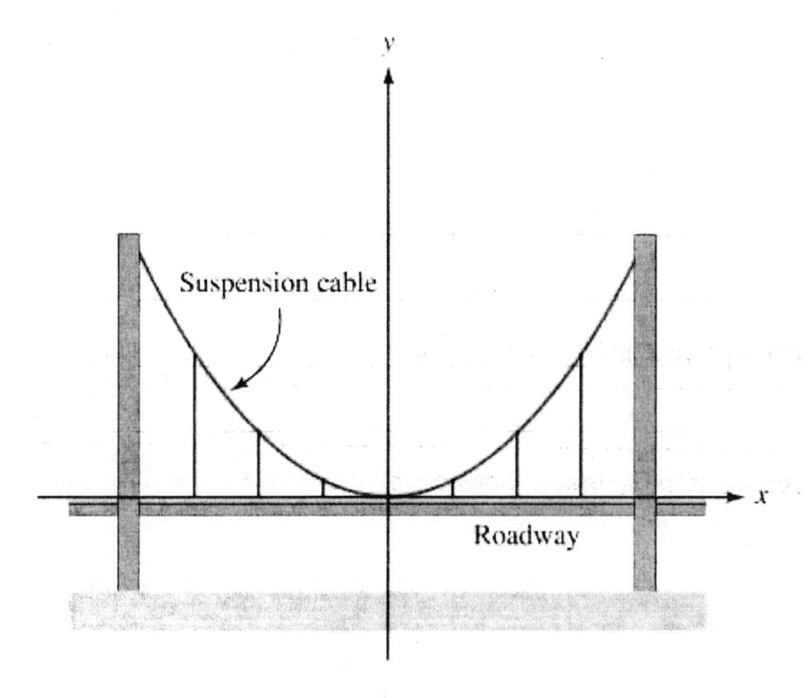

( ) 3
( ) -4
( ) -2
( ) -3
( ) 4
( ) 2

17. Add the polynomials:
$4a^2 + 6a^2$.

18. Choose the correct answers for adding the polynomials:
$(3a^2+4a)+(2a^2-2a+6)$.

( ) $5a^2+2a$
( ) $5a^2+2a+6$
( ) $5a^2+6a+6$
( ) $5a^2+2a-6$

19. Subtract the polynomials:
$(4b^2+5b+5)-(5b^2-8b+8)$.

20. If a house is purchased for $68000 and is expected to appreciate $600 per year, its value *y* after *x* years is given by the equation $y = 600x + 68000$.

A second house is purchased for $52000 and is expected to appreciate $500 per year.

Choose the correct answer for a single polynomial equation that will give the combined value *y* of both houses after *x* years.

( ) $y = 1100x + 120000$
( ) $y = 68500x + 52600$
( ) $y = 1300x + 120000$
( ) $y = 120000x + 1100$
( ) $y = 120000 - 1100x$

21. Find the product:
$(3y^{10})(4y^4)$.

22. Choose the correct answer for the product:

$(- \frac{1}{3}b^7)(\frac{1}{6}b^4)$.

( ) $-\frac{1}{9}b^{11}$

( ) $-\frac{1}{18}b^{11}$

( ) $\frac{1}{18}b^{11}$

23. Find the product:

$4(c + 3)$.

24. Choose the correct answer for the product:

$(x + 5)(x + 6)$.

( ) $x^2 + 30x + 30$

( ) $x^2 + 11x + 30$

( ) $x^2 + 11x + 11$

25. Express the area of the rectangle in the illustration if$x$= 6.

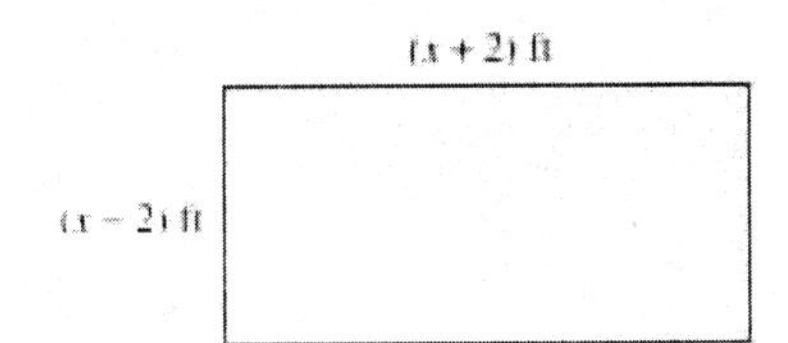

Answers For

1. 4, 4, 6, 6, 8, 8

2. 129

3. $(0, -40) | (8, -88)$

4. D

5. 4

6. g

7. (-6, -5)|(4, 5)|(-2, -1)

8. 2

9. 64

10. 4^{20}

11. $a^7 b^5$

12. $81x^{32}$

13. 7

14. 1

15. -4, 2, -2, 0.5, 0, 0, 2, 0.5, 4, 2

16. 4

17. $10a^2$

18. $5a^2 + 2a + 6$

19. $-1b^2 + 13b + -3$

20. $y = 1100x + 120000$

21. $12y^{14}$

22. $-\frac{1}{18}b^{11}$

23. $4c + 12$

24. $x^2 + 11x + 30$

25. 32

1. Consider the equation $7x + y = -14$.

Complete the statement: If*x*= -3, then

( ) *y*= 7
( ) *y*= -35
( ) *y*= -14

2. Which one of the points below is on the*y*-axis?

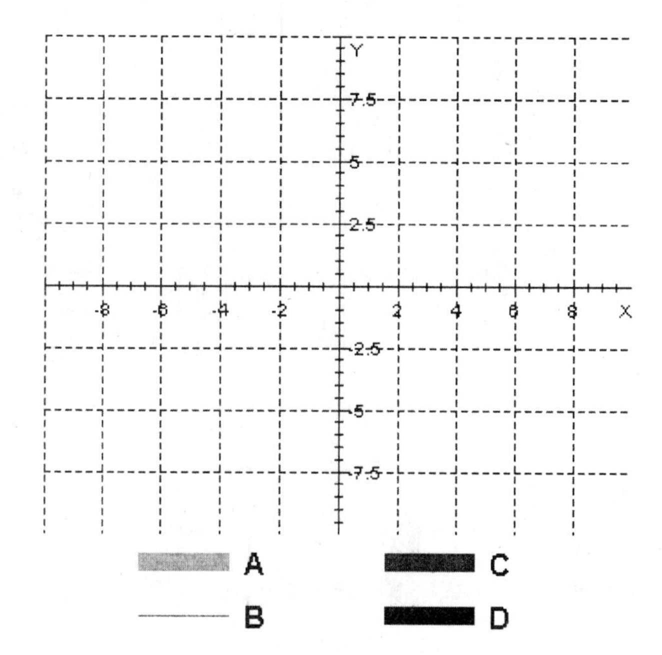

3. The map in the illustration below shows the areas where damage was caused by an earthquake.

At which points was damage done?

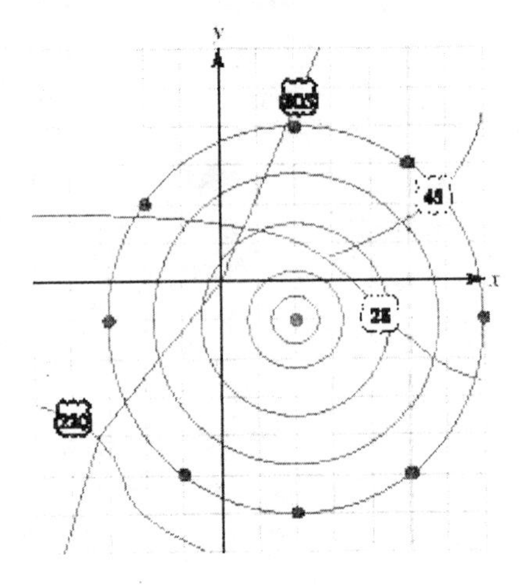

[] $(3, 3)$
[] $(-3, 2)$
[] $(-3, 6)$
[] $(2, 0)$

4. In the equation $f = -13v - 6$, which variable is the independent variable?

5. Select all the points that are eitherx-intercepts ory-intercepts of the line graphed below.

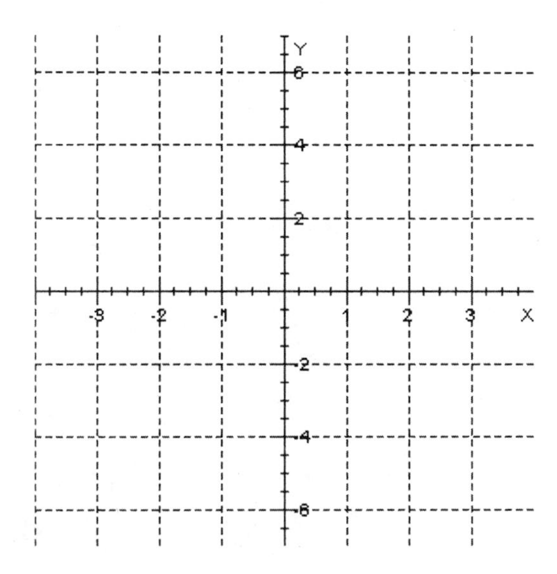

[] (-4,0)
[] (0,-4)
[] (0,-2)
[] (-2,0)

6. What is $c^8 \cdot c^9 \cdot c^4$ rewritten using only one exponent?

() c^{17}
() c^{13}
() c^{21}

7. Match each equation with the point that is a solution of the equation.

$(10, 2)$	$2x + 10y = -84$
$(1, 3)$	$10x - 2y = 96$
$(-7, -7)$	$10x + 2y = 16$

8. Complete the table and graph the equation $-2y + 5x = 8$.

x	y
-10	
-7	
	-9
7	
	21

9. The following graph shows the value$y$(in thousands of dollars) of a car that is$x$ years old. Estimate$x$, if the value of the car equals 5.

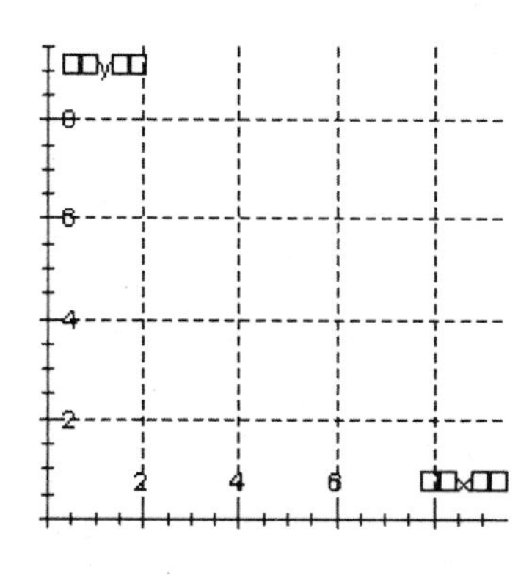

( ) 7
( ) 4
( ) 2

10. Rewrite the following expression using only one exponent:

$f^6 \cdot f^9$

11. Simplify the following expression:

$s^2 b^2 \cdot b^2 s^2$

12. Simplify the expression:

$(y^3 y^7)^2$

( ) y^{20}
( ) y^{14}
( ) y^{12}
( ) y^{23}

13. How many terms are contained in a monomial?

14. Choose the correct degree of the following polynomial:

$-5b^4 - 6b + 10$.

( ) 3
( ) 4
( ) -5

15. Graph the following equation by first making a table of solutions:

$y = -\frac{1}{2}x^2 + 1$.

x	y
-4	
-2	
0	
2	
4	

16. The number of feet that a car travels before stopping depends on the driver's reaction time and the braking distance. (See illustration.) For one driver, the stopping distance*d*is given by the equation $d = 0.15w^2 + 0.6w$, where*w*is the velocity of the car. Find the stopping distance for speed*w*= 70 mph.

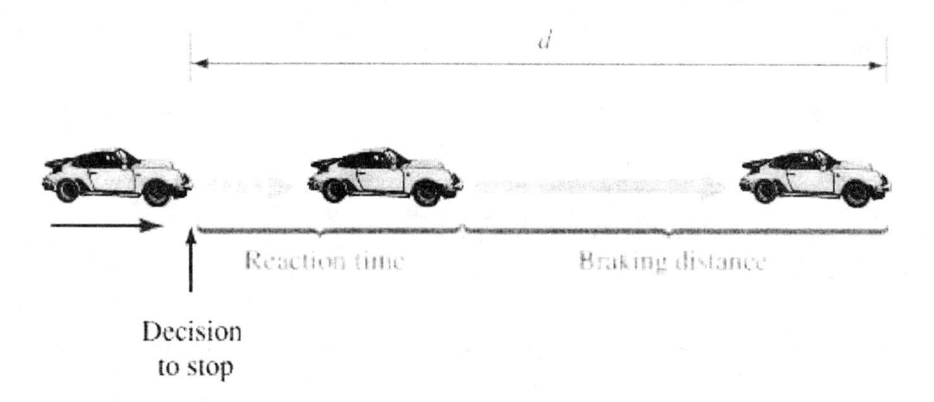

( ) 576 ft
( ) 1560 ft
( ) 777 ft
( ) 153 ft

17. Add the polynomials:

$5c^3 + 5c^3 - 8c^3$.

18. Choose the correct answer for adding the polynomials:

$(-3c^2 + 9) + (6c^2 - 9)$.

( ) $3c^4$
( ) $3c^2 + 18$
( ) $9c^2$
( ) $3c^2$

19. Subtract the polynomials:

$(8b^2+6b)-(3b^2-3b+5)$.

20. If a house is purchased for $79000 and is expected to appreciate $850 per year, its value*y*after*x*years is given by the equation*y*= 850*x*+ 79000.

A second house is purchased for $84000 and is expected to appreciate $500 per year.

Find the value of the two houses after 3 years.

( ) $165550
( ) $158950
( ) $167050
( ) $164350
( ) $83050

21. A young couple bought two cars, one for $7100 and the other for $8500. The first car is expected to depreciate $700 per year and the second car $800 per year.

Write the value of the two cars after 2 years.

22. Choose the correct product:

$(-10x^8)(-5x^2)$.

( ) $10x^{10}$
( ) $-50x^{16}$
( ) $50x^{10}$

23. Find the product:

$-9a(a^2-9)$.

24. Choose the correct answer for the square of the binomial:
$(10s + 8)^2$.

( ) $100s^2 + 160s + 64$

( ) $100s^2 + 160s + 8$

( ) $100s^2 + 80s + 64$

25. The revenue *R* received from selling clock radios is the product of their price and the number that are sold. If the price of each radio is given by the formula

$-\frac{x}{55} + 35$ and *x* is the number sold, write a formula that gives the amount of revenue received.

Answers For

1. $y = 7$

2. A

3. $(3\ ,\ 3)\ |\ (2\ ,\ 0)$

4. v

5. (0,-4)|(-2,0)

6. c^{21}

7. (1,3) -> 10*x+2*y=16, (-7,-7) -> 2*x+10*y=-84, (10,2) -> 10*x-2*y=96

8. -10, -29, -7, -21.5, -2, -9, 7, 13.5, 10, 21

9. 4

10. t^{15}

11. $a^4 b^4$

12. y^{20}

13. 1

14. 4

15. -4, -7, -2, -1, 0, 1, 2, -1, 4, -7

16. 777 ft

17. $2c^3$

18. $3c^2$

19. $5b^2 + 9b - 5$

20. $167050

21. $y=12600$

22. $50x^{10}$

23. $-9a^3+81a$

24. $100s^2 + 160s + 64$

25. $R=-\frac{x^2}{55}+35x$

1. See illustration below.
What percent of the figure is not shaded?

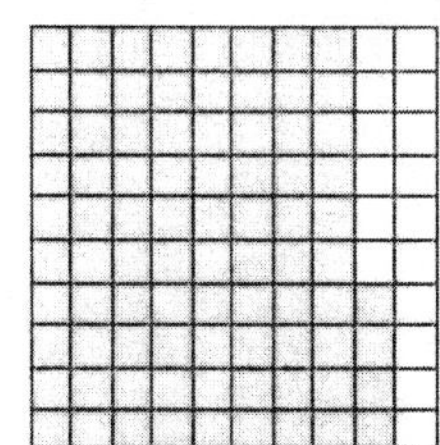

Unshaded area = __%

2. Change the following percent to a fraction.

$\frac{1}{23}\%$

3. Change the following percent to a fraction. Simplify when necessary.

89%

4. Change the following percent to a decimal.

490%

5. Change the following fraction to a percent.

$\frac{9}{2} =$ __%

6. Express the following fraction as a percent. Round to the nearest hundredth.

$\frac{1}{7} = \_\_\%$

7. The continental United States is divided into seven regions. (See illustration.)

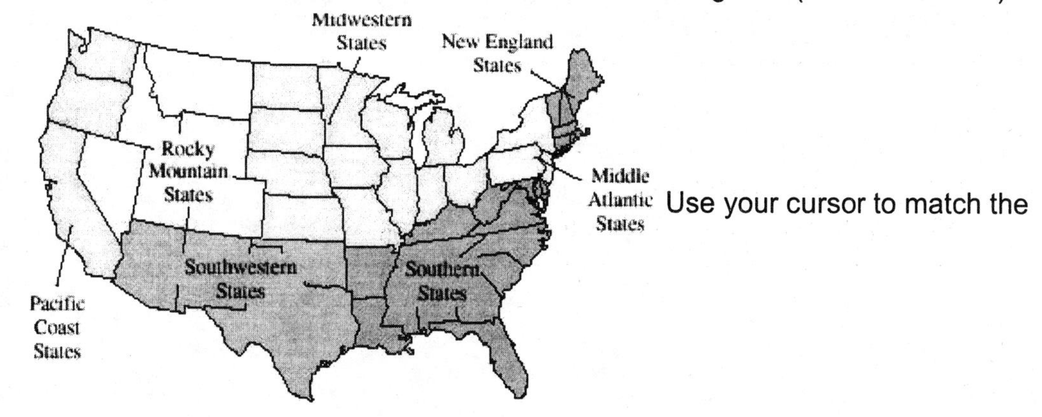

Use your cursor to match the percentages below.

percent of the 50 states in the Rocky Mountain region	24%
percent of the 50 states in the Midwestern region	12%

8. What number is 86% of 450?

9. 9.45 is 6.3% of what number?

10. What percent of 100 is 29?

___%

11. One month before a stock car race, advertising sales for the official race program were slow. Only 24 pages, or just 60% of the available pages, had been sold. What was the total number of pages devoted to advertising in the program?

12. A house has 1185 square feet on the first floor and 815 square feet on the second floor. What percent of the square footage of the house is on the first floor?

___%

13. NURSERY CENTER				
3	@	2.6	PLANTING MIX	$7.80
1	@	8.07	GROUND COVER	$8.07
2	@	13.95	SHRUBS	$27.90

Complete the sales receipt by finding the subtotal, the sales tax, and the total, if sales tax is 5%.

Sum	$
SUBTOTAL	
TAX	
TOTAL	

14. After flooding damaged much of the crop, the cost of a head of lettuce jumped from $0.80 to $1.92. What percent of increase is this?

___%

15. The illustration shows the typical change in soil volume during earth moving. (One cubic yard of soil fits in a cube that is 1 yard long, 1 yard wide, and 1 yard high.) Match the percent of increase in the soil volume as it goes through Step 1 and Step 2 of the process, if $A = 1$, $B = 1.24$, $C = 0.992$.

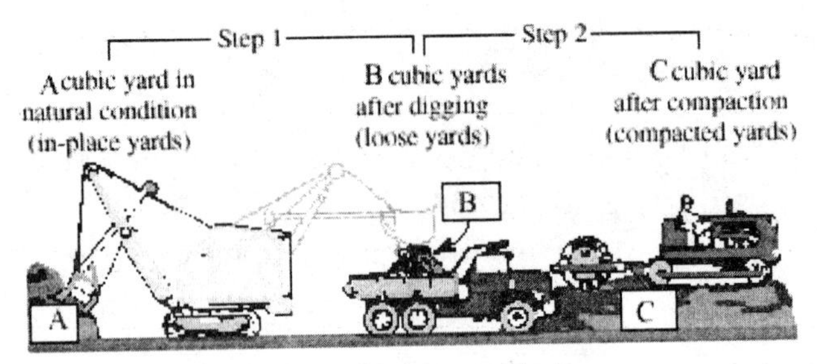

Source: U.S. Department of the Army

Step 1	20%
Step 2	24%

16. After selling a house for $88200, a real estate agent split the 2% commission with another agent. How much did each person receive?

17. What percent is the discount on a VCR with remote that regularly sells for $100 and is being discounted $40?

__%

18. When we do calculations with percents, they must be changed to decimals or fractions. Change the following percent to a decimal: 2.1%

19. Express the following as a fraction of a year, and simplify the fraction:

170 days

20. Complete the table by finding the simple interest earned.

Principal	Rate	Time	Interest earned
2000	6	5	

21. The compound interest is illustrated below, where $p1$=$1000.00, $p2$=$1010.82, $p3$ =$1022.53, $p4$=$1035.21 and $p5$=$1048.93. How much interest was earned on the first compound calculation?

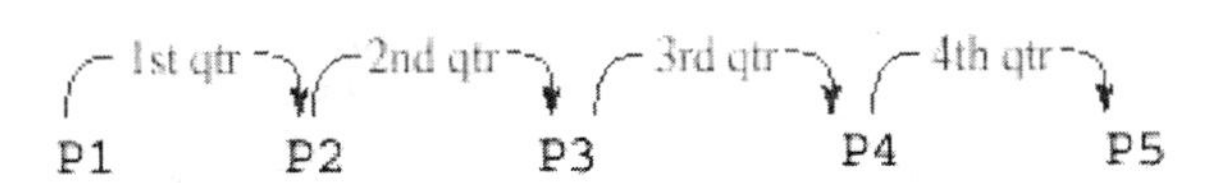

22. A developer promised a return of 2% annual interest on an investment of $17000 in her company. How much interest could an investor expect to make in the first year?

23. A student borrows $220 from an educational fund to pay for books for the spring semester. If the loan is for 43 days at $3\frac{1}{2}$% annual interest, what will the student owe at the end of the loan period? Round the result to the nearest cent.

24. A ninth-grade student opens a savings account that locks her money into a 4 year annual rate of 6%, compounded daily. If the initial deposit is $2100, how much money will be in the account when she begins college in four years? Round the result to the nearest cent.

25. Suppose you won $282000 in the lottery and deposited the money in a savings account that paid an annual rate of 7% interest, compounded daily. How much interest would you earn in a year? Round the result to the nearest cent.

Answers

1. 16

2. $\frac{1}{2300}$

3. $\frac{89}{100}$

4. 4.9

5. 450

6. 14.285714

7. percent of the 50 states in the Midwestern region -> 24%, percent of the 50 states in the Rocky Mountain region -> 12%

8. 387

9. 150

10. 29

11. 40

12. 59.25

13. SUBTOTAL, 43.77, TAX, 2.19, TOTAL, 45.96

14. 140

15. Step 1 -> 24%, Step 2 -> 20%

16. 882

17. 40

18. 0.021

19. $\frac{170}{365}$

20. 2000, 6, 5, 600

21. 10.82

22. 340

23. 220.907123

24. 2669.570561

25. 20445.277254

1. See illustration below.
What percent of the figure is not shaded?

Unshaded area = ___%

2. Change the percent to a fraction. Simplify if necessary.

125%

3. Change the following percent to a fraction.

1.3%

4. Change the following percent to a decimal.

0.3%

5. Change the following decimal to a percent.

3 = _____ %

6. 168 is 42% of what number?

7. 5.6 is 2.8% of what number?

8. Change the following fraction to a percent.

$\frac{7}{4} = \_\_\%$

9. Express the following fraction as a percent. Round to the nearest hundredth.

$\frac{1}{8} = \_\_\%$

10. The continental United States is divided into seven regions. (See illustration.)

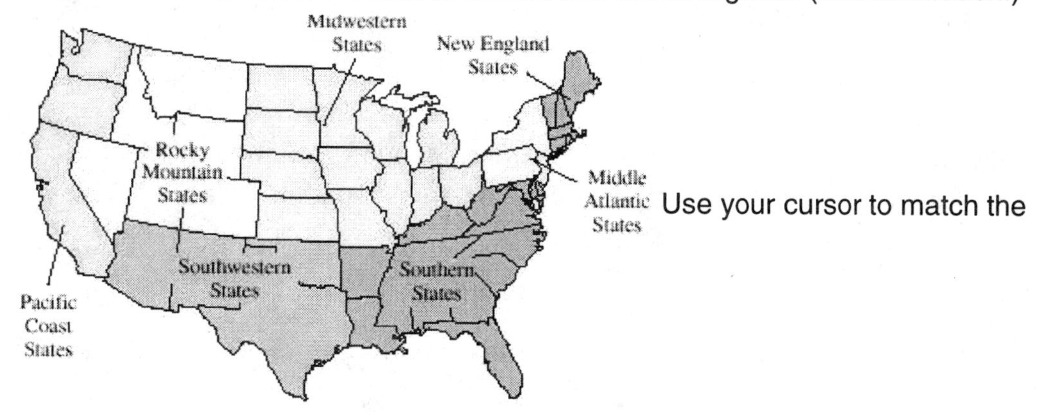

Use your cursor to match the percentages below.

percent of the 50 states in the Midwestern region	12%
percent of the 50 states in the Rocky Mountain region	24%

11. 18 is $33\frac{1}{3}\%$ of what number?

12. Promote sales, a free 10-ounce bottle of shampoo is packaged with every large bottle. (See Illustration.) Use the information on the package to determine how many ounces of shampoo the large bottle contains.

SHAMPOO

25% MORE FREE!

Large bottle = ___ oz.

13. The cost to repair a car after a collision was $3400. The automobile insurance policy paid the entire bill except for a $34 deductible, which the driver paid. What percent of the cost did he pay?

___%

14. A house has 1165 square feet on the first floor and 835 square feet on the second floor. What percent of the square footage of the house is on the first floor?

___%

15. While examining the monthly telephone bill, a man noticed an additional charge of $1.28 labeled federal excise tax. If the basic service charges for that billing period were $32, what is the federal excise tax rate?

__%

16. Some states use sales tax to raise revenue. How much money will be collected on the sale of a $19000 car if the sales tax rate is 1%?

17. Because of a heavy spring runoff, the shoreline of a lake increased from 6.6 miles to 7.92 miles. What was the percent of increase in the shoreline?

__%

18. What percent is the discount on a camcorder with remote that regularly sells for $100 and is being discounted $40?

__%

19. A shopper presents a coupon at a store. This store doubles the face value of the coupon (*a*= 18). Find the discount rate for the box of cereal that normally sells for $9.00.

___%

SAVE
a¢
GREAT HARVEST
CEREAL
WHOLE GRAIN GOODNESS
Manufacturer's coupon (Limit 1)

20. When we do calculations with percents, they must be changed to decimals or fractions. Change the following percent to a decimal: 7.5%

21. Express the following as a fraction of a year, and simplify the fraction:

50 days

22. \$8000 is deposited in a savings account that earns 10% interest compounded annually. Match the following to find how much money will be in the account at the end of 2 years.

Ending balance	\$8800
New principal	\$9680
Second year's interest	\$800
First year's interest	\$880

23. A farmer borrowed \$4000 from a credit union. The money was loaned at 9.3% annual interest. How many months was the money loaned for, if the credit union charged him \$434 for the use of the money?

24. How much money was initially invested in an account that earns annual interest of 4%, compounded semiannually, if the account balance at the end of 4 years is $641? Round the result to the nearest cent.

25. Suppose you won $116000 in the lottery and deposited the money in a savings account that paid an annual rate of 5% interest, compounded daily. How much interest would you earn in a year? Round the result to the nearest cent.

Answers

1. 16

2. $\frac{5}{4}$

3. $\frac{13}{1000}$

4. 0.003

5. 300

6. 400

7. 200

8. 175

9. 12.5

10. percent of the 50 states in the Midwestern region -> 24%, percent of the 50 states in the Rocky Mountain region -> 12%

11. 54

12. 40

13. 1

14. 58.25

15. 4

16. 190

17. 20

18. 40

19. 4

20. 0.075

21. $\frac{50}{365}$

22. First year's interest -> $800, New principal -> $8800, Second year's interest -> $880, Ending balance -> $9680

23. 14

24. 547.087328

25. 5947.02959

1. See illustration below.
What percent of the figure is not shaded?

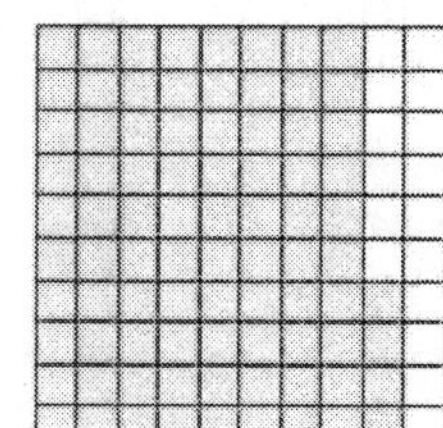

Unshaded area = __ %

2. Change the following percent to a fraction. Select the correct answer.

7.9%

( ) $\frac{79}{100}$

( ) $\frac{79}{1000}$

3. Change the following percent to a decimal.

300%

4. Change the following decimal to a percent. Select the correct answer.

3

( ) 30%

( ) 0.03%

( ) 300%

5. Change the following fraction to a percent. Select the correct answer.

$\frac{3}{8}$

( ) 3.75%

( ) 37.5%

( ) 24%

6. Express the following fraction as a percent. Round to the nearest hundredth.

$\frac{1}{8} = \_\_\%$

7. The illustration shows roughly what percent each section of the body represents of the total skin area. Determine the missing percent.

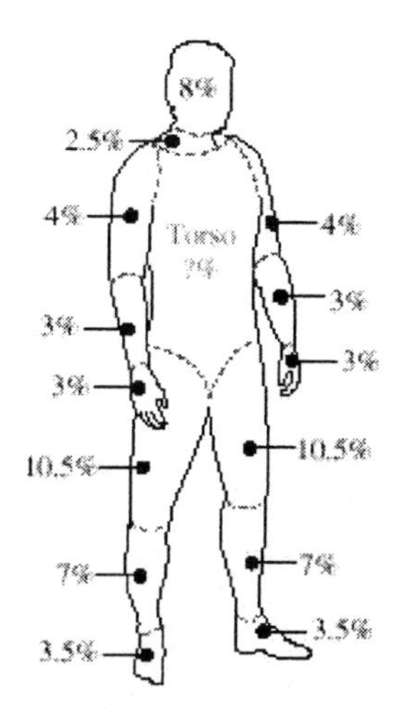

torso = ___%

8. If the day of your birthday represents $\frac{1}{365}$ of a year,is it true, that what percent of the year, rounded to the nearest hundredth of a percent, is 0.27%? A calculator may be helpful to solve this problem. Select the correct answer.

( ) True
( ) False

9. 414 is 92% of what number?

10. 18.2 is 9.1% of what number? Select the correct answer.

( ) 400
( ) 200
( ) 2000

11. What percent of 100 is 54?

__%

12. On the written part of his driving test, a man answered 12 out of 40 questions correctly. If 70% correct is passing, did he pass the test? Select the correct answer.

( ) yes
( ) no

13. To assure its customers of low prices, the Home Club offers a "10% Plus" guarantee. If the customer finds the same item selling for less somewhere else, he or she receives the difference in price, plus 10% of the difference. A woman bought miniblinds at the Home Club for $200 but later saw the same blinds on sale for $105 at another store. How much can she expect to be reimbursed?

14. The cost to repair a car after a collision was $5000. The automobile insurance policy paid the entire bill except for a $50 deductible, which the driver paid. What percent of the cost did he pay? Select the correct answer.

( ) 99%
( ) 1%

15. Use the information on the paycheck stub in the table to find the worker's compensation tax rate.

628644	Issue date: 03-27-00
GROSS PAY TAXES	\$270.00
FED. TAX	\$24.30
WORK. COMP.	\$4.94
MEDICARE	\$3.59
NET PAY	\$257.88

( ) 9%
( ) 1.33%
( ) 1.83%

16. In one state, a gallon of unleaded gasoline sells for \$2.34. This price includes federal and state taxes that total approximately \$0.39 per gallon. Therefore, the price of a gallon of gasoline, before taxes, is about \$1.95. What is the tax rate on gasoline?

__%

17. The illustration shows the typical change in soil volume during earth moving. (One cubic yard of soil fits in a cube that is 1 yard long, 1 yard wide, and 1 yard high.) Find the percent of increase in the soil volume as it goes through Step 1 of the process, if $A = 1, B = 1.36, C = 1.0744$.

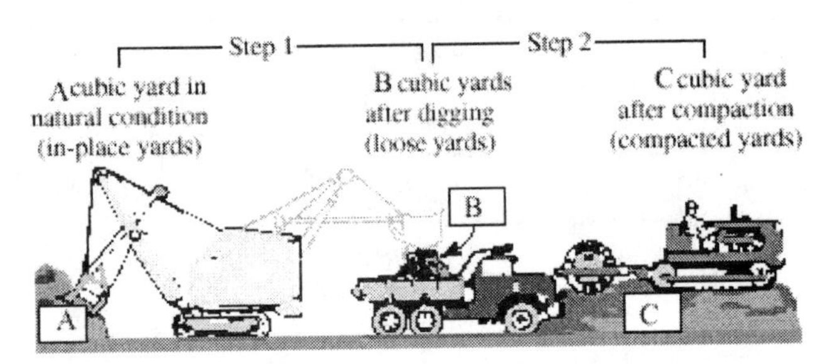

Source: U.S. Department of the Army

( ) 36%
( ) 21%

18. An art gallery displays paintings for artists and receives a commission from the artist when a painting is sold. What is the commission rate if a gallery received $151.50 when a painting was sold for $1010.00?

19. The host of a TV infomercial says that the suggested retail price of a rotisserie grill is $40.00 and that it is now offered "for just 4 easy payments of only $6.40." What is the discount? Select the correct answer.

( ) $25.60
( ) $33.60
( ) $6.40
( ) $14.40

20. When we do calculations with percents, they must be changed to decimals or fractions. Change the following percent to a decimal: 9%

21. Express the following as a fraction of a year, simplify the fraction:

150 daysSelect the correct answer.

( ) $\frac{32}{74}$

( ) $\frac{150}{12}$

( ) $\frac{150}{73}$

( ) $\frac{30}{73}$

22. How many times a year is the interest on a savings account calculated if the interest is compounded?

daily	365
quarterly	2
monthly	12
semiannually	4

23. In order to meet month's end payroll obligations, a small business had to borrow $4000 for 20 days. How much did the business have to repay if the interest rate was 16%? Round the result to the nearest cent. Select the correct answer.

( ) $4035.07
( ) $4045.07
( ) $3935.05
( ) $4035.06
( ) $4145.08

24. Use the loan application form illustrated below to complete the table.

1	**Amount of loan (principal)**	$3300
2	**Length of loan (time)**	1years
3	**Annual percentage rate**	9%
4	**Interest charged**	?
5	**Total amount to be repaid**	?

point from the form	answer
4	
5	

25. A 5 year certificate of deposit pays an annual rate of 2%, compounded daily. The maximum allowable deposit is $39000. What is the most interest a depositor can earn from the CD? Round the result to the nearest cent. Select the correct answer.

( ) $4111.56
( ) $4001.45
( ) $4091.54
( ) $4101.55
( ) $4201.65

Answers

1. 16

2. $\frac{79}{1000}$

3. 3

4. 300%

5. 37.5%

6. 12.5

7. 27.5

8. true

9. 450

10. 200

11. 54

12. no

13. 104.5

14. 1%

15. 1.83%

16. 20

17. 36%

18. 15

19. $14.40

20. 0.09

21. $\frac{30}{73}$

22. semiannually -> 2, daily -> 365, quarterly -> 4, monthly -> 12

23. $4035.07

24. 4, 297, 5, 3597

25. $4101.55

1. Change the following percent to a fraction. Simplify when necessary. Select the correct answer.

17%.

( ) $\frac{83}{100}$

( ) $\frac{17}{100}$

2. Change the following percent to a fraction.

$\frac{1}{7}\%$

( ) $\frac{1}{700}$

( ) $\frac{1}{7}$

( ) $\frac{1}{70}$

3. What percent of the figure is not shaded?

Select the correct answer.

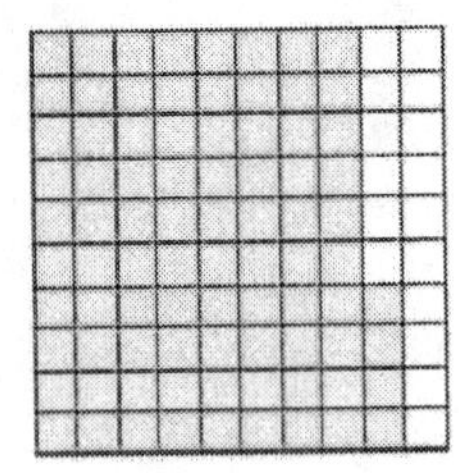

( ) 16%
( ) 84%

4. Change the following percent to a decimal. Select the correct answer.

130%

( ) 1.3

( ) 13

5. Change the following fraction to a percent. Select the correct answer.

$\frac{3}{8}$

( ) 3.75%

( ) 37.5%

( ) 24%

6. Express the following fraction as a percent. Round to the nearest hundredth. Select the correct answer.

$\frac{1}{8}$

( ) 12.51%

( ) 12.5%

7. The continental United States is divided into seven regions. (See illustration.) What percent of the 50 states are in the Rocky Mountain region? Choose your answer from below.

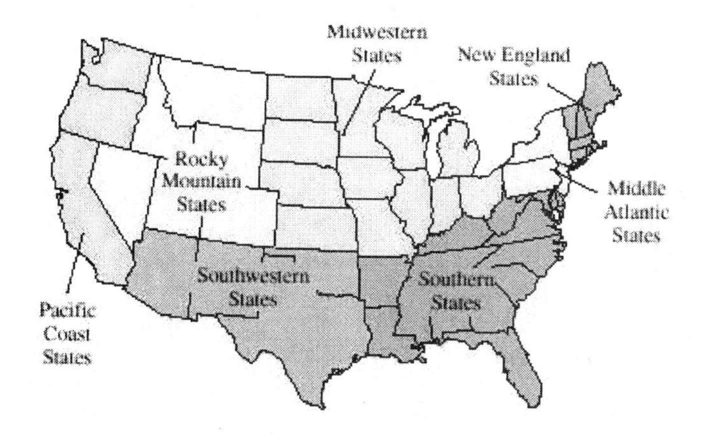

( ) 12%
( ) 24%

8. What number is 64% of 500?

( ) 420
( ) 32000
( ) 320

9. 12.6 is 6.3% of what number? Select the correct answer.

( ) 2000
( ) 400
( ) 200

10. What percent of 400 is 340? Select the correct answer.

( ) 85%
( ) 15%

11. One month before a stock car race, advertising sales for the official race program were slow. Only 12 pages, or just 30% of the available pages, had been sold. What was the total number of pages devoted to advertising in the program? Select the correct answer.

( ) 40
( ) 400

12. A house has 1140 square feet on the first floor and 860 square feet on the second floor. What percent of the square footage of the house is on the first floor? Select the correct answer.

( ) 43%
( ) 57%

13. NURSERY CENTER				
3	@	2.19	PLANTING MIX	$6.57
1	@	9.42	GROUND COVER	$9.42
2	@	14.86	SHRUBS	$29.72

Find the total purchase price, if sales tax is 5%.

( ) $48.00
( ) $2.29
( ) $45.71

14. After flooding damaged much of the crop, the cost of a head of lettuce jumped from $0.90 to $2.07. What percent of increase is this? Select the correct answer.

( ) 143.97 %
( ) 230 %
( ) 130 %
( ) 43.97 %

15. The illustration shows the typical change in soil volume during earth moving. (One cubic yard of soil fits in a cube that is 1 yard long, 1 yard wide, and 1 yard high.) Find the percent of increase in the soil volume as it goes through Step 1 of the process, if $A = 1, B = 1.31, C = 0.6812$.

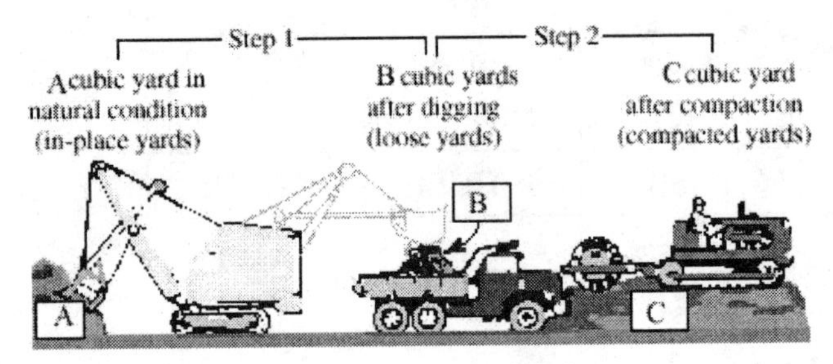

Source: U.S. Department of the Army

( ) 48%
( ) 31%

16. After selling a house for $91400.00, a real estate agent split the 6% commission with another agent. How much did each person receive? Select the correct answer.

( ) $88658.00
( ) $2742.00
( ) $5484.00
( ) $761666.71

17. What is the sale price on a VCR with remote that regularly sells for $500 and is being discounted $40? Select the correct answer.

( ) $460
( ) $540
( ) $40

18. When we do calculations with percents, they must be changed to decimals or fractions. Change the following percent to a decimal: 6.3%. Select the correct answer.

( ) 0.63
( ) 63
( ) 0.0063
( ) 0.063
( ) 630

19. Express the following as a fraction of a year, simplify the fraction:

80 daysSelect the correct answer.

( ) $\frac{80}{73}$

( ) $\frac{16}{73}$

( ) $\frac{18}{74}$

( ) $\frac{80}{12}$

20. Complete the table by finding the simple interest earned.

Principal	Rate	Time	Interest earned
10000	7	2	?

( ) $140000
( ) $1.40
( ) $14.00
( ) $1400

21. The compound interest is illustrated below, where$p1$=\$1000.00,$p2$=\$1010.40,$p3$ =\$1021.22,$p4$=\$1032.48 and$p5$=\$1044.20. How much interest was earned on the first compound calculation? Select the correct answer.

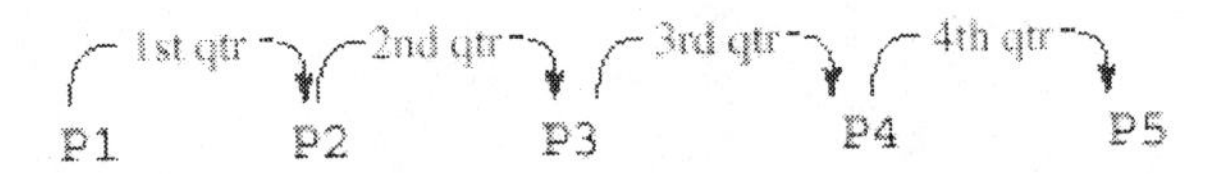

( ) \$44.20
( ) \$10.40
( ) \$11.26
( ) \$32.48
( ) \$10.82
( ) \$21.22
( ) \$11.72

22. A developer promised a return of 8% annual interest on an investment of \$15000 in her company. How much interest could an investor expect to make in the first year? Select the correct answer.

( ) \$1199
( ) \$1210
( ) \$1190
( ) \$1310
( ) \$1200

23. A student borrows $200 from an educational fund to pay for books for the spring semester. If the loan is for 35 days at $2\frac{1}{4}\%$ annual interest, what will the student owe at the end of the loan period? Round the result to the nearest cent. Select the correct answer.

( ) $210.43
( ) $100.41
( ) $310.44
( ) $200.43
( ) $200.42

24. A ninth-grade student opens a savings account that locks her money into a 4 year annual rate of 7%, compounded daily. If the initial deposit is $2300, how much money will be in the account when she begins college in four years? Round the result to the nearest cent. Select the correct answer.

( ) $3043.12
( ) $3043.13
( ) $3044.22
( ) $3033.11
( ) $3042.02

25. Suppose you won $607000 in the lottery and deposited the money in a savings account that paid an annual rate of 4% interest, compounded daily. How much interest would you earn in a year? Round the result to the nearest cent. Select the correct answer.

( ) $24770.76
( ) $24760.75
( ) $25770.77
( ) $24670.66
( ) $24771.86

Answers

1. $\frac{17}{100}$

2. $\frac{1}{700}$

3. 16%

4. 1.3

5. 37.5%

6. 12.5%

7. 12%

8. 320

9. 200

10. 85%

11. 40

12. 57%

13. $48.00

14. 130 %

15. 31%

16. $2742.00

17. $460

18. 0.063

19. $\frac{16}{73}$

20. $1400

21. $10.40

22. $1200

23. $200.43

24. $3043.12

25. $24770.76

1. What percent of the figure is not shaded?

Select the correct answer.

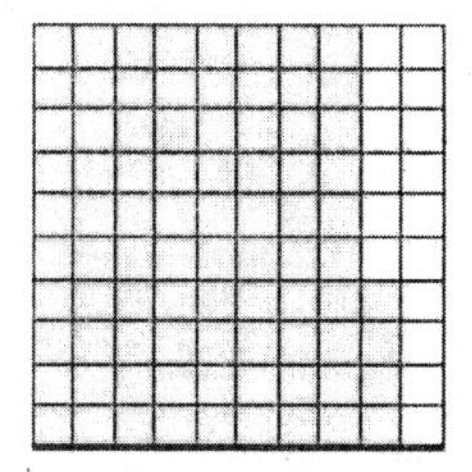

( ) 84%
( ) 16%

2. Change the following percent to a fraction. Simplify if necessary. Select the correct answer.

125%

( ) $\frac{5}{5}$

( ) $\frac{5}{4}$

( ) $\frac{5}{9}$

3. Change the following percent to a fraction. Select the correct answer.

5.7%

( ) $\frac{57}{1000}$

( ) $\frac{57}{100}$

4. Change the following percent to a decimal. Select the correct answer.

0.8%

( ) 80

( ) 0.008

( ) 0.08

5. Change the following decimal to a percent. Select the correct answer.

4

( ) 40%

( ) 0.04%

( ) 400%

6. Change the following fraction to a percent. Select the correct answer.

$$\frac{7}{2}$$

( ) 14%

( ) 35%

( ) 350%

7. Express the following fraction as a percent. Round to the nearest hundredth. Select the correct answer.

$$\frac{1}{8}$$

( ) 12.5%

( ) 12.51%

8. The continental United States is divided into seven regions. (See illustration.) What percent of the 50 states are in the Rocky Mountain region? Choose your answer from below.

( ) 24%
( ) 12%

9. 60 is 40% of what number? Select the correct answer.

( ) 150
( ) 300
( ) 250

10. 19.2 is 9.6% of what number? Select the correct answer.

( ) 200
( ) 400
( ) 2000

11. 39 is $33\frac{1}{3}\%$ of what number? Select the correct answer.

( ) 150
( ) 351
( ) 117

12. Promote sales, a free 7-ounce bottle of shampoo is packaged with every large bottle. (See Illustration.) Use the information on the package to determine how many ounces of shampoo the large bottle contains. Select the correct answer.

( ) 28oz.
( ) 14oz.

13. The cost to repair a car after a collision was $4600. The automobile insurance policy paid the entire bill except for a $46 deductible, which the driver paid. What percent of the cost did he pay? Select the correct answer.

( ) 99%
( ) 1%

14. A house has 1240 square feet on the first floor and 760 square feet on the second floor. What percent of the square footage of the house is on the first floor? Select the correct answer.

( ) 38%
( ) 62%

15. While examining the monthly telephone bill, a women noticed an additional charge of $0.60 labeled federal excise tax. If the basic service charges for that billing period were $30, what is the federal excise tax rate? Select the correct answer.

( ) 2%
( ) 20%
( ) 18%
( ) 98%

16. Some states use sales tax to raise revenue. How much money will be collected on the sale of a $16000 car if the sales tax rate is 3%? Select the correct answer.

( ) $480
( ) $15520
( ) $48000
( ) $4800

17. Because of a heavy spring runoff, the shoreline of a lake increased from 5 miles to 6.6 miles. What was the percent of increase in the shoreline? Select the correct answer.

( ) 32 %
( ) 131 %
( ) 132 %

18. What is the sale price on a camcorder with remote that regularly sells for $200 and is being discounted $30? Select the correct answer.

( ) $170
( ) $230
( ) $30

19. What is the discount on a box of cereal that normally sells for $3.60 if the shopper presents the coupon below to the store and the store doubles the face value of the coupon. (On the coupon below,*a*= 27.) Select the correct answer.

( ) $0.27
( ) $3.33
( ) $3.06
( ) $0.54

20. When we do calculations with percents, they must be changed to decimals or fractions. Change the following percent to a decimal: 7.1%. Select the correct answer.

( ) 0.71
( ) 0.0071
( ) 0.071
( ) 710
( ) 71

21. Express the following as a fraction of a year, simplify the fraction:

280 daysSelect the correct answer.

( ) $\frac{56}{73}$

( ) $\frac{58}{74}$

( ) $\frac{280}{12}$

( ) $\frac{280}{73}$

22. $2000 is deposited in a savings account that earns 5% interest compounded annually. How much money will be in the account at the end of 2 years? Select the correct answer.

( ) $2215.00
( ) $2200.00
( ) $2100.00
( ) $2205.00

23. A farmer borrowed $8000 from a credit union. The money was loaned at 6.6% annual interest. How many months was the money loaned for, if the credit union charged him $528 in interest for the use of the money? Select the correct answer.

( ) 12 months
( ) 8 months
( ) 22 months
( ) 10 months
( ) 17 months

24. How much money was initially invested in an account that earns annual interest of 9%, compounded semiannually, if the account balance at the end of 4 years is $652? Round the result to the nearest cent. Select the correct answer.

( ) $458.48
( ) $459.58
( ) $558.49
( ) $457.38
( ) $448.47

25. Suppose you won $355000 in the lottery and deposited the money in a savings account that paid an annual rate of 9% interest, compounded daily. How much interest would you earn in a year? Round the result to the nearest cent. Select the correct answer.

( ) $33428.66
( ) $33327.46
( ) $34427.57
( ) $33427.56
( ) $33417.55

Answers

1. 16%

2. $\frac{5}{4}$

3. $\frac{57}{1000}$

4. 0.008

5. 400%

6. 350%

7. 12.5%

8. 12%

9. 150

10. 200

11. 117

12. 28oz.

13. 1%

14. 62%

15. 2%

16. $480

17. 32 %

18. $170

19. $0.54

20. 0.071

21. $\frac{56}{73}$

22. $2205.00

23. 12 months

24. $458.48

25. $33427.56

1. What percent of 200 is 140?

__%

2. When we do calculations with percents, they must be changed to decimals or fractions. Change the following percent to a decimal: 8%

3. In one state, a gallon of unleaded gasoline sells for $2.28. This price includes federal and state taxes that total approximately $0.38 per gallon. Therefore, the price of a gallon of gasoline, before taxes, is about $1.90. What is the tax rate on gasoline?

__%

4. Change the following percent to a fraction. Select the correct answer.

3.1%

( ) $\frac{31}{1000}$

( ) $\frac{31}{100}$

5. A 3 year certificate of deposit pays an annual rate of 5%, compounded daily. The maximum allowable deposit is $84000. What is the most interest a depositor can earn from the CD? Round the result to the nearest cent. Select the correct answer.

( ) $13583.06
( ) $13603.08
( ) $13693.17
( ) $13593.07
( ) $13492.97

6. The cost to repair a car after a collision was $3500. The automobile insurance policy paid the entire bill except for a $350 deductible, which the driver paid. What percent of the cost did he pay? Select the correct answer.

( ) 90%
( ) 10%

7. Change the following decimal to a percent. Select the correct answer.

5

( ) 50%

( ) 500%

( ) 0.05%

8. An art gallery displays paintings for artists and receives a commission from the artist when a painting is sold. What is the commission rate if a gallery received $130.00 when a painting was sold for $1040.00?

9. Change the following fraction to a percent. Select the correct answer.

$$\frac{3}{8}$$

( ) 3.75%

( ) 24%

( ) 37.5%

10. How many times a year is the interest on a savings account calculated if the interest is compounded?

daily	2
monthly	365
semiannually	12
quarterly	4

11. Change the following percent to a decimal.

320%

12. The host of a TV infomercial says that the suggested retail price of a rotisserie grill is $64.00 and that it is now offered "for just 4 easy payments of only $10.88." What is the discount? Select the correct answer.

( ) $10.88
( ) $53.12
( ) $43.52
( ) $20.48

13. 14 is 7% of what number? Select the correct answer.

( ) 200
( ) 2000
( ) 400

14. In order to meet month's end payroll obligations, a small business had to borrow $7000 for 20 days. How much did the business have to repay if the interest rate was 17%? Round the result to the nearest cent. Select the correct answer.

( ) $7065.21
( ) $7065.20
( ) $6965.19
( ) $7075.21
( ) $7175.22

15. The illustration shows the typical change in soil volume during earth moving. (One cubic yard of soil fits in a cube that is 1 yard long, 1 yard wide, and 1 yard high.) Find the percent of increase in the soil volume as it goes through Step 1 of the process, if$A$= 1,B= 1.31,C= 0.7467.

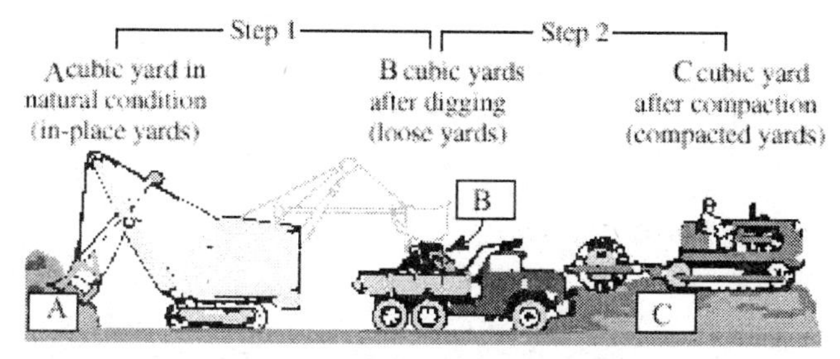

Source: U.S. Department of the Army

( ) 31%
( ) 43%

16. See illustration below.
What percent of the figure is not shaded?

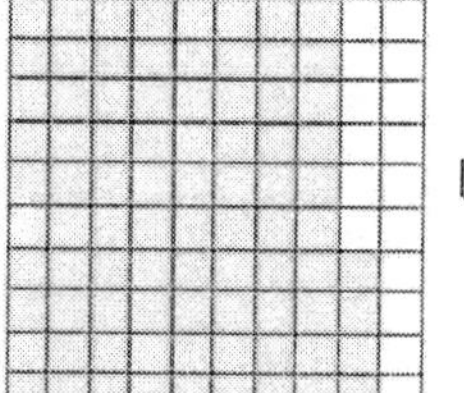

Unshaded area = __ %

17. Express the following as a fraction of a year, simplify the fraction:

120 daysSelect the correct answer.

( ) $\frac{120}{12}$

( ) $\frac{24}{73}$

( ) $\frac{120}{73}$

( ) $\frac{26}{74}$

18. The illustration shows roughly what percent each section of the body represents of the total skin area. Determine the missing percent.

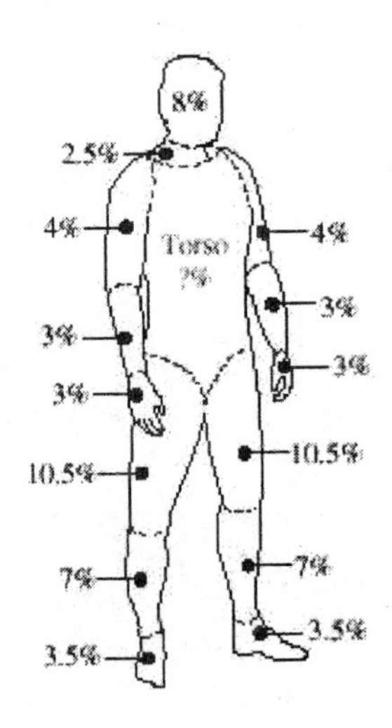

torso = ___%

19. To assure its customers of low prices, the Home Club offers a "10% Plus" guarantee. If the customer finds the same item selling for less somewhere else, he or she receives the difference in price, plus 10% of the difference. A woman bought miniblinds at the Home Club for $146 but later saw the same blinds on sale for $101 at another store. How much can she expect to be reimbursed?

20. On the written part of his driving test, a man answered 27 out of 40 questions correctly. If 70% correct is passing, did he pass the test? Select the correct answer.

( ) no
( ) yes

21. Use the information on the paycheck stub in the table to find the worker's compensation tax rate.

628644	Issue date: 03-27-00
GROSS PAY TAXES	$320.00
FED. TAX	$25.60
WORK. COMP.	$4.35
MEDICARE	$5.28
NET PAY	$305.09

( ) 1.65%
( ) 1.36%
( ) 8%

22. If the day of your birthday represents $\frac{1}{365}$ of a year,is it true, that what percent of the year, rounded to the nearest hundredth of a percent, is 0.27%? A calculator may be helpful to solve this problem. Select the correct answer.

( ) True
( ) False

23. 480 is 96% of what number?

24. Use the loan application form illustrated below to complete the table.

1	**Amount of loan (principal)**	$5600
2	**Length of loan (time)**	2years
3	**Annual percentage rate**	4%
4	**Interest charged**	?
5	**Total amount to be repaid**	?

point from the form	answer
4	
5	

25. Express the following fraction as a percent. Round to the nearest hundredth.

$\frac{1}{7} = \_\_\%$

Answers

1. 70

2. 0.08

3. 20

4. $\frac{31}{1000}$

5. $13593.07

6. 10%

7. 500%

8. 12.5

9. 37.5%

10. semiannually -> 2, daily -> 365, quarterly -> 4, monthly -> 12

11. 3.2

12. $20.48

13. 200

14. $7065.21

15. 31%

16. 16

17. $\frac{24}{73}$

18. 27.5

19. 49.5

20. no

21. 1.36%

22. true

23. 500

24. 4, 448, 5, 6048

25. 14.285714

1. See illustration below.
What percent of the figure is not shaded?

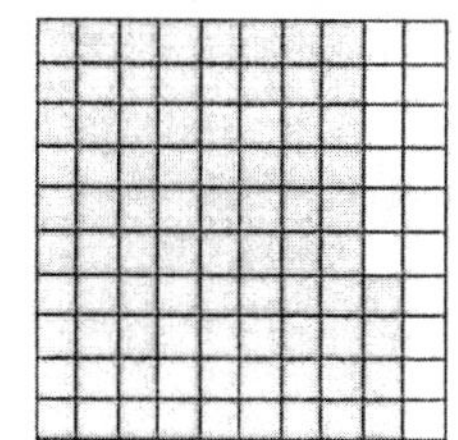

Unshaded area = __ %

2. Change the following percent to a fraction. Simplify when necessary. Select the correct answer.

89%.

( ) $\frac{11}{100}$

( ) $\frac{89}{100}$

3. Change the following percent to a fraction.

$\frac{1}{33}\%$

4. Change the following decimal to a percent. Select the correct answer.

0.69

( ) 69%

( ) 0.0069%

( ) 6.9%

5. Change the following decimal to a percent.

8.29 = _____ %

6. Find the exact equivalent percent for the following fraction. Select the correct answer.

$\frac{1}{3}$

( ) $297\frac{1}{3}\%$

( ) $297\frac{2}{3}\%$

7. In the last quarter of 1999, approximately 105.3 million housing units in the United States were occupied. Use the data in the illustration to determine what percent were owner occupied, if a= 30.2%.

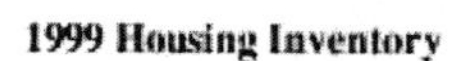

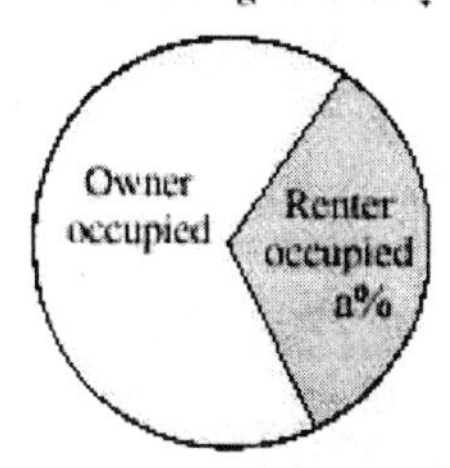

Owner occupied = ___ %

8. The illustration shows roughly what percent each section of the body represents of the total skin area. Determine the missing percent.

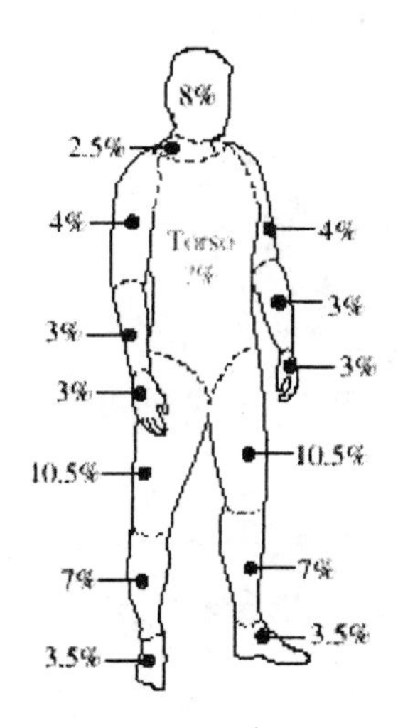

torso = ___ %

9. 20 is what percent of 40? Select the correct answer.

( ) 100%
( ) 50%
( ) 5%

10. 78 is $33\frac{1}{3}\%$ of what number? Select the correct answer.

( ) 702
( ) 267
( ) 234

11. On the written part of his driving test, a man answered 27 out of 40 questions correctly. If 70% correct is passing, did he pass the test? If "yes" put 1, if "no" put 0.

12. Find the number of gallons of sulfuric acid in 80 gallons of solution in a tank, if the percent of sulfuric acid is 50%. Select the correct answer.

( ) 9 gal
( ) 40 gal

13. A house has 1135 square feet on the first floor and 865 square feet on the second floor. What percent of the square footage of the house is on the first floor?

__%

14. The state sales tax rate in Utah is 4.75%. Find the sales tax on bedroom suite that sells for $1100. Select the correct answer.

( ) $1047.75
( ) $577.5
( ) $522.5
( ) $52.25

15. Factory management wants to reduce the number of overtime hours by 20%. If the total number of overtime hours is 340 this month, what is the target reduced number of overtime hours for next month?

16. A police department plans to increase its 140 person force by 15%. What will be the total number of officers after the new officers have been hired? Select the correct answer.

( ) 10
( ) 150
( ) 21
( ) 161

17. After flooding damaged much of the crop, the cost of a head of lettuce jumped from $1.00 to $2.20. What percent of increase is this?

__%

18. The host of a TV infomercial says that the suggested retail price of a rotisserie grill is $40.00 and that it is now offered "for just 4 easy payments of only $8.00." What is is the discount rate?

__%

SAVE

a¢

GREAT HARVEST

CEREAL

WHOLE GRAIN GOODNESS

Manufacturer's coupon (Limit 1)

19. The illustration shows the typical change in soil volume during earth moving. (One cubic yard of soil fits in a cube that is 1 yard long, 1 yard wide, and 1 yard high.) Find the percent of increase in the soil volume as it goes through Step 1 of the process, if $A = 1, B = 1.44, C = 0.7632$.

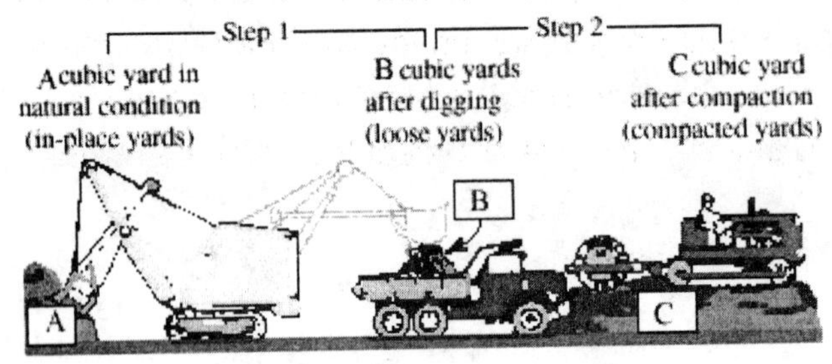

Source: U.S. Department of the Army

( ) 47%
( ) 44%

20. Express the following as a fraction of a year, simplify the fraction:

360 daysSelect the correct answer.

( ) $\frac{360}{12}$

( ) $\frac{72}{73}$

( ) $\frac{74}{74}$

( ) $\frac{360}{73}$

21. A homeowner borrows $13000 to pay for a kitchen remodeling project. The terms of the loan are 9.3% annual interest and repayment in 2 years. How much total interest will be paid on the loan?

22. A farmer borrowed $2000 from a credit union. The money was loaned at 6.9% annual interest. How many months was the money loaned for, if the credit union charged him $161 in interest for the use of the money? Select the correct answer.

( ) 14 months
( ) 10 months
( ) 12 months
( ) 19 months
( ) 24 months

23. Find the interest earned on $40000 at $6\frac{1}{5}$ % for 4 years. Fill the table to organize your work.

P	r	t	I

24. If $860 is invested in an account that earns 3%, compounded annually, what will the account balance be after 3 years? Round the result to the nearest cent. Select the correct answer.

( ) $929.74
( ) $939.75
( ) $939.76
( ) $938.65
( ) $940.85

25. Suppose you won $482000 in the lottery and deposited the money in a savings account that paid an annual rate of 8% interest, compounded daily. How much interest would you earn in a year? Round the result to the nearest cent.

Answers For

1. 16

2. $\frac{89}{100}$

3. $\frac{1}{3300}$

4. 69%

5. 829

6. $297\frac{1}{3}\%$

7. 69.8

8. 27.5

9. 50%

10. 234

11. 0

12. 40 gal

13. 56.75

14. $52.25

15. 272

16. 161

17. 120

18. 20

19. 44%

20. $\frac{72}{73}$

21. 2418

22. 14 months

23. 40000, 0.062, 4, 9920

24. $939.75

25. 40139.789604

1. Change the following percent to a fraction. Simplify when necessary.

47%

2. Change the following percent to a fraction. Simplify when necessary. Select the correct answer.

230%.

( ) $\frac{23}{100}$

( ) $\frac{23}{10}$

3. Change the following percent to a decimal.

530%

4. Change the following fraction to a percent. Select the correct answer.

$\frac{7}{100}$

( ) 70%

( ) 7%

( ) 700%

5. Change the following fraction to a percent.

$\frac{3}{4} = \_\_\%$

6. Express the following fraction as a percent. Round to the nearest hundredth. Select the correct answer.

$\frac{1}{8}$

( ) 12.5%

( ) 12.51%

7. What number is 22% of 90?

8. In the statement9 *is 90% of 10*, which value is the total amount? Select the correct answer.

( ) 9
( ) 90
( ) 10

9. 292 is 73% of what number?

10. What percent of 150 is 130.5? Select the correct answer.

( ) 87%
( ) 13%

11. Promote sales, a free 5-ounce bottle of shampoo is packaged with every large bottle. (See Illustration.) Use the information on the package to determine how many ounces of shampoo the large bottle contains.

Large bottle = __ oz.

12. Find the number of gallons of sulfuric acid in 70 gallons of solution in a tank, if the percent of sulfuric acid is 50%. Select the correct answer.

( ) 12 gal
( ) 35 gal

13. A house has 1115 square feet on the first floor and 885 square feet on the second floor. What percent of the square footage of the house is on the first floor?

__%

14. After checking out of a hotel, a man noticed that the hotel bill included an additional charge labeled room tax. If the price of the room was $51, and the room tax was $3.57, find the room tax rate. Select the correct answer.

( ) 93%
( ) 7%
( ) 70%
( ) 182.07%

15. After selling a house for $98700.00, a real estate agent split the 4% commission with another agent. How much did each person receive? Select the correct answer.

( ) $1974.00
( ) $3948.00
( ) $96726.00
( ) $1233750.05

16. Complete the sales receipt by finding the subtotal, the sales tax, and the total, if sales tax is 6%.

NURSERY CENTER				
3	@	3.17	PLANTING MIX	$9.51
1	@	8.76	GROUND COVER	$8.76
2	@	14.62	SHRUBS	$29.24

Sum	$
SUBTOTAL	
TAX	
TOTAL	

17. Use the information on the paycheck stub in the table to find the worker's compensation tax rate.

628644	Issue date: 03-27-00
GROSS PAY TAXES	$370.00
FED. TAX	$37.00
WORK. COMP.	$3.81
MEDICARE	$5.33
NET PAY	$355.53

( ) 10%
( ) 1.44%
( ) 1.03%

18. A police department plans to increase its 80 person force by 10%. What will be the new size of the department?

19. An art gallery displays paintings for artists and receives a commission from the artist when a painting is sold. What is the commission rate if a gallery received $135.00 when a painting was sold for $1080.00?

20. When we do calculations with percents, they must be changed to decimals or fractions. Change the following percent to a decimal: 7.1%. Select the correct answer.

( ) 71
( ) 0.0071
( ) 0.071
( ) 710
( ) 0.71

21. A retiree invests \$5000 in a savings plan that pays 7% per year. What will the account balance be at the end of the first year?

22. A homeowner borrows \$12000 to pay for a kitchen remodeling project. The terms of the loan are 9.3% annual interest and repayment in 2 years. How much total interest will be paid on the loan? Select the correct answer.

( ) \$2231
( ) \$2342
( ) \$2132
( ) \$2232
( ) \$2242

23. A student borrows \$230 from an educational fund to pay for books for the spring semester. If the loan is for 31 days at $2\frac{1}{3}$% annual interest, what will the student owe at the end of the loan period? Round the result to the nearest cent.

24. A municipality receives a low-interest loan for \$13 million from a bank to finance the construction of a water treatment plant. What is the annual interest of the loan if the amount paid back at the end of 2 years is \$13.546 million? Select the correct answer.

( ) 1.9%
( ) 2.1%
( ) 1.6%
( ) 3.1%
( ) 2.2%

25. A 2 year certificate of deposit pays an annual rate of 9%, compounded daily. The maximum allowable deposit is \$58000. What is the most interest a depositor can earn from the CD? Round the result to the nearest cent.

Answers For

1. $\frac{47}{100}$

2. $\frac{23}{10}$

3. 5.3

4. 7%

5. 75

6. 12.5%

7. 19.8

8. 9

9. 400

10. 87%

11. 20

12. 35 gal

13. 55.75

14. 7%

15. $1974.00

16.

17. 1.03%

18. 88

19. 12.5

20. 0.071

21. 5350

22. $2232

23. 230.455799

24. 2.1%

25. 11437.066365

1. Write a fraction in simplified form that expresses the ratio of 15 to 20.

2. Refer to the monthly budget shown in the illustration. Find the ratio of the amount budgeted for food to the total budget in lowest terms.

Item	Amount
Rent	$100
Food	$600
Gas and electric	$160
Phone	$160
Entertainment	$780

3. A 40-pound bag of grass seed costs $144. Find the cost per pound of grass seed.

4. How many minutes are in 9 hours?

5. A certain brand of cold and sinus medication is sold in 30-tablet boxes for $36 and in 15-tablet boxes for $19.8. Which is the better buy (i.e. less expensive per tablet) and which is the worse buy (i.e. more expensive per tablet)? Use your cursor to match up the choices below for both answers.

15 - tablet boxes	Better buy
30 - tablet boxes	Worse buy

6. Tell whether the statement is a proportion. $\frac{28}{36} = \frac{49}{64}$.

7. Solve for the variable in the proportion:

$$\frac{7}{8} = \frac{x}{16}$$

8. Convert 60 inches to feet.

9. In one community, a bill for 515 kilowatt hours of electricity is $54. In a second community, a bill for 760 kwh is $47. In which community is electricity cheaper and in which is it more expensive? Use your cursor to match up the choices below.

In the second community	electricity is more expensive
In the first community	electricity is cheaper

10. Solve for the variable in the proportion: $\frac{s+4}{4} = \frac{-9}{4}$

11. Out of a sample of 500 men's shirts, 16 were rejected because of crooked collars. How many crooked collars would you expect to find in a run of 1500 shirts?

12. The school board has determined that there should be 3 teachers for every 40 students. Complete the table by filling in the number of teachers needed at each school.

	Glenwood High	Goddard Junior High	Sellers Elementary
Enrollment	840	1080	1040
Teachers			

13. Convert 10 feet to inches.

14. Convert 8 yards to feet.

15. To the nearest centimeter, tell which measurement the arrow points to on the ruler in the illustration.

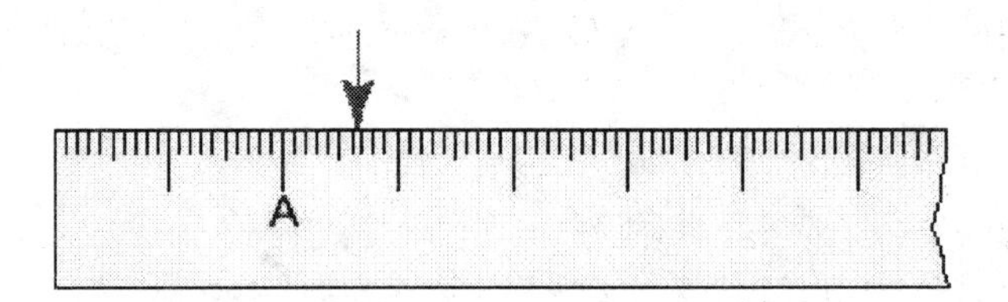

A= 2 cm.

16. Convert 16 kL to liters.

17. Blood pressure is measured by a sphygmomanometer (see the illustration). The measurement is read at two points and is expressed, for example, as 129/83. This indicates a systolic pressure of 129 millimeters of mercury and a diastolic pressure of 83 millimeters of mercury. Convert either of these measurements to centimeters of mercury.

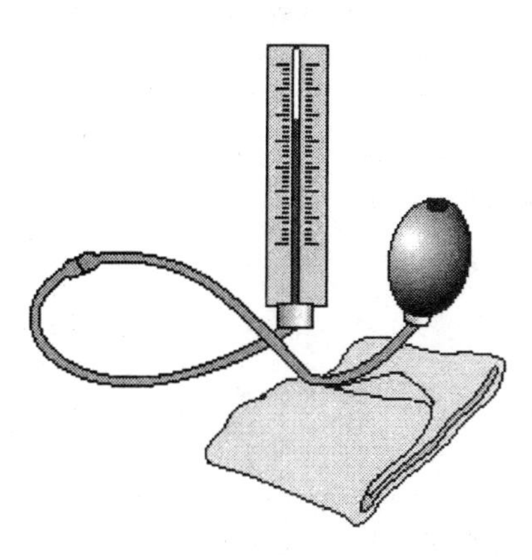

18. A baby weighs 3.517 kilograms. Give this weight in centigrams.

19. The net weight of a bottle of olives is 387 grams. Find the smallest number of bottles that must be purchased to have at least 4 kilograms of olives.

20. Convert 4700 feet to kilometers. Round your answer to the nearest hundredth.

21. onvert 121 kilograms into pounds.

22. THE MIDDLE EAST: The distance between Eilat and Jerusalem is 309 kilometers. To the nearest tenth, give this distance in miles.

23. HAIR GROWTH: When hair is short, its rate of growth averages about 0.6 inch per month. How many centimeters is this a month? (Round your answer to the nearest tenth).

24. SNOWY WEATHER: At which temperature might it snow or rain? Match the each item on the left with the items on the right.

snow	-8° C
rain	15° C

25. Convert 20000 pounds to tons.

Answers

1. $\frac{3}{4}$

2. $\frac{1}{3}$

3. $3.6

4. 540

5. 30 - tablet boxes -> Better buy, 15 - tablet boxes -> Worse buy

6. no

7. 14

8. 5

9. In the first community -> electricity is more expensive, In the second community -> electricity is cheaper

10. -13

11. 48

12. Enrollment, 840, 1080, 1040, Teachers, 63, 81, 78

13. 120

14. 24

15. 3

16. 16000

17. 12.9

18. 351700

19. 11

20. 1.43

21. 266.2

22. 192

23. 1.5

24. snow -> -8° C , rain -> 15° C

25. 10

1. Write a fraction in simplified form that expresses the ratio of 0.02 to 0.08.

2. Write a fraction in simplified form that expresses the ratio of 15 months to 16 years.

3. A driver pumped 8 gallons of gasoline into his tank at a total cost of $38.4. Find the cost per gallon of gasoline.

4. A car travels 310 miles in 4.5 hours and a truck travels 400 miles in 2 hours. Which vehicle is going faster? Using your cursor, match up the choices below.

Truck is	faster
Car is	slower

5. Ricardo worked for 25 hours to help insulate a hockey arena. For his work, he received $287.5. Find his hourly rate of pay.

6. Solve for the variable in the proportion:

$$\frac{3}{24} = \frac{8}{c}$$

7. Solve for the variable in the proportion: $\frac{a}{24} = \frac{9}{8}$

8. The bar graph in the illustration shows the yearly costs incurred and the revenue received by a business. Write a proportion for the ratios of costs to revenue for 1999 and 2000.

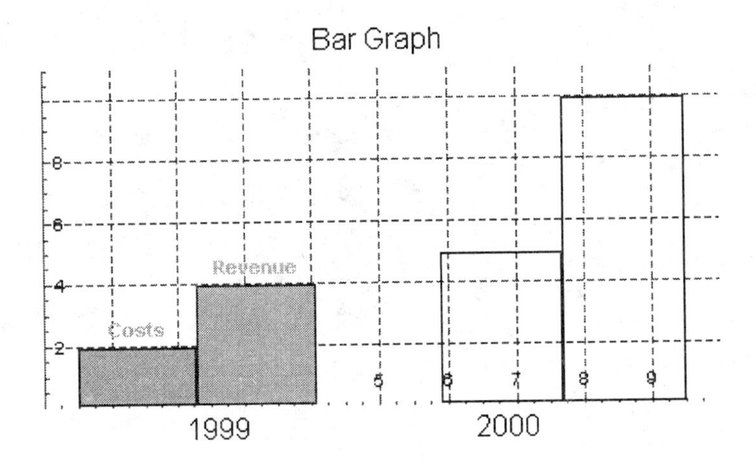

9. A florist sells a dozen long-stemmed white lilies for $62.07. In honor of their 20th wedding anniversary, a man wants to buy 20 lilies for his wife. What will the lilies cost?

10. The ratio in the illustration indicates that 1 inch on the model carousel is equivalent to A= 236 inches on the actual carousel. How wide should the model be if the actual carousel is 118 feet wide?

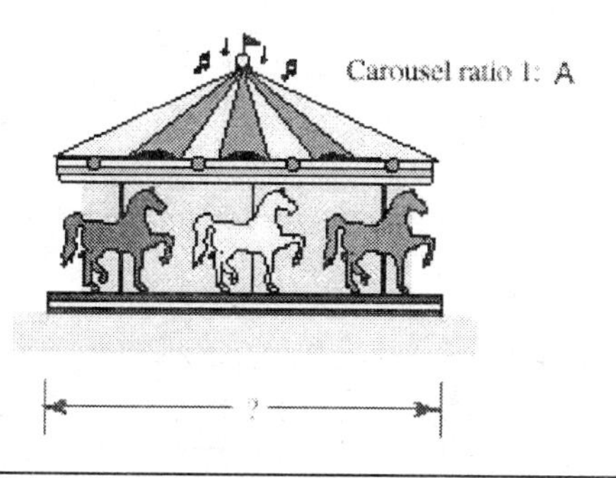

11. How many pounds are in 1 tons?

12. Convert $8\frac{5}{6}$ feet to inches.

13. Convert 42240 feet to miles.

14. Convert 180 minutes to hours.

15. AMELIA EARHART: In 1932, Amelia Earhart became the first woman to fly across the Atlantic Ocean alone, establishing a new record for the crossing: 13 hours and 30 minutes. How many minutes did her flight take?

16. To the nearest centimeter, tell which measurement the arrow points to on the ruler in the illustration.

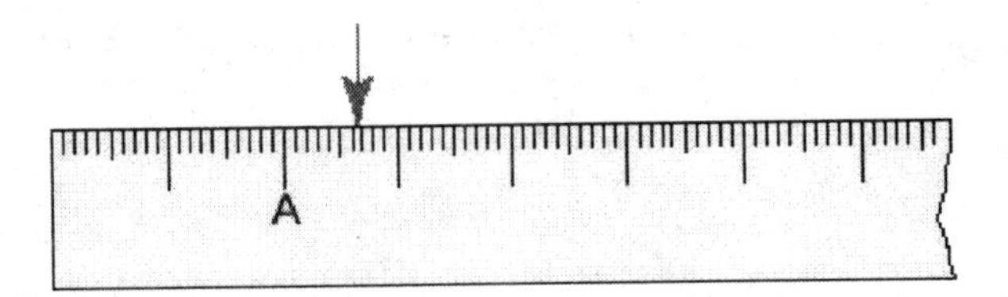

A= 2 cm.

17. Match each item with its most realistic measurement.

Item	Measurement
Thickness of a phone book	9 cm
Height of a soccer goal	2737 km
Length of the River	2 m

18. Convert 0.08 mm to meters.

19. How many deciliters of root beer are there in two 2.5-liter bottles?

20. A bottle of hydrochlorothiazine contains 30 tablets. If each tablet contains 80 milligrams of the active ingredient, how many grams of the active ingredient are in the bottle?

21. Convert 6000 inches into meters.

22. Convert 4000 milliliters to gallons. Round to the nearest tenth.

23. TRACK AND FIELD: Track meets are held on an oval track like the one shown in the illustration. One lap around the track is usually 403 meters. However, for some older tracks in the United States, one lap is 447 yards. Are these two types of tracks the same length? If the answer is no, enter 0; if the answer is yes, enter 1.

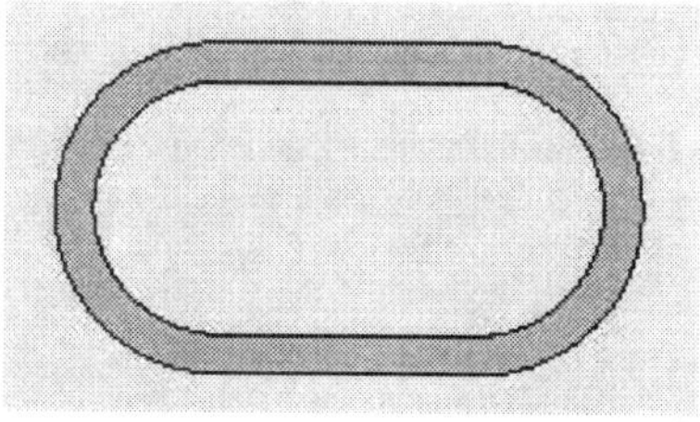

24. POSTAL REGULATIONS: You can mail a package weighing up to 70 pounds via priority mail. Can you mail a package that weighs 35 kilograms by priority mail? If the answer is yes enter a 1; if the answer is no, enter 0.

25. Match the corresponding statements.

warm water	$-2°$ C
cold water	$24°$ C
frozen water	$8°$ C

Answers

1. $\frac{1}{4}$

2. $\frac{5}{64}$

3. $4.8

4. Truck is -> faster, Car is -> slower

5. 11.5

6. 64

7. 27

8. $\frac{2}{4}=\frac{5}{10}$

9. 103.45

10. 6

11. 2000

12. 106

13. 8

14. 3

15. 810

16. 3

17. Thickness of a phone book -> 9 cm, Length of the River -> 2737 km, Height of a soccer goal -> 2 m

18. 0.00008

19. 50

20. 2.4

21. 152.4

22. 1.1

23. 0

24. 0

25. frozen water -> $-2°$ C, cold water -> $8°$ C, warm water -> $24°$ C

1. Write a fraction in simplified form that expresses the ratio of 2 to 32.

( ) $\frac{16}{1}$

( ) $\frac{2}{32}$

( ) $\frac{1}{16}$

2. Write a fraction in simplified form that expresses the ratio of 15 minutes to 1 hour.

3. An airline had 5.9 complaints for every 200 passengers. Write this rate as a fraction in simplified form. Choose your answer from below.

( ) $\frac{59}{2000}$

( ) $\frac{2000}{59}$

( ) $\frac{59}{200}$

4. An 40000-gallon tank can be emptied in 80 minutes. Find the rate of flow in gallons per minute.

5. Ricardo worked for 43 hours to help insulate a hockey arena. For his work, he received $860. Find his hourly rate of pay. Choose your answer from below.

( ) 40
( ) 20
( ) 60

6. For every 27 feet of chain link fencing, 15 support posts are used. How many support posts will be needed for 81 feet of chain link fence? Write the proportion that could be used to solve this problem, using the variable*x*.

7. Solve for the variable in the proportion: $\frac{a+2}{36} = \frac{-5}{6}$.

Choose your answer from below.

[ ] -7

[ ] -28

[ ] -32

8. Solve for the variable in the proportion: $\frac{\frac{1}{9}}{\frac{1}{6}} = \frac{f}{\frac{1}{10}}$

9. In a red blood cell count, a drop of the patient's diluted blood is placed on a grid like that shown in the illustration. Instead of counting each and every red blood cell in the 25-square grid, a technician just counts the number of cells in the five highlighted squares. Then he or she uses a proportion to estimate the total red blood cell count. If there are 200 red blood cells in the blue squares, about how many red blood cells would there be in the entire grid? Choose your answer from below.

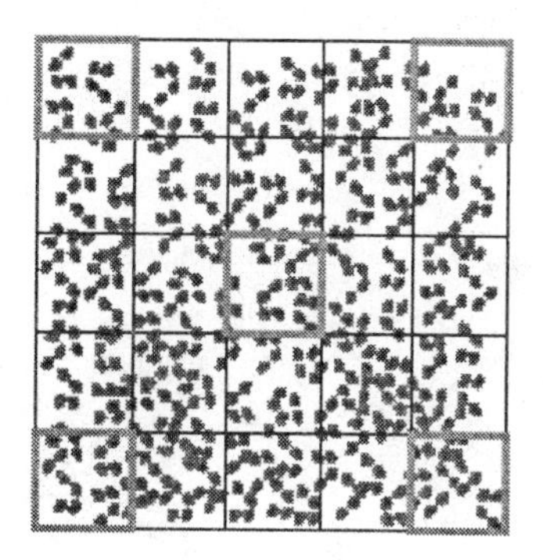

( ) 1000

( ) $\frac{1}{1000}$

( ) 40

10. The ratio in the illustration indicates that 1 inch on the model carousel is equivalent to$A$= 164 inches on the actual carousel. How wide should the model be if the actual carousel is 123 feet wide?

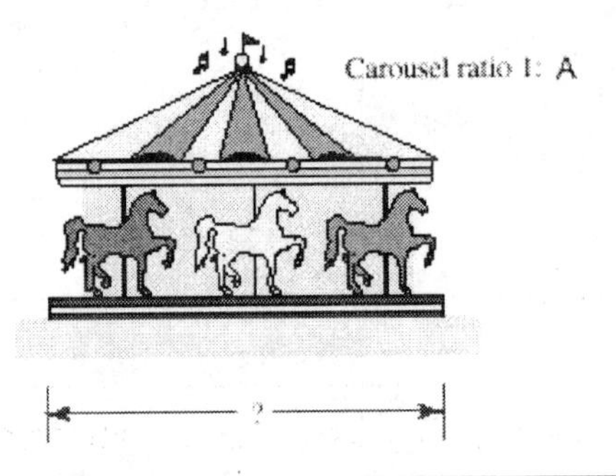

11. What is the appropriate measurement for the weight of an African elephant? Choose your answer from below.

( ) 1.4tons
( ) 18lb
( ) 1.8oz

12. Convert 36 inches to feet.

13. Convert 4 yards to feet.

Choose your answer from below.

( ) 48
( ) 12

14. Convert 5760 minutes to days.

15. AMELIA EARHART: In 1932, Amelia Earhart became the first woman to fly across the Atlantic Ocean alone, establishing a new record for the crossing: 13 hours and 30 minutes. How many minutes is this? Choose your answer frow below.

( ) 810 minutes
( ) 792 minutes
( ) 809

16. Convert 6 m to centimeters.

17. Convert 3.8 m to centimeters. Choose your answer from below.

( ) 38 cm
( ) 3800 cm
( ) 0.38 cm
( ) 380 cm

18. Convert 56000 cc to liters.

19. A baby weighs 4.003 kilograms. Give this weight in centigrams. Choose your answer from below.

( ) 40030 cg
( ) 400300 cg
( ) 4003 cg
( ) 0.04003 cg

20. The net weight of a bottle of olives is 241 grams. Find the smallest number of bottles that must be purchased to have at least 5 kilograms of olives.

21. Convert 4 feet to centimeters. Choose the answer, rounded to the nearest hundredth, from below.

( ) 121.92
( ) 400.00
( ) 1219.20

22. Convert 5 pints into liters.

23. Convert -10°C to degrees Fahrenheit. Choose your answer from below.

( ) -58 ° C
( ) -18 ° C
( ) 14 ° C

24. CHEETAH: A cheetah can run 115 kilometers per hour. How fast is this in mph? Round your answer to the nearest tenth.

25. HOT SPRINGS: The thermal springs in Hot Springs National Park in central Arkansas emit water as warm as 155°F. Change this temperature to degrees Celsius. Choose your answer from below.

( ) $\left(\frac{775}{9}\right)^{\circ}$
( ) $\left(\frac{615}{9}\right)^{\circ}$
( ) $\left(\frac{155}{9}\right)^{\circ}$

Answers

1. $\frac{1}{16}$

2. $\frac{1}{4}$

3. $\frac{59}{2000}$

4. 500

5. 20

6. $\frac{27}{15} = \frac{81}{x}$

7. -28

I-32

8. $\frac{1}{540}$

9. 1000

10. 9

11. 1.4tons

12. 3

13. 12

14. 4

15. 810 minutes

16. 600

17. 380 cm

18. 56

19. 400300 cg

20. 21

21. 121.92

22. 0.15

23. 14 ° C

24. 71.5

25. $\left(\frac{615}{9}\right)^{\circ}$

1. Write a fraction in simplified form that expresses the ratio of 5 to 10. Choose your answer from below.

( ) $\frac{1}{2}$
( ) $\frac{1}{10}$
( ) $\frac{5}{2}$

2. Refer to the monthly budget shown in the illustration. Find the ratio of the amount budgeted for food to the total budget in lowest terms. Choose your answer from below.

Item	Amount
Rent	$290
Food	$600
Gas and electric	$240
Phone	$250
Entertainment	$420

( ) $\frac{1}{5}$
( ) $\frac{1}{4}$
( ) $\frac{1}{3}$

3. A 65 pound bag of wheat seed costs $149.5. Find the cost per pound of wheat seed. Choose your answer from below.

( ) $4.6
( ) $6.9
( ) $2.3

4. A certain brand of cold and sinus medication is sold in 20-tablet boxes for $22 and in 10-tablet boxes for $12.1. Which is the better buy (i.e. less expensive per tablet)? Choose your answer from below.

( ) 20 - tablet box is better buy
( ) No difference
( ) 10 - tablet box is better buy

5. In one community, a bill for 845 kilowatt hours of electricity is $52. In a second community, a bill for 805 kwh is $41. In which community is the unit cost of electricity cheaper? Choose your answer from below.

( ) In the second community the unit cost of electricity is cheaper.
( ) In both communities the unit costs of electricity are the same.
( ) In the first community the unit cost of electricity is cheaper.

6. Which of these statements are proportions?

[ ] $\frac{21}{56} = \frac{30}{80}$

[ ] $\frac{80}{48} = \frac{42}{24}$

[ ] $\frac{9.75}{36.27} = \frac{15.5}{57.66}$

7. Solve for the variable in the proportion: $\frac{9}{10} = \frac{b}{60}$.

Choose your answer from below.

[ ] $\frac{1}{54}$

[ ] 54

[ ] $\frac{9}{600}$

8. Solve for the variable in the proportion: $\frac{a + 9}{5} = \frac{-5}{1}$.

Choose your answer from below.

[ ] -14

[ ] -34

[ ] -16

[ ] 34

9. Out of a sample of 400 men's shirts, 19 were rejected because of crooked collars. How many crooked collars would you expect to find in a run of 800 shirts? Choose your answer from below.

( ) 38
( ) 2
( ) 48
( ) 16843.1

10. See the table for the number of teachers needed at each school. How many teachers should there be for every 60 students? Choose your answer from below.

	Glenwood High	Goddard Junior High	Sellers Elementary
Entrollment	1260	1980	1080
Teachers	84	132	72

( ) 18
( ) 240
( ) 33
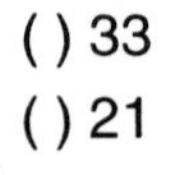
( ) 21
( ) 4

11. How many minutes are in 9 hours? Choose your answer from below.

( ) 180
( ) 540
( ) 5400

12. Convert 3 feet to inches.

Choose your answer from below.

( ) 30
( ) 18
( ) 36

13. Convert 24 inches to feet.

Choose your answer from below.

( ) 1
( ) 12
( ) 2

14. Convert 8 yards to feet.

Choose your answer from below.

( ) 96
( ) 24

15. To the nearest centimeter, tell which measurement the arrow points to on the ruler in the illustration. Choose your answer from below.

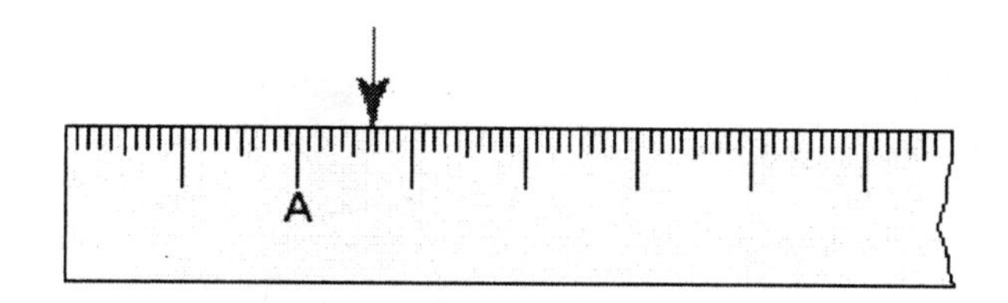

A= 2 cm.

( ) 2 cm
( ) 3 cm

16. Convert 68 kL to liters. Choose your answer from below.

( ) 680000 L
( ) 6800 L
( ) 68000 L
( ) 0.068 L

17. Blood pressure is measured with a sphygmomanometer (see the illustration). The measurement is read at two points and is expressed, for example, as 115/89. This indicates a systolic pressure of 115 millimeters of mercury and a diastolic pressure of 89 millimeters of mercury. Convert these measurement to centimeters of mercury. Choose your answer from below.

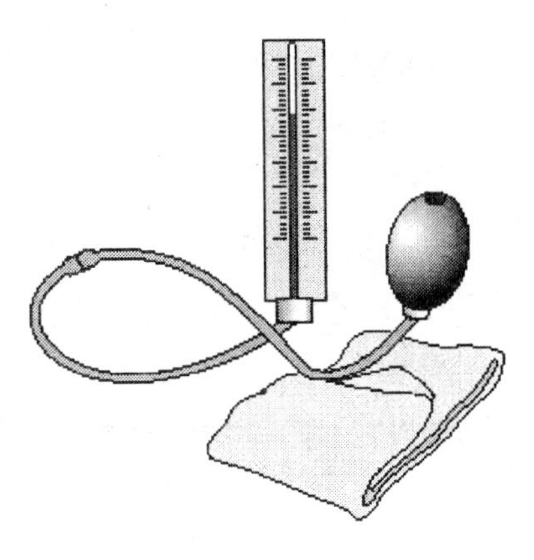

( ) systolic: 1.15 cm, diastolic: 0.89 cm
( ) systolic: 11.5 cm, diastolic: 8.9 cm
( ) systolic: 1150 cm, diastolic: 890 cm

18. A baby weighs 4.462 kilograms. Give this weight in centigrams. Choose your answer from below.

( ) 446200 cg
( ) 44620 cg
( ) 4462 cg
( ) 0.04462 cg

19. The net weight of a bottle of olives is 381 grams. Find the smallest number of bottles that must be purchased to have at least 5 kilograms of olives. Choose your answer from below.

( ) 13 bottles
( ) 15 bottles
( ) 14 bottles
( ) 16 bottles

20. Convert 3400 feet to kilometers. Choose your answer, rounded to the nearest hundredth, from below.

( ) 1.04 kilometers
( ) 3.40 kilometers
( ) 1036.32 kilometers

21. Convert 88 kilograms to pounds. Choose the answer from the list below.

( ) 193.4
( ) 193.6
( ) 1936

22. THE MIDDLE EAST: The distance between Eilat and Jerusalem is 309 kilometers. What is this distance in miles? Choose your answer from below.

( ) 201 miles
( ) 497 miles.
( ) 192 miles.

23. HAIR GROWTH: When hair is short, its rate of growth averages about 0.7 inch per month. How many centimeters is this a month? Choose your answer from below.

( ) 1.778 cm.
( ) 0.1778 cm.
( ) 17.78 cm.

24. SNOWY WEATHER: At which temperature might it snow: -8°C or 12°C? Choose your answer from below.

( ) 12° C
( ) -8° C

25. Convert 16000 pounds to tons.

Choose your answer from below.

( ) 9
( ) 8
( ) 7

Answers

1. $\frac{1}{2}$

2. $\frac{1}{3}$

3. $2.3

4. 20 - tablet box is better buy

5. In the second community the unit cost of electricity is cheaper.

6. $\frac{21}{56} = \frac{30}{80}$

I $\frac{9.75}{36.27} = \frac{15.5}{57.66}$

7. 54

I $\frac{9}{600}$

8. -14

I-34

9. 38

10. 4

11. 540

12. 36

13. 2

14. 24

15. 3 cm

16. 68000 L

17. systolic: 11.5 cm, diastolic: 8.9 cm

18. 446200 cg

19. 14 bottles

20. 1.04 kilometers

21. 193.6

22. 192 miles.

23. 1.778 cm.

24. -8° C

25. 8

1. Write a fraction in simplified form that expresses the ratio of 0.06 to 0.08.

( ) $\frac{3}{4}$
( ) $\frac{4}{3}$
( ) $\frac{6}{4}$

2. Write a fraction in simplified form that expresses the ratio of 27 months to 16 years. Choose your answer from below.

( ) $\frac{9}{64}$
( ) $\frac{9}{16}$
( ) $\frac{9}{192}$

3. A driver pumped 12 gallons of gasoline into his tank at a total cost of $25.2. Find the cost per gallon of the gasoline. Choose your answer from below.

( ) $2.1
( ) $6.3
( ) $4.2

4. A car travels 365 miles in 4.5 hours and a truck travels 320 miles in 2 hours. Which vehicle is going faster? Choose your answer from below.

( ) The car is faster then the truck.
( ) Both vehicles have the same rate.
( ) The truck is faster then the car.

5. Ricardo worked for 22 hours to help insulate a hockey arena. For his work, he received $440. Find his hourly rate of pay. Choose your answer from below.

( ) 40
( ) 60
( ) 20

6. Solve for the variable in the proportion: $\frac{7}{35} = \frac{10}{t}$.

Choose your answer from below.

( ) 50

( ) $\frac{10}{5}$

( ) $\frac{1}{50}$

7. Solve for the variable in the proportion: $\frac{s}{12} = \frac{2}{4}$.

Choose your answer from below.

( ) 6

( ) 4

( ) $\frac{1}{6}$

8. The bar graph in the illustration shows the yearly costs incurred and the revenue received by a business. How do the ratios of costs to revenue for 1999 and 2000 compare? Choose your answer from below.

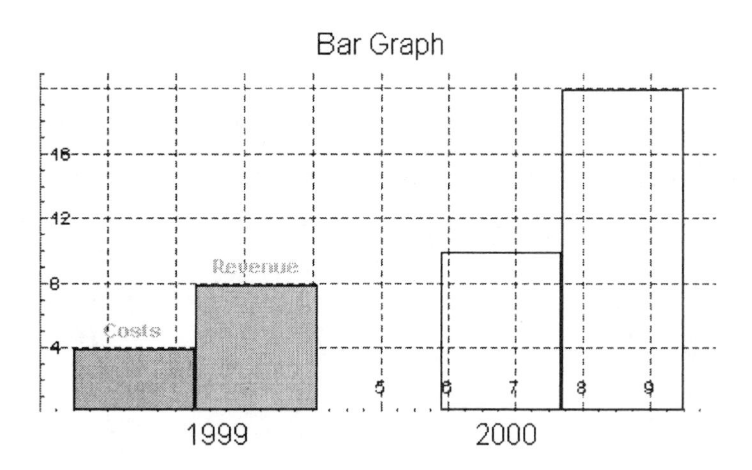

( ) in 1999 larger then in 2000
( ) in 1999 less then in 2000
( ) the same

9. A florist sells a dozen long-stemmed white lilies for $69.18. In honor of their 28th wedding anniversary, a man wants to buy 28 lilies for his wife. What will the lilies cost? Choose your answer from below.

( ) 161.42
( ) 92.24
( ) 29.69

10. The ratio in the illustration indicates that 1 inch on the model carousel is equivalent to$A$= 216 inches on the actual carousel. How wide should the model be if the actual carousel is 216 feet wide? Choose your answer from below.

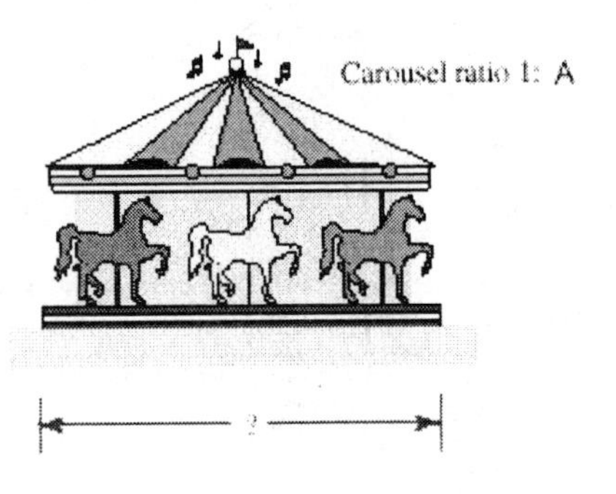

( ) $\frac{216}{216}$

( ) 144

( ) 12

11. How many pounds are in 5 tons? Choose your answer from below

( ) 100

( ) 10000

( ) 100000

12. Convert $5\frac{1}{4}$ feet to inches.

Choose your answer from below.

( ) 63

( ) 31.5

( ) 60

13. Convert 21120 feet to miles.

Choose your answer from below.

( ) 4
( ) 4.2

14. Do the conversion:
120 minutes to hours.

Choose your answer from below.

( ) 2
( ) 1
( ) 3

15. AMELIA EARHART: In 1932, Amelia Earhart became the first woman to fly across the Atlantic Ocean alone, establishing a new record for the crossing: 13 hours and 30 minutes. How many minutes is this? Choose your answer frow below.

( ) 809
( ) 785 minutes
( ) 810 minutes

16. To the nearest centimeter, tell which measurement the arrow points to on the ruler in the illustration. Choose your answer from below.

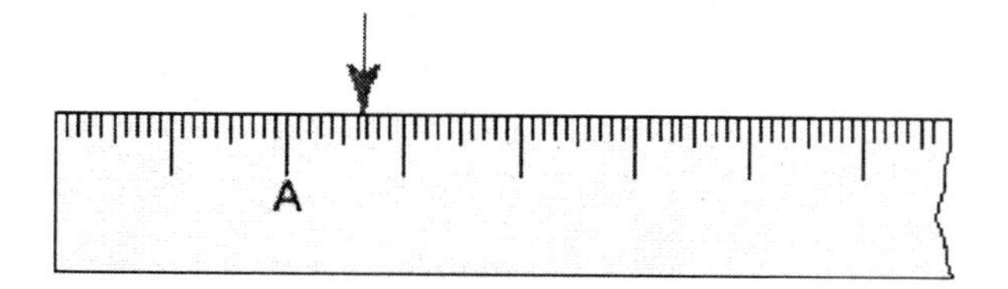

A= 2 cm.

( ) 3 cm
( ) 2 cm

17. What is the most realistic measurement for the thickness of a phone book? Choose your answer from below.

( ) 2 m
( ) 7 cm
( ) 1281 km

18. Convert 0.036 mm to meters. Choose your answer from below.

( ) 0.00036 m
( ) 0.000036 m
( ) 0.0036 m
( ) 36 m

19. How many deciliters of root beer are there in two 2.5-liter bottles? Choose your answer from below.

( ) 0.5 dL
( ) 500 dL
( ) 50 dL
( ) 25 dL

20. A bottle of hydrochlorothiazine contains 50 tablets. If each tablet contains 70 milligrams of the active ingredient, how many grams of the active ingredient are in the bottle? Choose your answer from below.

( ) 0.35 g
( ) 3.5 g
( ) 35 g

21. Convert 3500 inches into meters.

( ) 8890
( ) 88.9
( ) 8.89

22. Convert 4500 milliliters to gallons. Choose your answer, rounded to the nearest tenth, from below.

( ) 11.9
( ) 118.8
( ) 1.2

23. TRACK AND FIELD: Track meets are held on an oval track like the one shown in the illustration below. One lap around the track is usually 404 meters. However, for some older tracks in the United States, one lap is 448 yards. Are these two types of tracks the same length? Choose your answer from below.

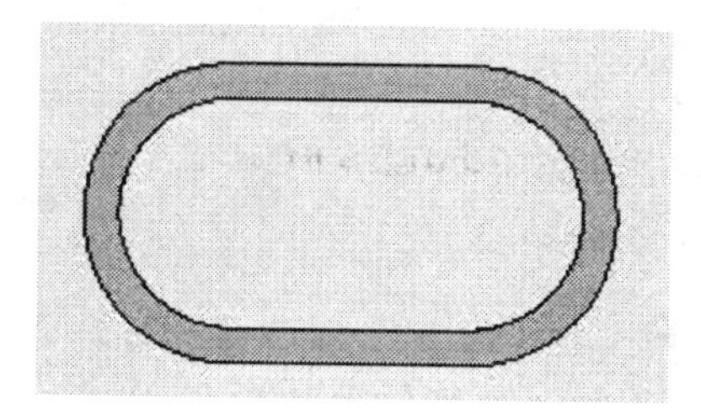

( ) yes
( ) I don't know
( ) no

24. POSTAL REGULATIONS: You can mail a package weighing up to 70 pounds via priority mail. Can you mail a package that weighs 38 kilograms by priority mail? Choose your answer from below.

( ) yes
( ) no
( ) I don't know

25. DRINKING WATER: To get a cold drink of water, which temperature would you choose: -3°C, 6°C, or 28°C? Choose your answer from below.

( ) 28° C
( ) -3° C
( ) 6° C

Answers

1. $\frac{3}{4}$

2. $\frac{9}{64}$

3. $2.1

4. The truck is faster then the car.

5. 20

6. 50

7. 6

8. the same

9. 161.42

10. 12

11. 10000

12. 63

13. 4

14. 2

15. 810 minutes

16. 3 cm

17. 7 cm

18. 0.000036 m

19. 50 dL

20. 3.5 g

21. 88.9

22. 1.2

23. no

24. no

25. 6° C

1. Convert -10°C to degrees Fahrenheit. Choose your answer from below.

( ) -58° C
( ) -18° C
( ) 14° C

2. Convert 84 inches to feet.

[ ]

3. Write a fraction in simplified form that expresses the ratio of 10 to 16.

( ) $\frac{5}{8}$
( ) $\frac{10}{16}$
( ) $\frac{8}{5}$

4. CHEETAH: A cheetah can run 110 kilometers per hour. How fast is this in mph? Round your answer to the nearest tenth.

[ ]

5. Convert 78000 cc to liters.

[ ]

6. Write a fraction in simplified form that expresses the ratio of 10 minutes to 1 hour.

[ ]

7. A baby weighs 2.956 kilograms. Give this weight in centigrams. Choose your answer from below.

( ) 29560 cg
( ) 2956 cg
( ) 295600 cg
( ) 0.02956 cg

8. What is the appropriate measurement for the weight of an African elephant? Choose your answer from below.

( ) 19lb
( ) 1.1tons
( ) 1.7oz

9. An airline had 4.1 complaints for every 300 passengers. Write this rate as a fraction in simplified form. Choose your answer from below.

( ) $\frac{41}{3000}$

( ) $\frac{41}{300}$

( ) $\frac{3000}{41}$

10. An 6900-gallon tank can be emptied in 15 minutes. Find the rate of flow in gallons per minute.

11. Convert 10 yards to feet.

Choose your answer from below.

( ) 30
( ) 120

12. Ricardo worked for 37 hours to help insulate a hockey arena. For his work, he received $721.5. Find his hourly rate of pay. Choose your answer from below.

( ) 39
( ) 19.5
( ) 58.5

13. AMELIA EARHART: In 1932, Amelia Earhart became the first woman to fly across the Atlantic Ocean alone, establishing a new record for the crossing: 13 hours and 30 minutes. How many minutes is this? Choose your answer frow below.

( ) 786 minutes
( ) 809
( ) 810 minutes

14. Convert 7 m to centimeters.

15. For every 30 feet of chain link fencing, 50 support posts are used. How many support posts will be needed for 3 feet of chain link fence? Write the proportion that could be used to solve this problem, using the variable*x*.

16. HOT SPRINGS: The thermal springs in Hot Springs National Park in central Arkansas emit water as warm as 150°F. Change this temperature to degrees Celsius. Choose your answer from below.

( ) $\left(\frac{150}{9}\right)^{\circ}$

( ) $\left(\frac{750}{9}\right)^{\circ}$

( ) $\left(\frac{590}{9}\right)^{\circ}$

17. Solve for the variable in the proportion: $\frac{z + 7}{27} = \frac{-8}{9}$.

Choose your answer from below.

[ ] -17

[ ] -31

[ ] -15

[ ] 31

18. The net weight of a bottle of olives is 347 grams. Find the smallest number of bottles that must be purchased to have at least 5 kilograms of olives.

19. Convert 4 feet to centimeters. Choose the answer, rounded to the nearest hundredth, from below.

( ) 1219.20
( ) 400.00
( ) 121.92

20. In a red blood cell count, a drop of the patient's diluted blood is placed on a grid like that shown in the illustration. Instead of counting each and every red blood cell in the 25-square grid, a technician just counts the number of cells in the five highlighted squares. Then he or she uses a proportion to estimate the total red blood cell count. If there are 130 red blood cells in the blue squares, about how many red blood cells would there be in the entire grid? Choose your answer from below.

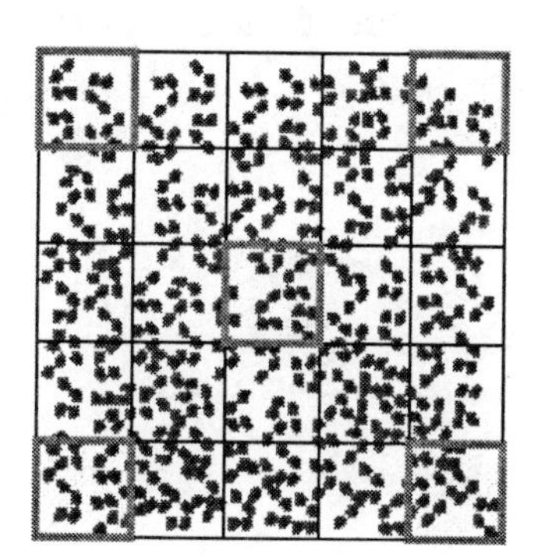

( ) $\frac{1}{650}$

( ) 650

( ) 26

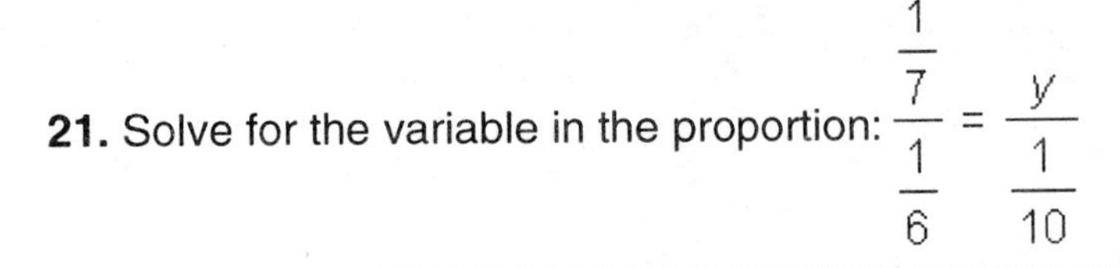

21. Solve for the variable in the proportion: $\dfrac{\frac{1}{7}}{\frac{1}{6}} = \dfrac{y}{\frac{1}{10}}$

22. Convert 8.1 m to centimeters. Choose your answer from below.

( ) 81 cm
( ) 810 cm
( ) 0.81 cm
( ) 8100 cm

23. The ratio in the illustration indicates that 1 inch on the model carousel is equivalent to$A$= 164 inches on the actual carousel. How wide should the model be if the actual carousel is 164 feet wide?

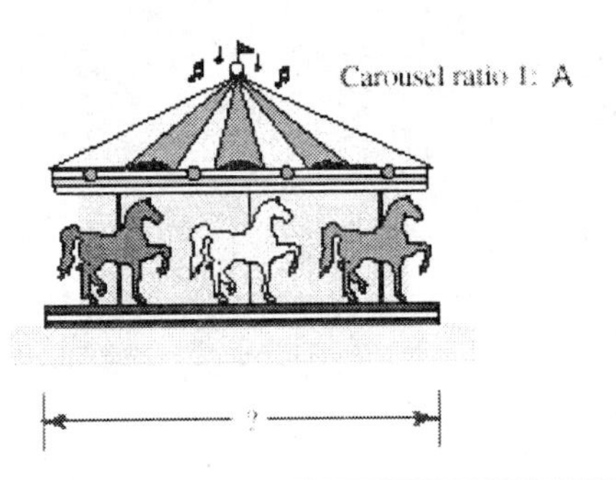

24. Convert 2880 minutes to days.

25. Convert 2 pints into liters.

Answers

1. 14° C

2. 7

3. $\frac{5}{8}$

4. 68.4

5. 78

6. $\frac{1}{6}$

7. 295600 cg

8. 1.1tons

9. $\frac{41}{3000}$

10. 460

11. 30

12. 19.5

13. 810 minutes

14. 700

15. $\frac{30}{50} = \frac{3}{x}$

16. $\left(\frac{590}{9}\right)^{\circ}$

17. -31
I-15

18. 15

19. 121.92

20. 650

21. $\frac{1}{420}$

22. 810 cm

23. 12

24. 2

25. 0.06

1. To write the ratio $\frac{27}{36}$ in lowest terms, we divide out any common factors of the numerator and denominator. What common factor do they have?

2. Write the phrase "18 presents for 9 children" as a unit rate. Choose your answer from below.

( ) 4
( ) 6
( ) 2

3. A secretary typed a document containing 700 words in 10 minutes. How many words per minute did he type?

4. A certain brand of cold and sinus medication is sold in 25-tablet boxes for $27.5 and in 10-tablet boxes for $12.1. Which is the better buy (i.e. less expensive per tablet)? Choose your answer from below.

( ) No difference
( ) 10 - tablet box is better buy
( ) 25 - tablet box is better buy

5. What are the means of the proportion $\frac{60}{10} = \frac{c}{6}$?

Choose your answer from below.

( ) 60 and 6
( ) 60 and$c$
( ) $c$and 10
( ) 10 and 6

6. Solve for the variable in the proportion: $\frac{b+8}{20} = \frac{-10}{4}$

7. Solve for the variable in the proportion: $\frac{\frac{1}{2}}{\frac{1}{6}} = \frac{c}{\frac{1}{10}}$.

Choose your answer from below.

( ) $\frac{20}{186}$

( ) $\frac{1}{120}$

( ) $\frac{120}{31}$

( ) $\frac{31}{120}$

8. Write a ratio of the rise to the run for each ramp shown in the illustration, where a= 7, b= 9, c= 81, d= 63. Set the ratios equal to each other.

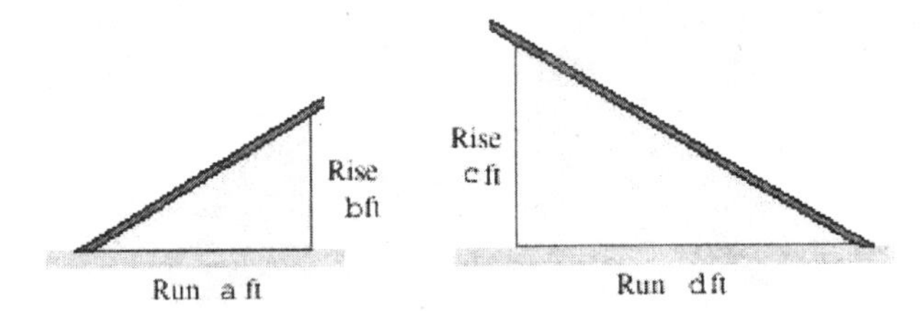

9. The ratio in the illustration indicates that 1 inch on the model carousel is equivalent to$A$= 160 inches on the actual carousel. How wide should the model be if the actual carousel is 160 feet wide? Choose your answer from below.

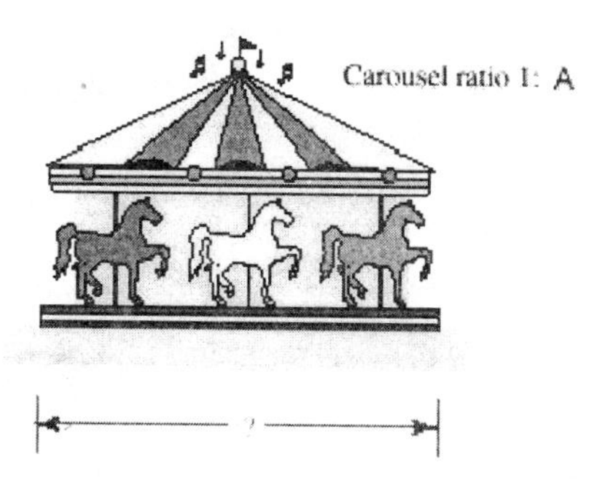

( ) 144
( ) 12
( ) $\frac{160}{160}$

10. How many pounds are in 3 tons?

11. Convert 24 inches to feet.

Choose your answer from below.

( ) 12
( ) 2
( ) 1

12. In one community, a bill for 625 kilowatt hours of electricity is $55. In a second community, a bill for 800 kwh is $56. In which community is electricity cheaper and in which is it more expensive? Use your cursor to match up the choices below.

In the second community	electricity is cheaper
In the first community	electricity is more expensive

13. Convert 144 ounces to pounds.

14. Do the conversion:
360 minutes to hours.

Choose your answer from below.

( ) 7
( ) 6
( ) 5

15. HIKING: A college student walks 14 miles in 157 minutes. How many hours does he walk? Round your answer to the nearest tenth of an hour.

16. To the nearest centimeter, tell which measurement the arrow points to on the ruler in the illustration. Choose your answer from below.

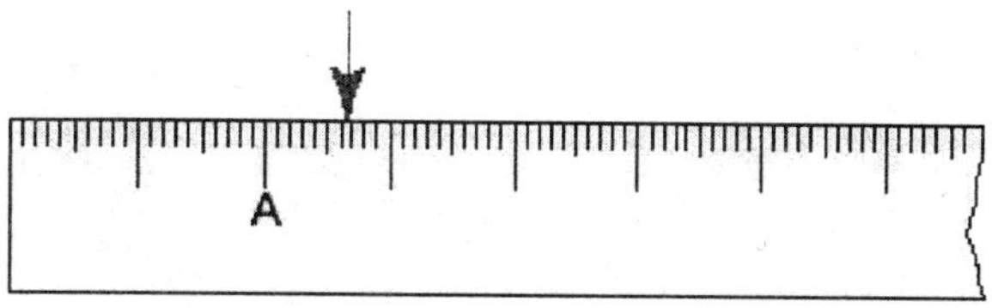

A= 2 cm.

( ) 2 cm
( ) 3 cm

17. Convert 3.9 m to centimeters.

18. Convert 518 mg to grams. Choose your answer from below.

( ) 51.8 g
( ) 5.18 g
( ) 518000 g
( ) 0.518 g

19. Convert 36 mL to cubic centimeters.

20. The net weight of a bottle of olives is 354 grams. Find the smallest number of bottles that must be purchased to have at least 5 kilograms of olives. Choose your answer from below.

( ) 15 bottles
( ) 16 bottles
( ) 14 bottles
( ) 17 bottles

21. Convert 11 liters to gallons. Round your answer to the nearest hundredth.

22. Convert 3000 inches into meters.

( ) 7.62
( ) 76.2
( ) 7620

23. THE MIDDLE EAST: The distance between Eilat and Jerusalem is 309 kilometers. To the nearest tenth, give this distance in miles.

24. A tiger can run 45 mph. How fast is this in kilometers per hour, rounded to the nearest tenth? Choose your answer from below.

( ) 7.2 kph.
( ) 724.2 kph.
( ) 72.4 kph.

25. HOT SPRINGS: The thermal springs in Hot Springs National Park in central Arkansas emit water as warm as 155°F. Change this temperature to degrees Celsius. (Round to the nearest tenths).

Answers For

1. 9

2. 2

3. 70

4. 25 - tablet box is better buy

5. *c*and 10

6. -58

7. $\frac{1}{120}$

8. $\frac{9}{7}=\frac{81}{63}$

9. 12

10. 6000

11. 2

12. In the first community -> electricity is more expensive, In the second community -> electricity is cheaper

13. 9

14. 6

15. 2.616667

16. 3 cm

17. 390

18. 0.518 g

19. 36

20. 15 bottles

21. 2.90

22. 76.2

23. 192

24. 72.4 kph.

25. 68.333333

1. Write a fraction in simplified form that expresses the ratio of 2 to 4.

2. Write a fraction in simplified form that expresses the ratio of 15 minutes to 1 hour. Choose your answer from below.

( ) $\frac{1}{4}$

( ) $\frac{1}{12}$

( ) $\frac{1}{8}$

3. Find the unit cost if 130 barrels cost $2990.

4. A 45 pound bag of corn seed costs $306. Find the cost per pound of corn seed. Choose your answer from below.

( ) $20.4
( ) $6.8
( ) $13.6

5. Ricardo worked for 49 hours to help insulate a hockey arena. For his work, he received $808.5. Find his hourly rate of pay.

6. Write the following statement as a proportion: 8 is to 16 as 20 is to 40. Choose your answer from below.

( ) $\frac{8}{40} = \frac{20}{16}$

( ) $\frac{8}{16} = \frac{20}{40}$

7. Solve for the variable in the proportion:

$$\frac{7}{9} = \frac{c}{45}$$

8. Solve for the variable in the proportion: $\frac{b}{45} = \frac{8}{9}$.

Choose your answer from below.

( ) 9

( ) 40

( ) $\frac{1}{40}$

9. The bar graph in the illustration shows the yearly costs incurred and the revenue received by a business. Write a proportion for the ratios of costs to revenue for 1999 and 2000.

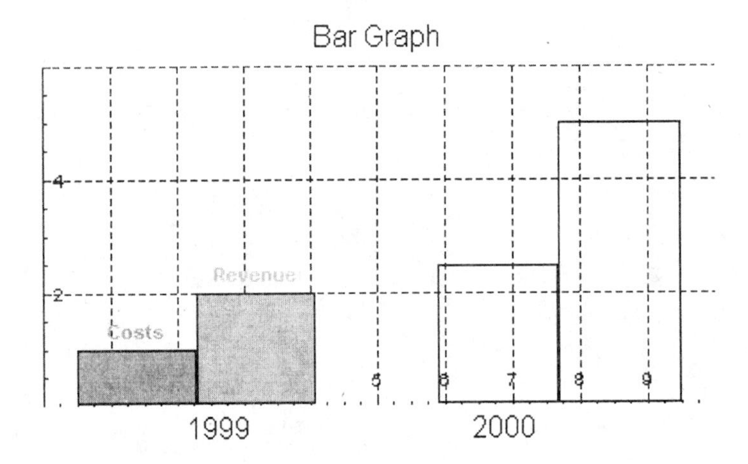

10. See the table for the number of teachers needed at each school. How many teachers should there be for every 20 students? Choose your answer from below.

	Glenwood High	Goddard Junior High	Sellers Elementary
Entrollment	540	780	720
Teachers	108	156	144

( ) 4
( ) 39
( ) 36
( ) 27
( ) 80

11. How many inches are in 4 feet?

12. How many minutes are in 3 hours? Choose your answer from below.

( ) 1800
( ) 180
( ) 60

13. Convert 0.7 miles to feet.

14. Convert 14000 pounds to tons.

Choose your answer from below.

( ) 6
( ) 8
( ) 7

15. AMELIA EARHART: In 1932, Amelia Earhart became the first woman to fly across the Atlantic Ocean alone, establishing a new record for the crossing: 13 hours and 30 minutes. How many minutes did her flight take?

16. What is the most realistic measurement for the thickness of a phone book? Choose your answer from below.

( ) 2 m
( ) 8 cm
( ) 1861 km

17. Convert 0.89 dm to centimeters.

18. Convert 8 g to milligrams. Choose your answer from below.

( ) 800 mg
( ) 0.008 mg
( ) 8000 mg
( ) 80 mg

19. Convert 18 kL to liters.

20. Change -5°C to degrees Fahrenheit.

21. Convert 3600 feet to kilometers. Round your answer to the nearest hundredth.

22. Convert 70°C to degrees Fahrenheit.

23. Convert 0.7 kilograms to ounces.

24. A baby weighs 3.569 kilograms. Give this weight in centigrams. Choose your answer from below.

( ) 3569 cg
( ) 35690 cg
( ) 356900 cg
( ) 0.03569 cg

25. HOT SPRINGS: The thermal springs in Hot Springs National Park in central Arkansas emit water as warm as 146°F. Change this temperature to degrees Celsius. (Round to the nearest tenths).

Answers For

1. $\frac{1}{2}$

2. $\frac{1}{4}$

3. $23

4. $6.8

5. 16.5

6. $\frac{8}{16} = \frac{20}{40}$

7. 35

8. 40

9. $\frac{1}{2} = \frac{2.5}{5}$

10. 4

11. 48

12. 180

13. 3696

14. 7

15. 810

16. 8 cm

17. 8.9

18. 8000 mg

19. 18000

20. 23

21. 1.10

22. 158

23. 24.5

24. 356900 cg

25. 63.333333

1. Look at the illustration and match each angle with its type. $\angle 1 = 62^{\circ}$ and $\angle 2 = 28^{\circ}$.

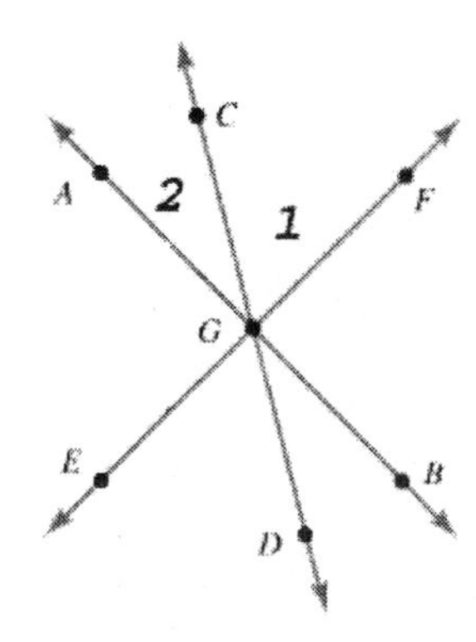

BGE	obtuse
BGA	acute
FGD	right
AGC	straight

2. In the figure below angle *a*= 76° and angle *b*= 35°.
What is the measure of angle *x*.

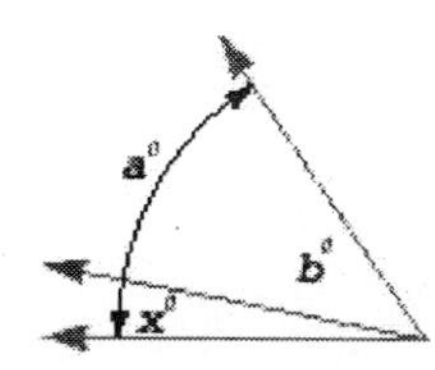

3. In the figure below $a = 4$, $b = 9$, $c = 3$, and $d = 54$. Find x.

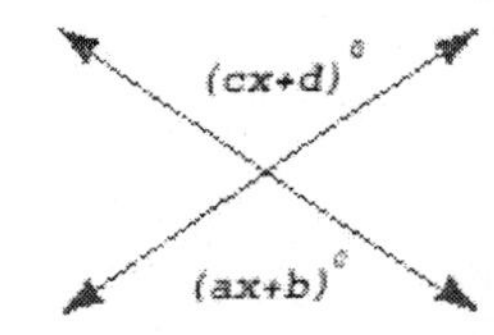

4. Look at the illustration. Find $m(\angle 4)$ if $m(\angle 1) = 29^\circ$

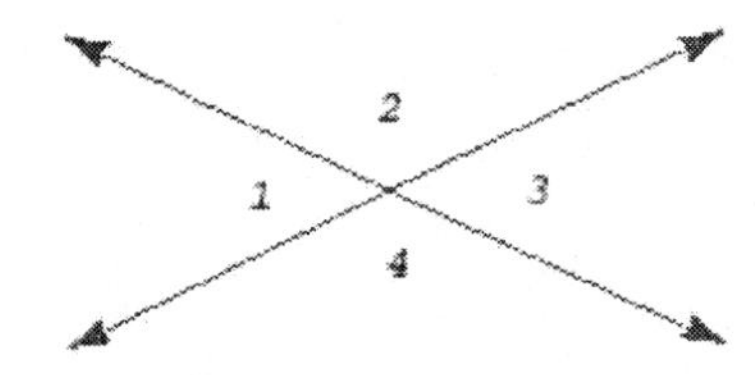

5. In the figure below, find the alternate interior angle to the angle 6.

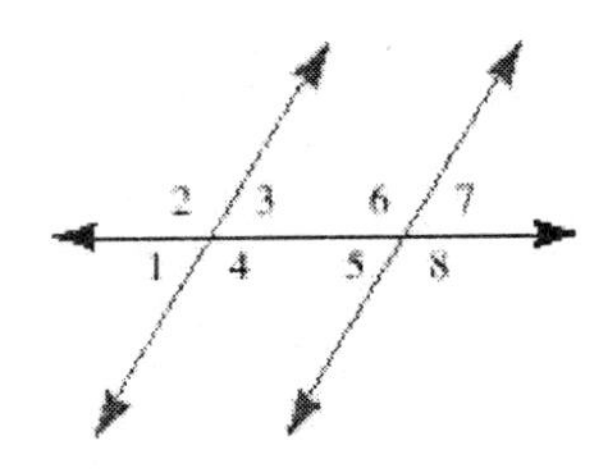

6. In the figure below, l_1 is parallel to l_2 and $\angle 4 = 149$. Complete the table with the measurements of the other angles.

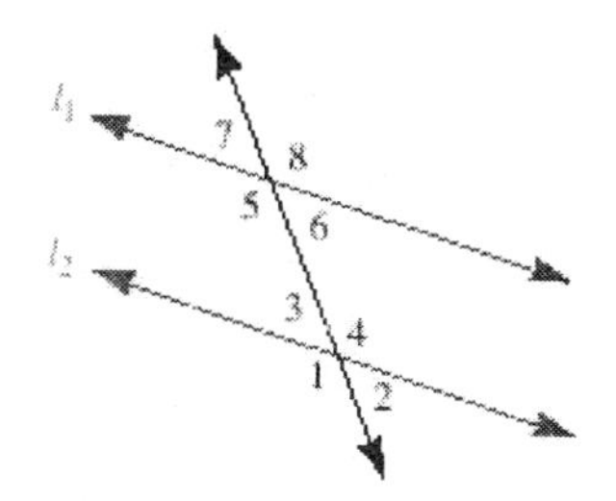

angle	measure
1	
2	
3	
5	
6	
7	
8	

7. In the figure below, line AB is parallel with line DE. Complete the table with the measurements of the other angles, if $\angle a = 32^\circ$ and $\angle b = 58^\circ$.

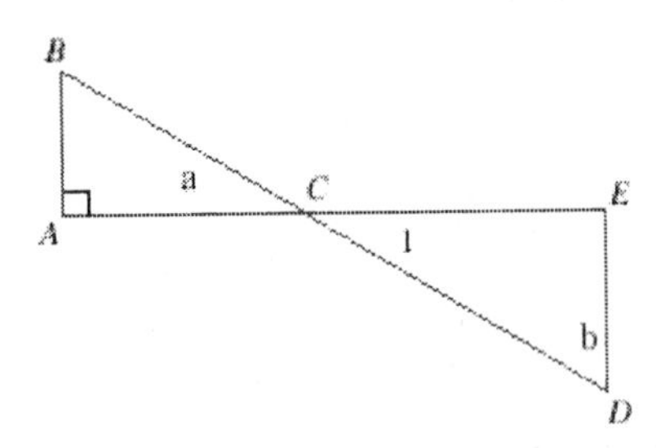

angle	measure
B	
1	
E	

In the figure below, l_1 is parallel with l_2. Find x, if $a = 6$, $b = -8$, $c = 2$ and $d = 12$.

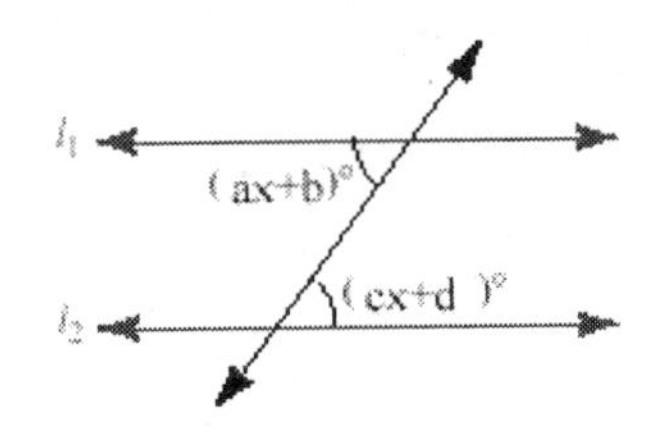

8. How many sides does the following polygon have?

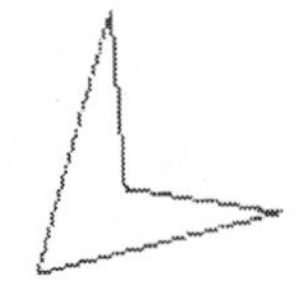

9. Find $\angle 2$ if

$\angle 1 = 13^{\circ}$.

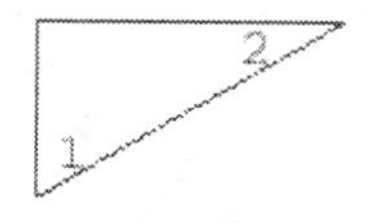

right triangle

10. Find b if $a = 71$.

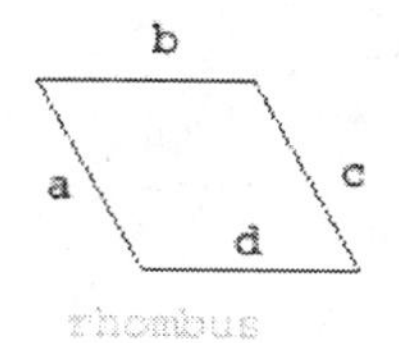

rhombus

11. Fill in the table by referring to the rectangle ABCD, shown below, where

$m(\angle 4) = 44^{\circ}$

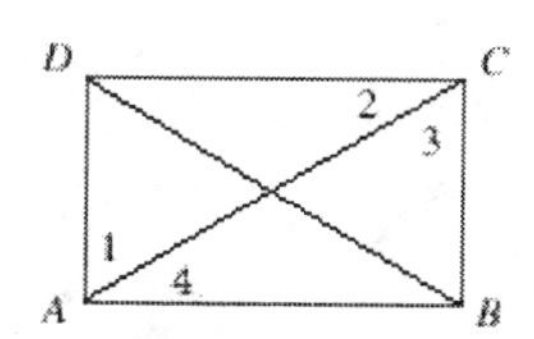

Angle	Measure
1	
2	
3	

12. The triangles shown in the illustration are congruent. The sides of the triangles are $a = 3$, $b = 9$, $c = 3$. Find d.

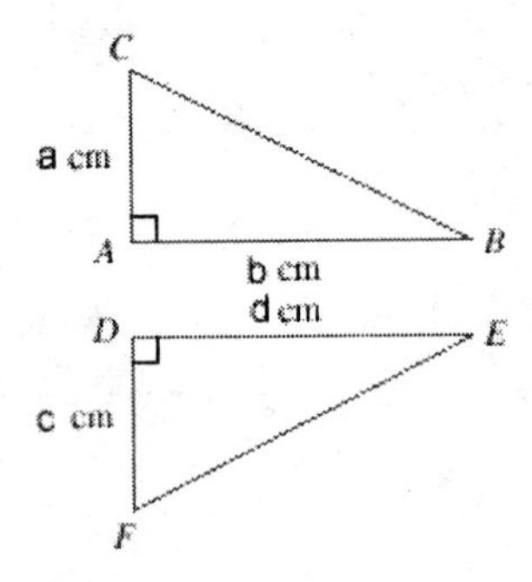

13. Find x, if $a = 8$ and $b = 9$.

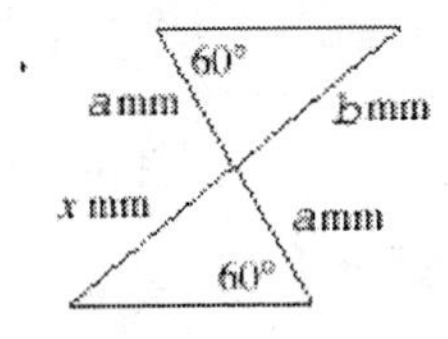

14. If segment DE in the illustration is parallel to segment AB, then $\triangle ABC$ is similar to $\triangle DEC$. Assuming this is the case, find x if $a = 100$, $b = 30$, and $c = 70$.

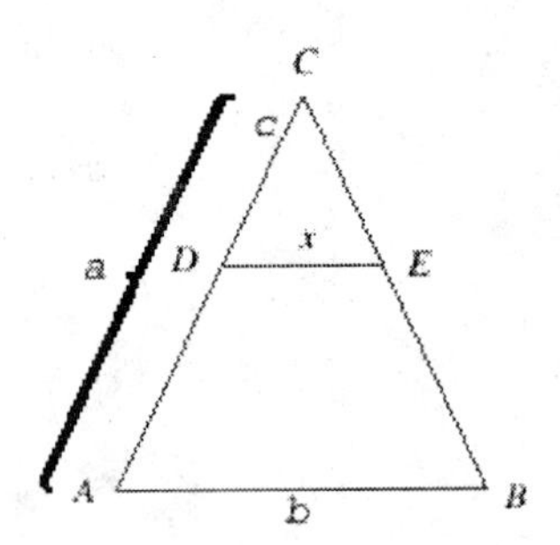

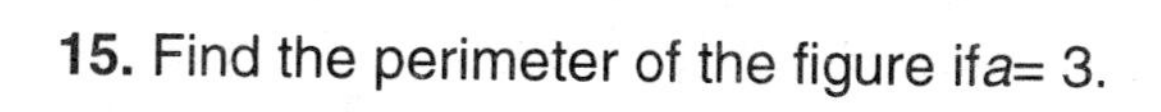

15. Find the perimeter of the figure if $a = 3$.

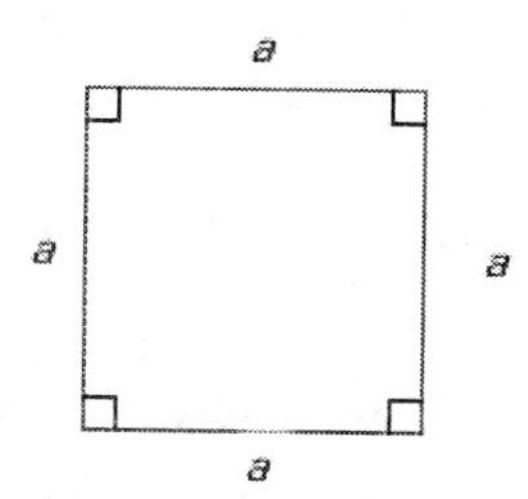

16. Find the area of the shaded part of the figure if $a = 6, b = 8$.

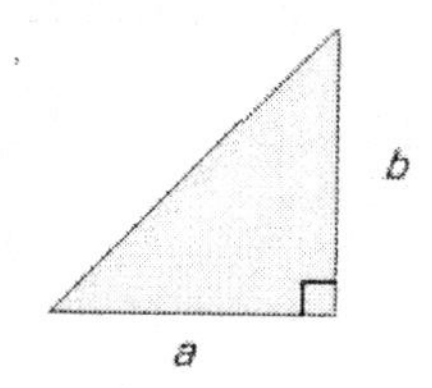

17. Match the corresponding statements.

segment joining two points on a circle	chord
A segment drawn from the center of a circle to a point on the circle	radius

18. Suppose the two "legs" of the compass shown in the illustration are adjusted so that the distance between the pointed ends is 10 inches. Complete the table with the corresponding measurements, if $\pi = 3.14$.

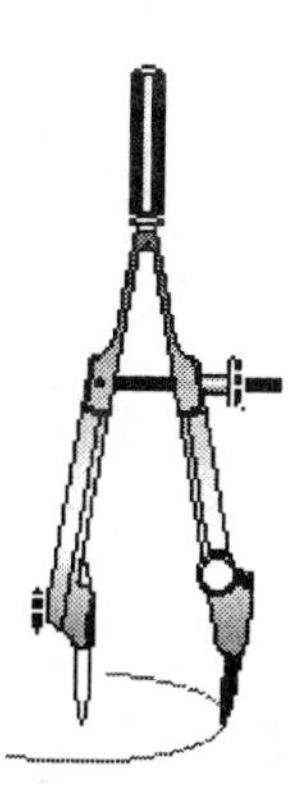

diameter	
area	
circumference	

19. Find the radius of a circle that has a circumference of 18π meters.

20. Find the total area of the figure to the nearest tenth, if $\pi = 3.14$, b= 8 cm and a= 6 cm.

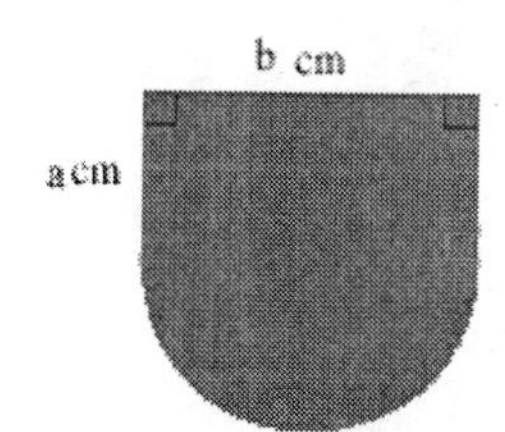

21. The rotunda at a state capitol is a circular area 120 feet in diameter. The legislature wishes to appropriate money to have the floor of the rotunda tiled. The lowest bid is $79 per square yard, including installation.
How much must the legislature spend to tile the floor?

22. Find the volume of a rectangular solid with dimensions of 5 by 2 by 4 centimeters.

23. Find the volume of a sphere with a radius of 4 inches.

24. Find the surface area of a rectangular solid with dimensions of 7 by 4 by 8 centimeters.

Answers

1. AGC -> acute, FGD -> obtuse, BGE -> right, BGA -> straight

2. 41

3. 45

4. 151

5. 4

6. 1, 149, 2, 31, 3, 31, 5, 149, 6, 31, 7, 31, 8, 149

7. B, 58, 1, 32, E, 90

8. 4

9. 77

10. 71

11. 1, 46, 2, 44, 3, 46

12. 9

13. 9

14. 21

15. 12

16. 24

17. A segment drawn from the center of a circle to a point on the circle -> radius, segment joining two points on a circle -> chord

18. diameter, 20, area, 314, circumference, 62.8

19. 9

20. 73.1

21. 99224.00

22. 40

23. 267.95

24. 232

1. What is the sum of $\angle a$ and $\angle f$? They are complementary angles.

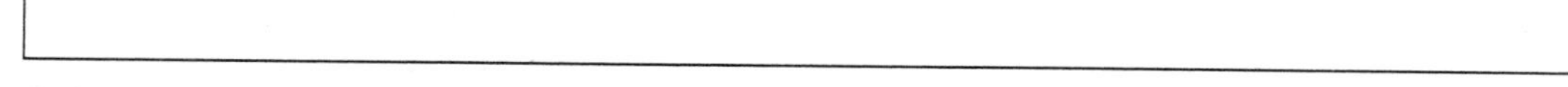

2. In the figure below $a = 6$, $b = 5$, and $c = 28$.
What is the measure of angle y?

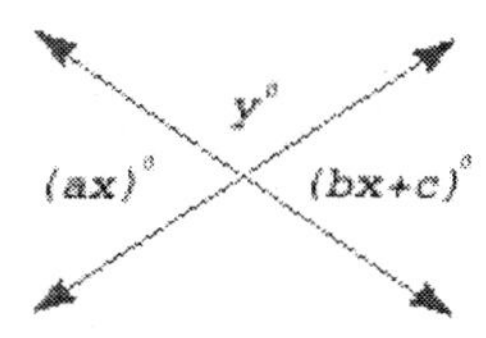

3. Find the supplement of each angle and complete the table.

Measure of x	Measure of supplement of x
166	
39	
122.5	
106	

4. In the figure below, find the corresponding angle that completes each pair.

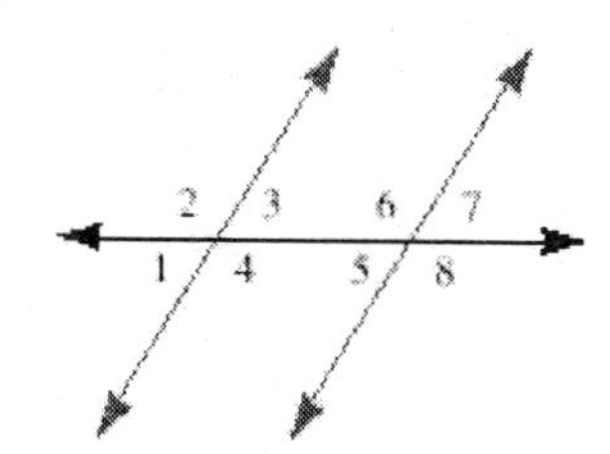

2	
4	

5. In the figure below, l_1 is parallel to l_2 with $\angle 2 = 60^{\circ}$ Find $\angle 1$.

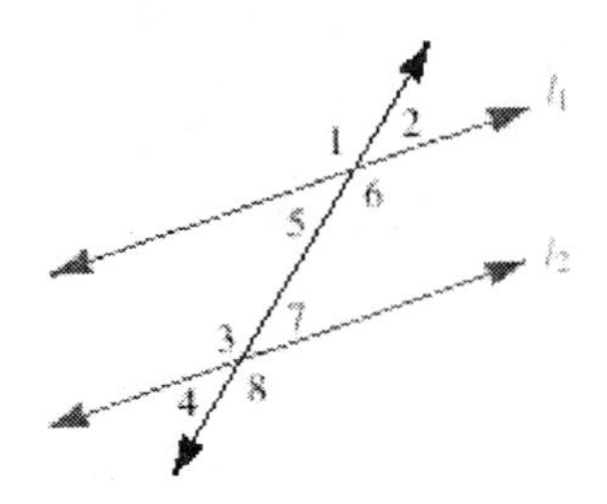

6. In the figure below, line AB is parallel to line DE. Find x, if $a = 5$, $b = -6$, $c = 2$ and $d = 9$.

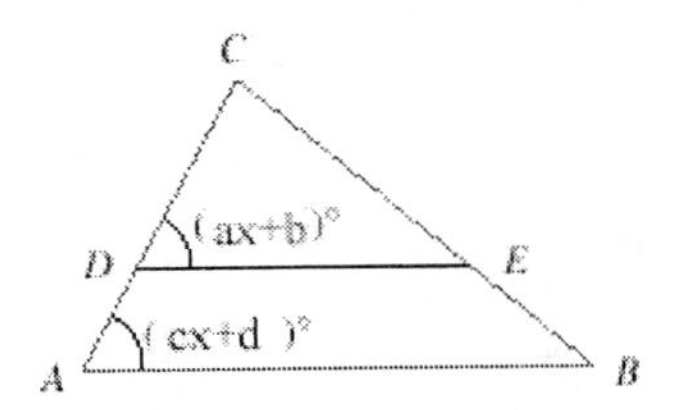

7. Find

$\angle 2$ if $\angle 1 = 49^{\circ}$.

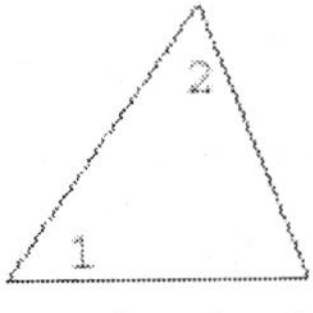

isosceles triangle

8. Classify the following polygons:

1.

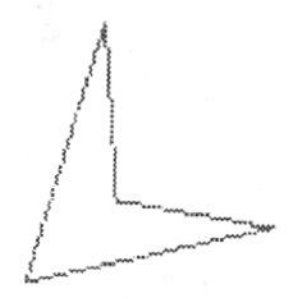

2.

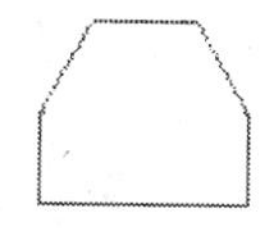

3.

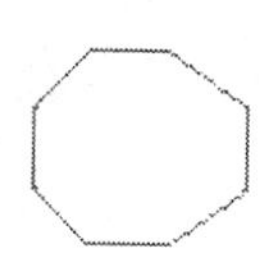

4.

5.

Picture 4	quadrilateral
Picture 1	pentagon
Picture 3	hexagon
Picture 2	octagon
Picture 5	triangle

9. Find $\overline{AB}$ if $\overline{AC} = 65.$

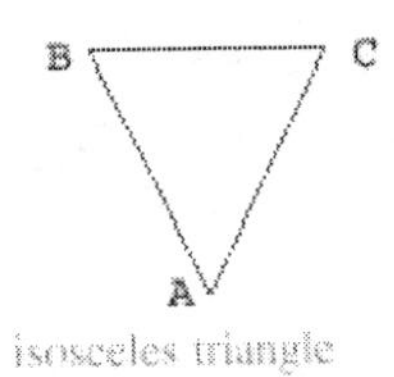

10. Refer to the illustration below to find $m(\overset{\frown}{BD})$, if $m(\overset{\frown}{AC}) = 18cm$.

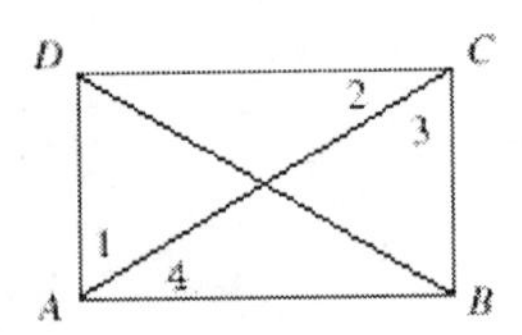

11. The angle a shown in the illustration is 44°. Find b, if the triangles are similar.

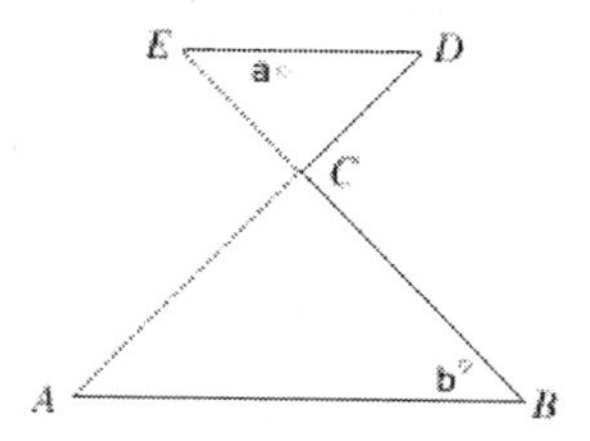

12. The two triangles shown in the illustration are congruent. Find b, if angle a is 45°.

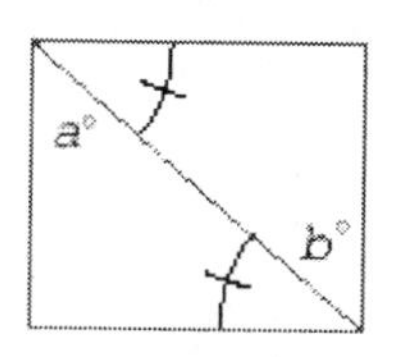

13. Find x if $a = 6$, $b = 8$, and $c = 10$.

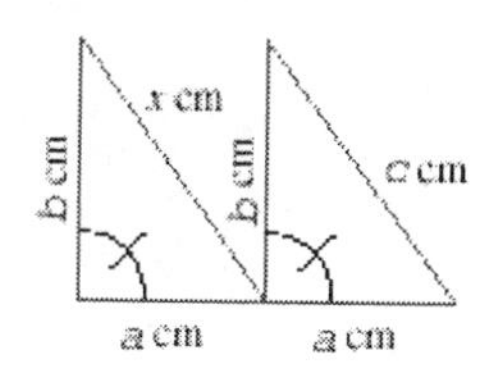

14. The airplane in the illustration ascends $c = 700$ feet as it flies a horizontal distance $b = 4000$ feet. How much altitude is gained as it flies a horizontal distance of $a = 1$ mi?

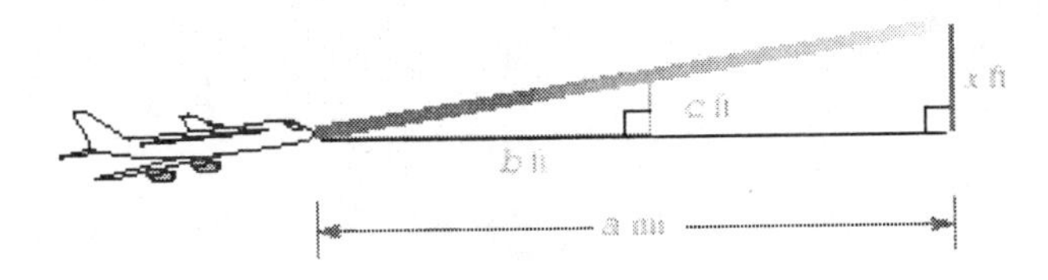

15. What size is the television screen shown in the illustration? Find d if $a = 8$ and $b = 15$.

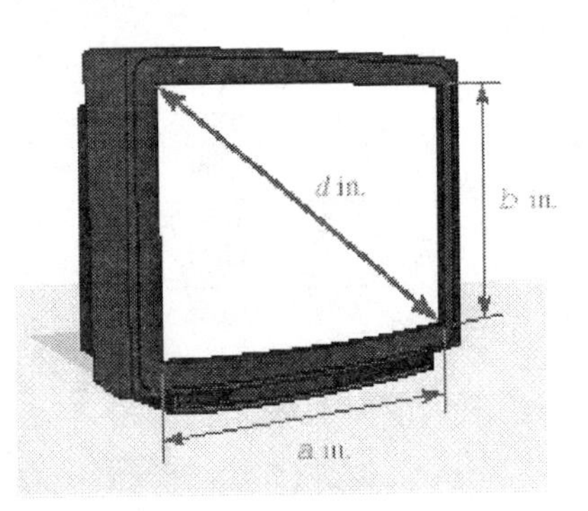

16. Find the perimeter of the figure if $a = 10$, $b = 6$, $c = 3$.

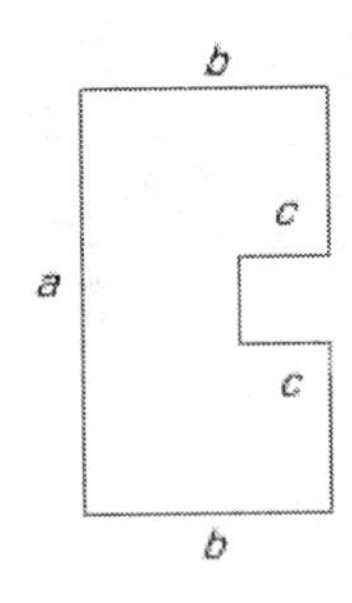

17. Find the area of the shaded part of the figure if $a = 8, b = 9, c = 3$.

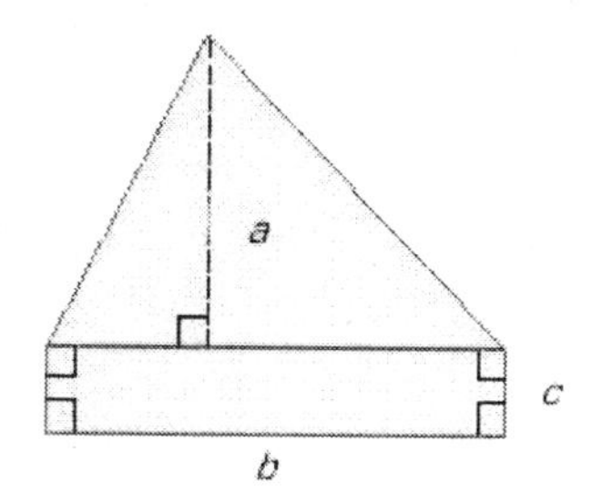

18. A rectangular living room measures 9 by 15 feet. At $20 per square yard, how much will it cost to carpet the room?

19. Match the corresponding statements.

an arc longer than a semicircle	major
an arc shorter than a semicircle	minor

20. To the nearest hundredth, find the circumference of a circle that has a diameter of 12 inches, if $\pi = 3.1415$.

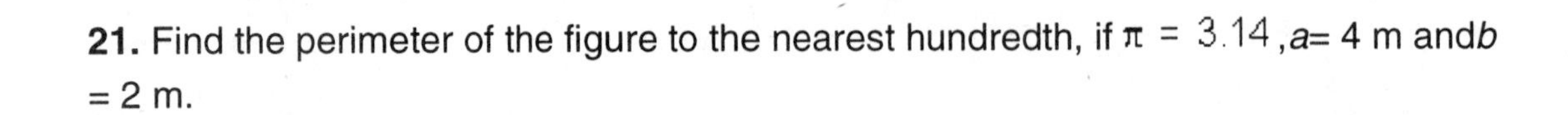

21. Find the perimeter of the figure to the nearest hundredth, if $\pi = 3.14$, a= 4 m and b = 2 m.

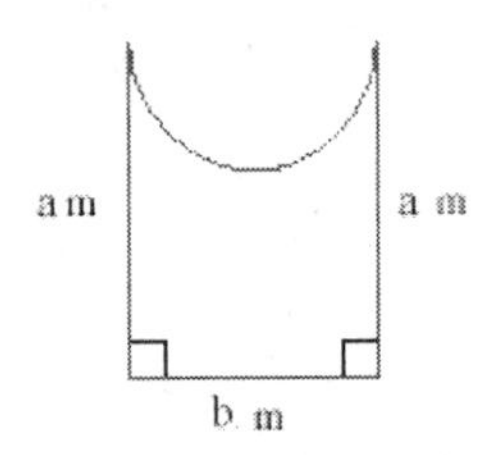

22. Joan wants to jog 17 miles on a circular track $\frac{1}{2}$ mile in diameter. How many times, to the nearest hundredth, must she circle the track?

23. Find the volume of a prism whose base is a right triangle with legs 5 and 8 meters long and whose height is 4 meters.

24. Find the volume of the figure if a= 4, b= 15.

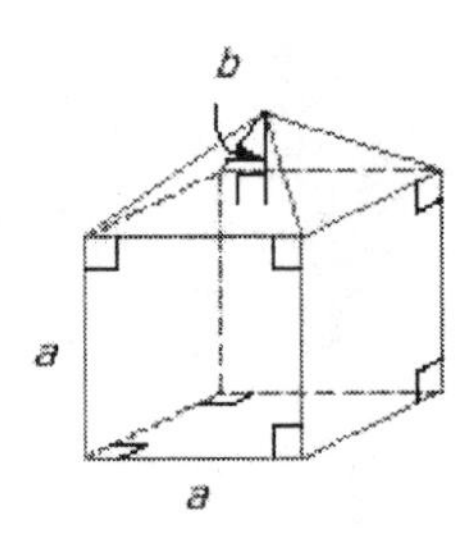

25. A restaurant serves pudding in a conical dish that has a diameter of 6 inches. If the dish is 7 inches deep, how many cubic inches of pudding are in each dish? If an answer is not exact, round to the nearest hundredth.

Answers

1. 90

2. 12

3. 166, 14, 39, 141, 122.5, 57.5, 106, 74

4. 2, 6, 4, 8

5. 120

6. 5

7. 49

8. Picture 1 -> quadrilateral, Picture 2 -> hexagon, Picture 3 -> octagon, Picture 4 > triangle, Picture 5 -> pentagon

9. 65

10. 18

11. 44

12. 45

13. 10

14. 924

15. 17

16. 38

17. 63

18. $300

19. an arc shorter than a semicircle -> minor, an arc longer than a semicircle -> major

20. 37.70

21. 13.14

22. 10.83

23. 80

24. 144

25. 65.95

1. $\angle c$ and $\angle d$ are complementary angles. What is their sum?

( ) 90°
( ) 360°
( ) 180°

2. In the figure below angle a = 25°. What is the measure of angle*x*.

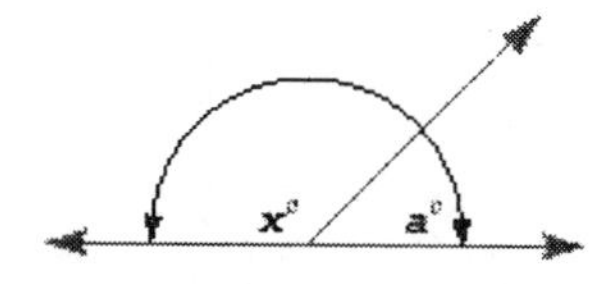

3. Look at the illustration. Find $m(\angle 4)$ if $m(\angle 1) = 19^{\circ}$

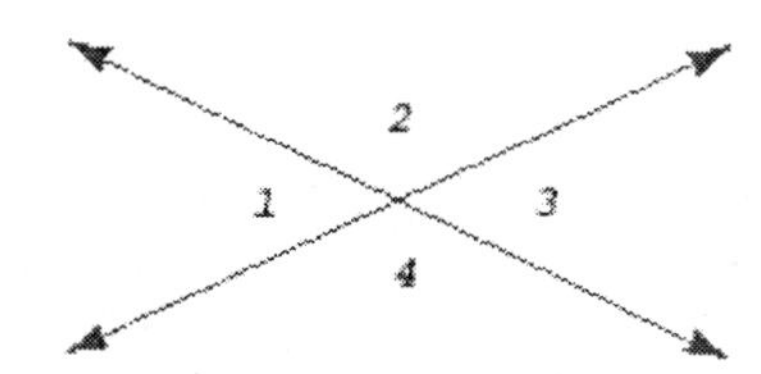

( ) 161
( ) 19
( ) 71

4. In the figure below $a = 63$. How many degrees from the horizontal position are the wings of the airplane?

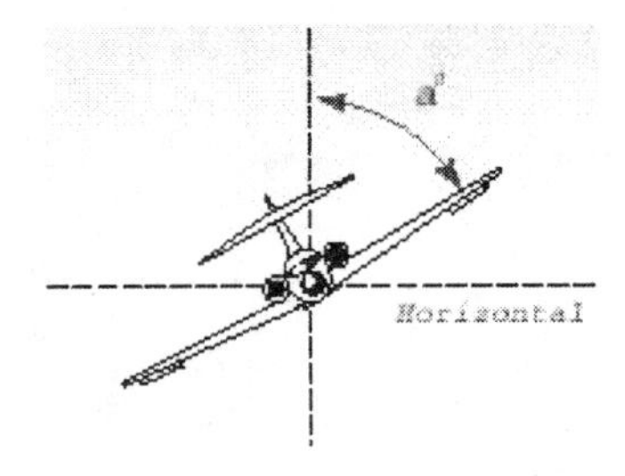

5. How many interior angles are shown in the figure below?

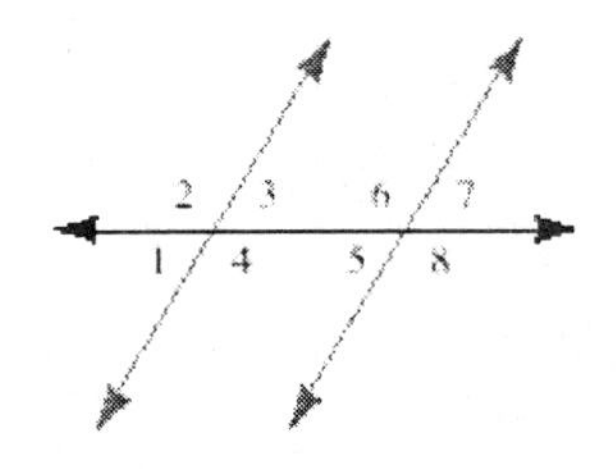

6. Using the figure below, find $\angle 8$ if l_1 is parallel to l_2 with $\angle 2 = 15^\circ$

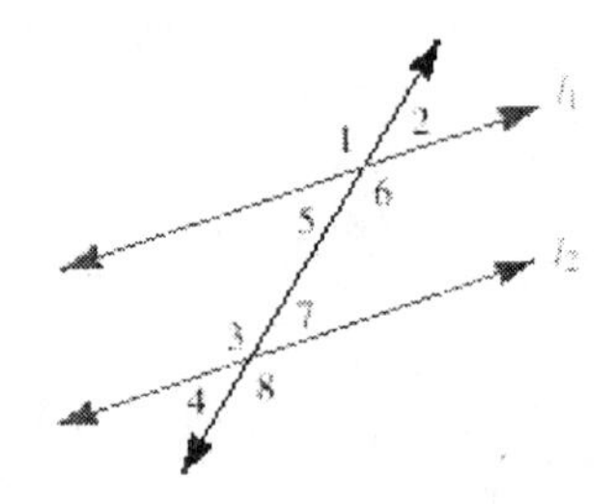

( ) 165°

( ) 15°

7. In the figure below, line AB is parallel to line DE. Find *x*, if *a* = 7, *b* = -4, *c* = 5 and *d* = 6.

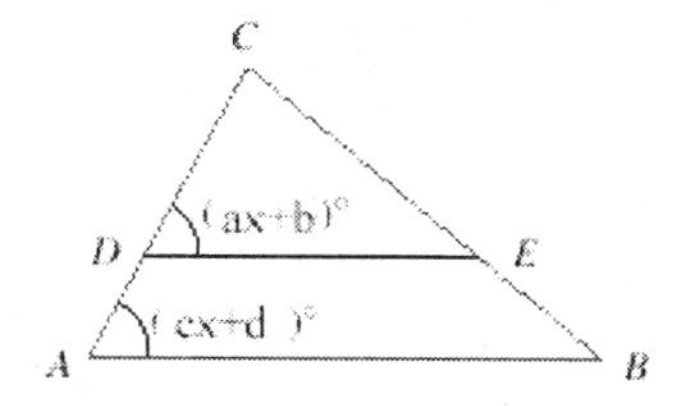

8. In the figure below, line AC is parallel to line BD. Find *x*, if *a* = 7, *b* = -10, *c* = 2 and *d* = 15.

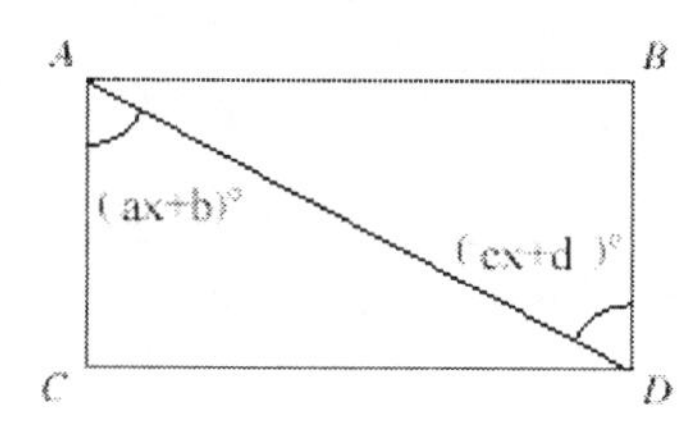

( ) 5°

( ) 31°

9. Find

$\angle 2$ if $\angle 1 = 63^\circ$

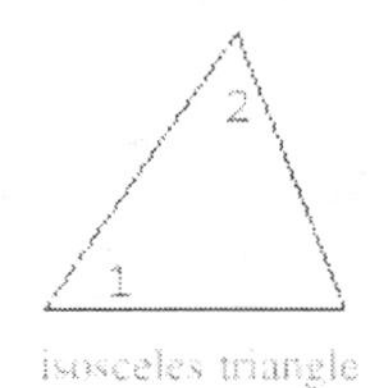

Choose your answer from below.

( ) 64°

( ) 27°

( ) 63°

10. Find c if a = 77.

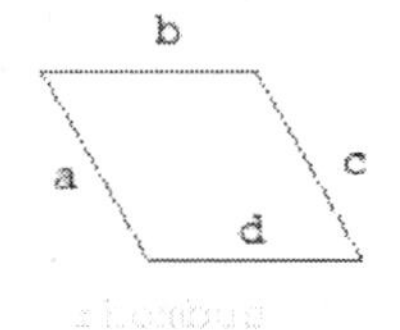

Choose your answer from below.

( ) 77cm
( ) 72cm
( ) 87cm

11. Refer to the illustration below to find $m(\overline{BD})$, if $m(\overline{AC}) = 12\text{cm}$.

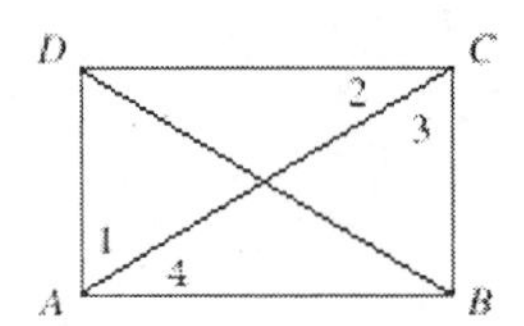

12. The triangles shown in the illustration are congruent. The sides of the triangles shown in the illustration are $a = 7, b = 13, c = 7$. True or False? $d = 13$.

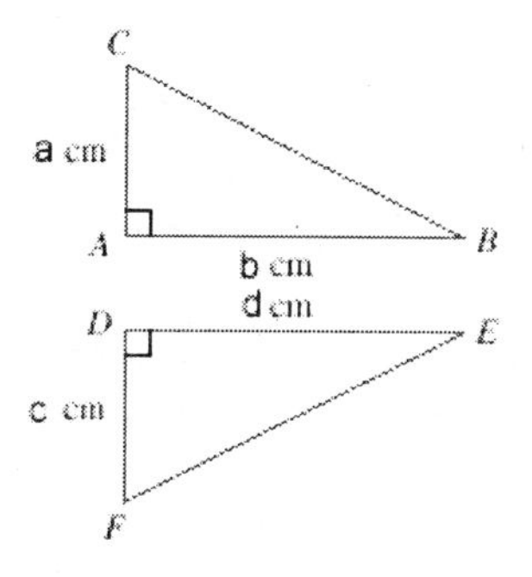

( ) True
( ) False

13. The two triangles shown in the illustration are congruent. Find b, if angle a is 45°.

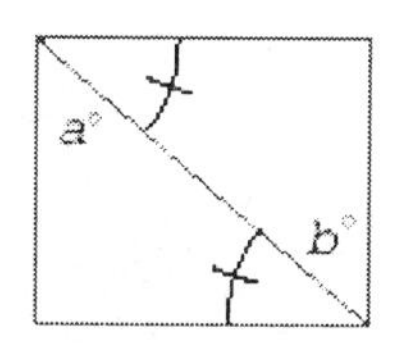

14. Match the sides of a right triangle with the lengths of the sides.

Hypotenuse	5
Least Leg	3
Greatest Leg	4

15. A man places a mirror on the ground and sees the reflection of the top of a building, as shown in the illustration. Find the height of the man,*a*, if *b*= 40,*c*= 300, and*h*= 30.

Choose the answer from below.

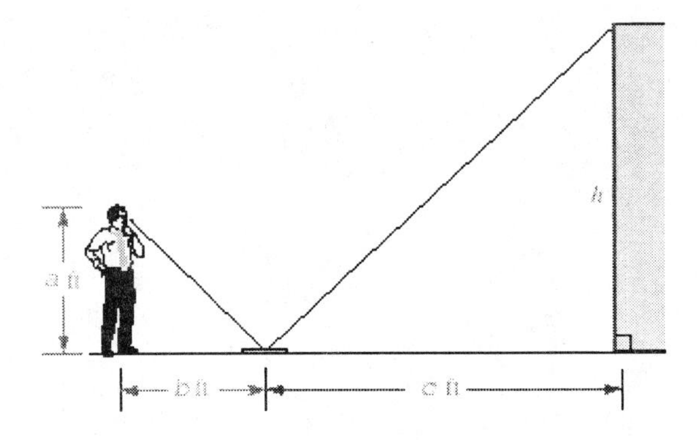

( ) $\frac{1}{4}$

( ) 4

( ) 34

( ) $\frac{450}{2}$

16. Find the perimeter of the figure if*a*= 9.

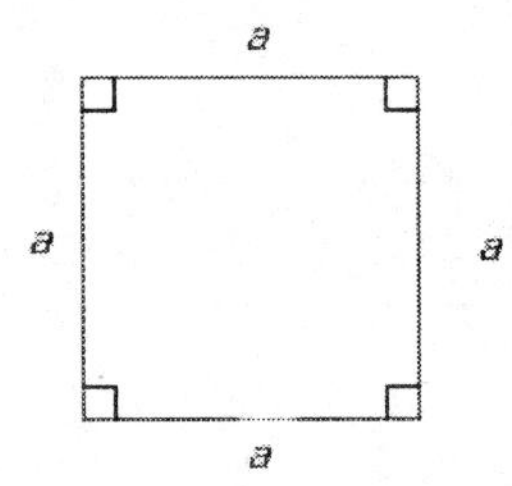

17. Find the area of the shaded part of the figure if $a = 6, b = 7$. Select the correct answer.

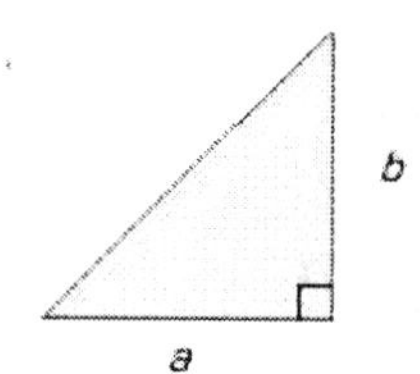

( ) 13
( ) 21
( ) 84

18. Find the area of the shaded part of the figure if $a = 8, b = 9, c = 3$.

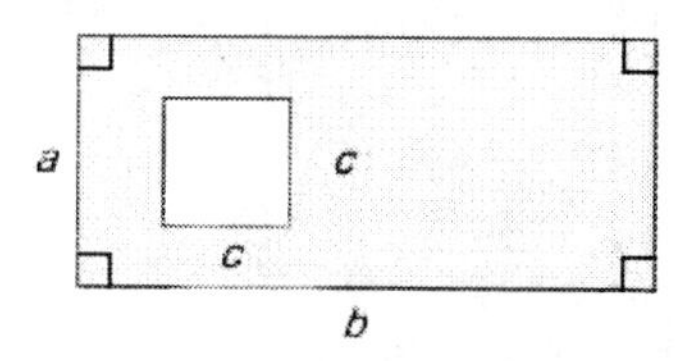

19. Round π to the nearest hundredth.

20. Find the perimeter of the figure to the nearest hundredth, if $\pi = 3.14$, $a = 5$ in. and $b = 8$ in.

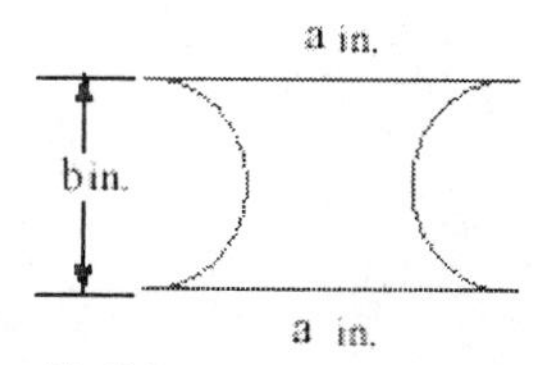

21. Find the total area of the shaded figure.

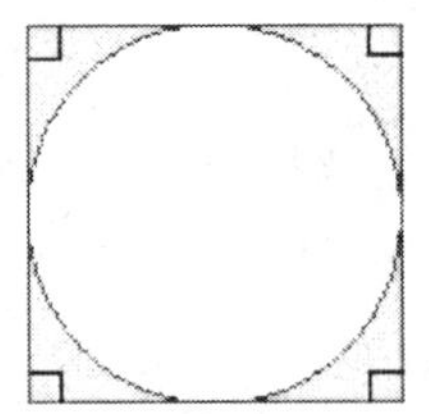

The side of the square is equal to 12.

( ) 30.9
( ) 1614.9
( ) 113.1
( ) 115.7

22. Refer to the illustration. How far does a point on the tip of a rotor blade travel when it makes one complete revolution?

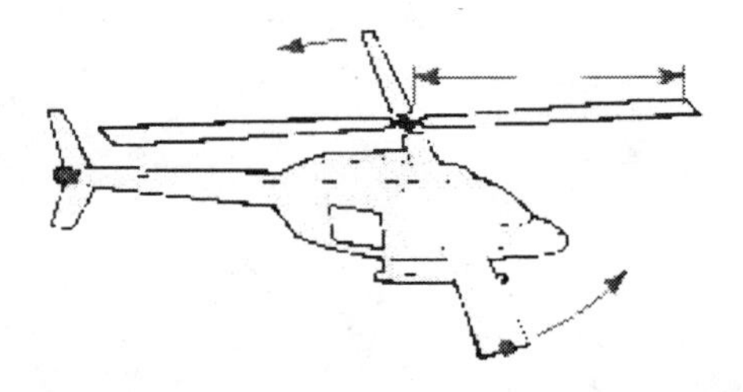

The length of the blade is equal to 18 feet.

( ) 1017.36 ft
( ) 56.52 ft
( ) 2034.72 ft
( ) 113.04 ft

23. Find the volume of a cylinder with a height of 3 meters and a circular base with a radius of 10 meters.

24. Find the volume of the figure if a= 16 cm, b= 4 cm.

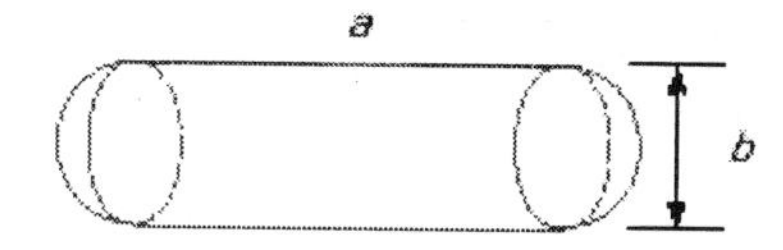

25. A classroom is 11 feet long, 10 feet wide, and 10 feet high. Find the number of cubic feet of air in the room.

( ) 1100 ft^3

( ) 31 ft^3

( ) 124 ft^3

Answers

1. 90°

2. 155

3. 161

4. 27

5. 4

6. 165°

7. 5

8. 5°

9. 63°

10. 77cm

11. 12

12. true

13. 45

14. Hypotenuse -> 5, Greatest Leg -> 4, Least Leg -> 3

15. 4

16. 36

17. 21

18. 63

19. 3.14

20. 35.12

21. 30.9

22. 113.04 ft

23. 942.00

24. 234.45

25. 1100 ft^3

1. In the figure below $\angle 1 = 64^\circ$ and $\angle 2 = 26^\circ$.
Which of the choices is an acute angle?

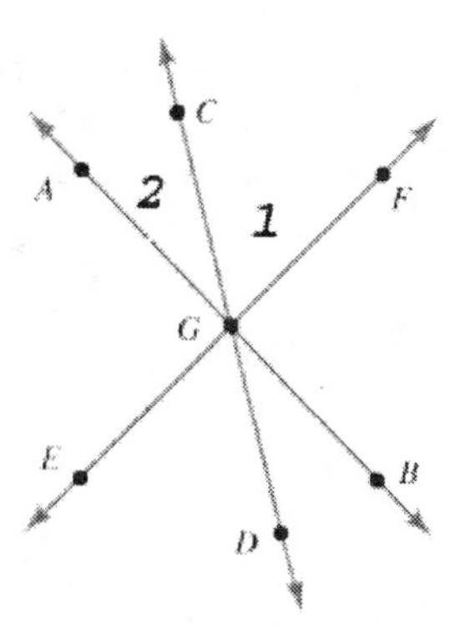

( ) *BGA*
( ) *BGE*
( ) *AGC*
( ) *FGD*

2. In the figure below angle $a = 80^\circ$ and angle $b = 32^\circ$.
What is the measure of angle x.

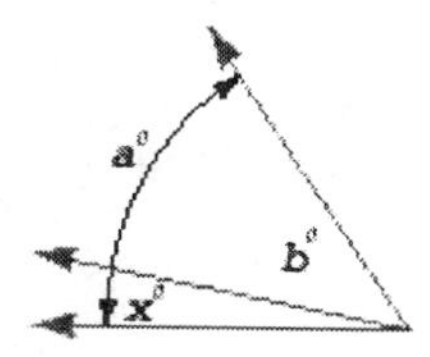

( ) 112
( ) 48
( ) 49

3. In the figure below $a = 6$, $b = 4$, $c = 2$, and $d = 148$. Find x.

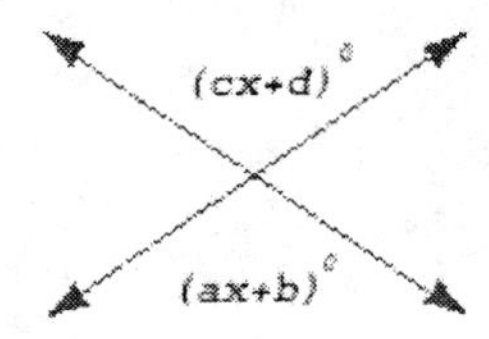

( ) 35
( ) 36
( ) 37

4. Look at the illustration. Find $m(\angle 4)$ if $m(\angle 1) = 15^{\circ}$

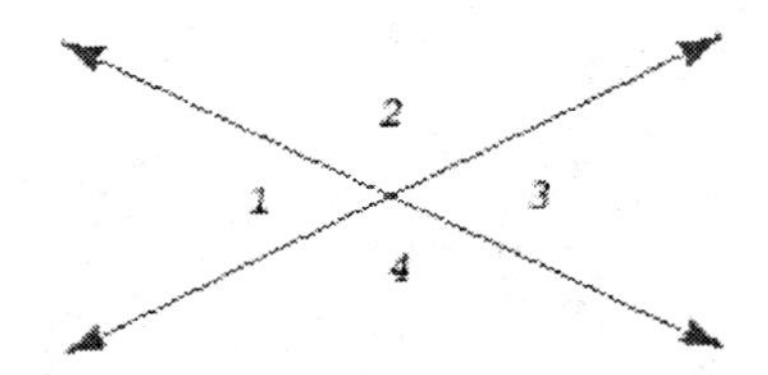

( ) 15
( ) 75
( ) 165

5. In the figure below, find the pair of alternate interior angles.

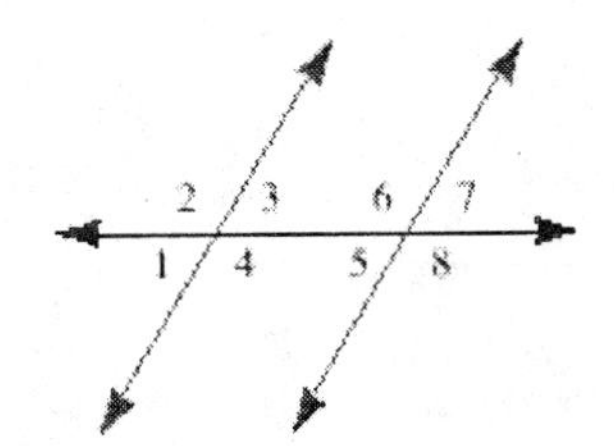

( ) $\angle 7$ and $\angle 2$
( ) $\angle 5$ and $\angle 1$
( ) $\angle 4$ and $\angle 6$

6. In the figure below, l_1 is parallel to l_2 with $\angle 4 = 103^\circ$ Find $\angle 2$.

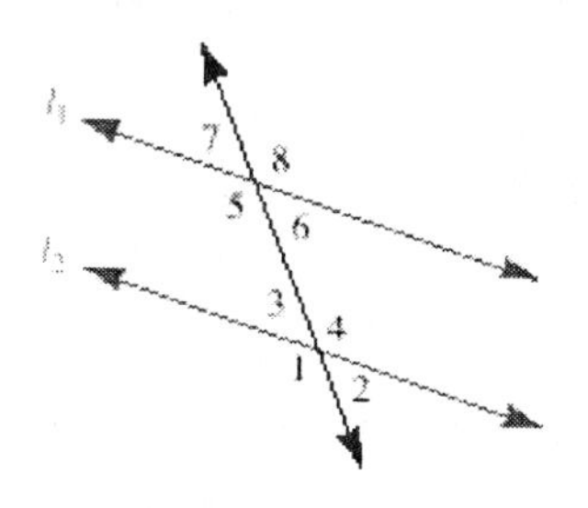

() 103°

() 77°

7. In the figure below, line AB is parallel to line DE. Find $\angle B$, if $\angle a = 27^\circ$ and $\angle b = 63^\circ$.

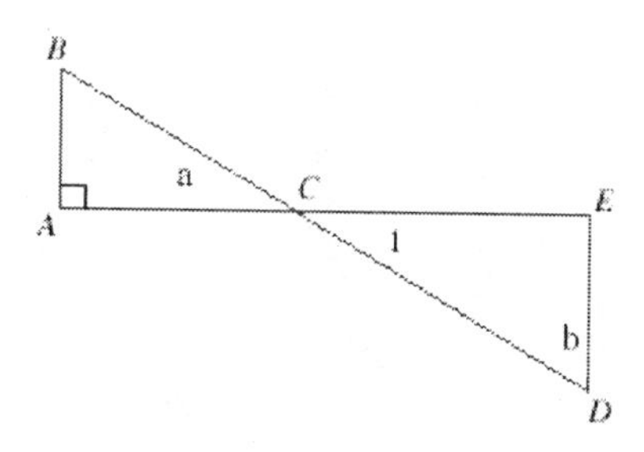

() 63°

() 90°

() 27°

8. In the figure below, l_1 is parallel with l_2. Find x, if $a= 4$, $b= -2$, $c= 3$ and $d= 3$.

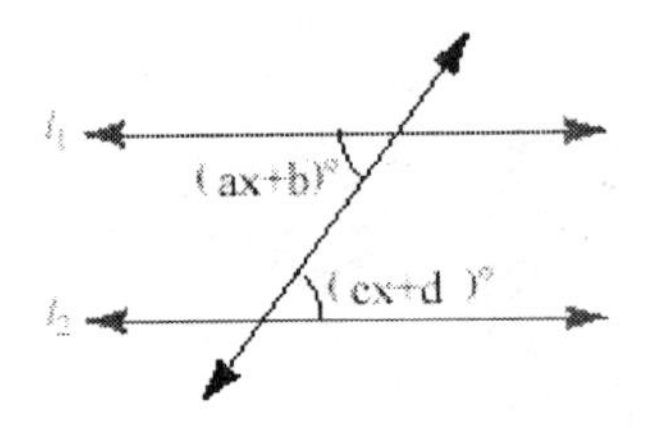

( ) 5°

( ) 175°

9. How many sides does the following polygon have? Choose the answer from below.

( ) 15
( ) 16
( ) 3

10. Find $\angle 2$ if

$\angle 1 = 33^{\circ}$.

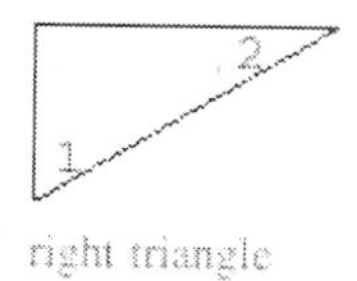

right triangle

Choose your answer from below.

( ) 57°

( ) 58°

( ) 33°

11. Find d if a = 49.

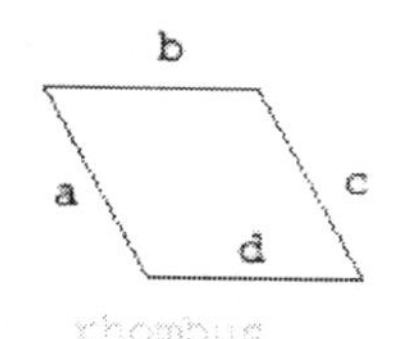

rhombus

Choose your answer from below.

( ) 49cm
( ) 59cm
( ) 44cm

12. Refer to the rectangle ABCD, shown below, where $m(\angle 4) = 38^\circ$. Choose the correct statement.

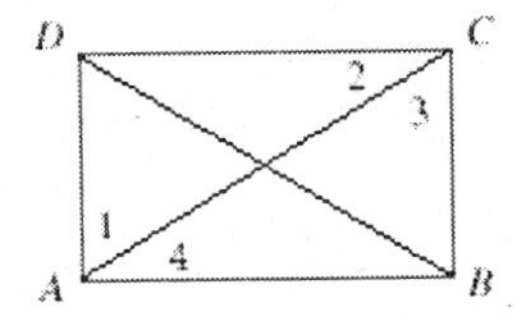

( ) $m(\angle 1) = 52^\circ$, $m(\angle 2) = 52^\circ$ and $m(\angle 3) = 38^\circ$.
( ) $m(\angle 1) = 38^\circ$, $m(\angle 2) = 38^\circ$ and $m(\angle 3) = 52^\circ$.
( ) $m(\angle 1) = 52^\circ$, $m(\angle 2) = 38^\circ$ and $m(\angle 3) = 52^\circ$.
( ) $m(\angle 1) = 38^\circ$, $m(\angle 2) = 52^\circ$ and $m(\angle 3) = 38^\circ$.

13. The angle*a*shown in the illustration is 48°. Find*b*, if the two triangles are similar. Choose your answer from below.

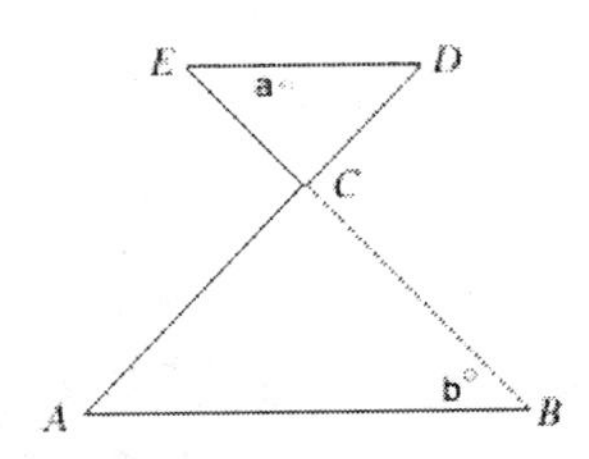

( ) 96°
( ) 48°
( ) 24°

14. Find x, if a= 8 and b= 10. Choose the answer from below.

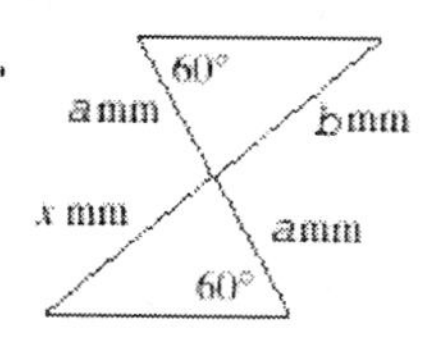

( ) 60
( ) 2
( ) 8
( ) 10

15. If segment DE in the illustration is parallel to segment AB, then $\triangle ABC$ is similar to $\triangle DEC$. Assuming this is the case, find x if a= 50 , b= 35 , and c= 10. Choose the answer from below.

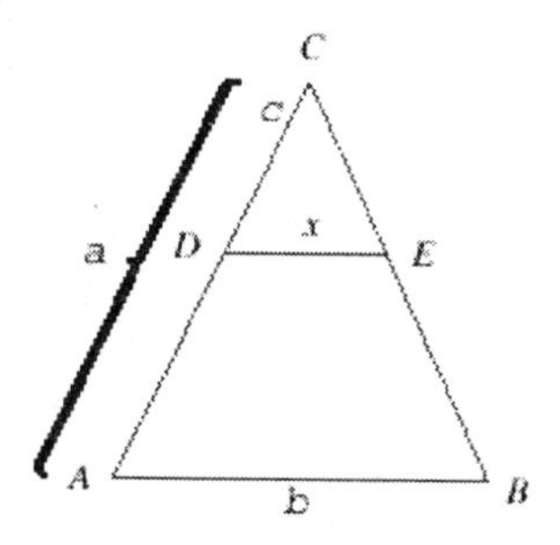

( ) 7

( ) $\frac{7}{100}$

( ) $\frac{100}{7}$

( ) $\frac{1}{7}$

16. Find the perimeter of the figure if $a = 14$. Select the correct answer.

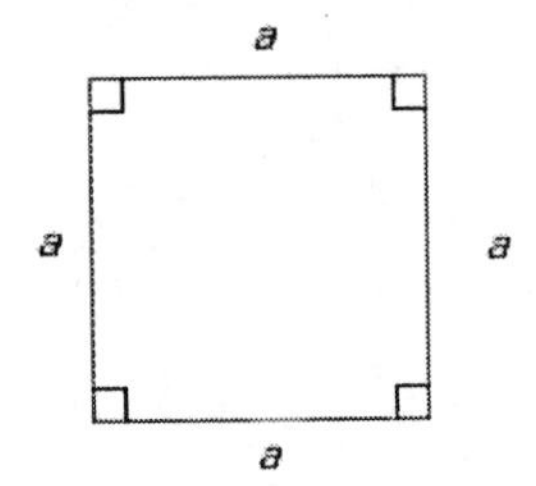

( ) 196
( ) 28
( ) 56

17. Find the area of the shaded part of the figure if $a = 6$, $b = 7$. Select the correct answer.

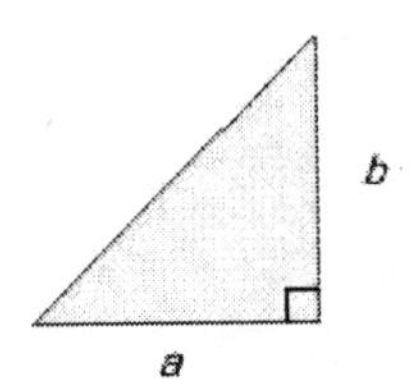

( ) 84
( ) 13
( ) 21

18. What is a segment drawn from the center of a circle to a point on the circle called?

( ) chord
( ) radius
( ) diameter

19. Suppose the two "legs" of the compass shown in the illustration are adjusted so that the distance between the pointed ends is 9 inches. What will the area of the circle be, if $\pi = 3.14$?

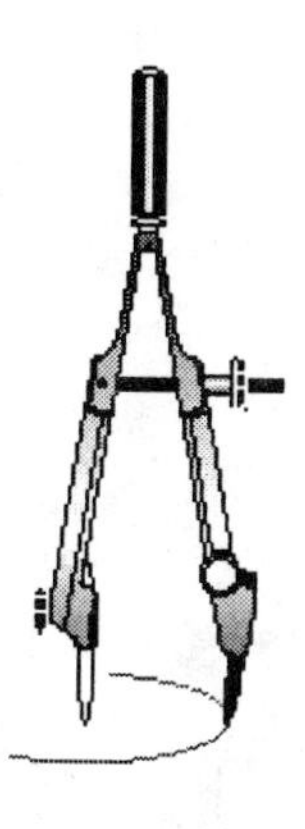

( ) 254.34
( ) 18
( ) 56.52

20. Find the radius of a circle that has a circumference of 16π meters.

( ) 16 m
( ) 32 m
( ) 25.12 m
( ) 8 m

21. Find the total area of the figure to the nearest tenth, if $\pi = 3.14$, b= 8 cm and$a$= 6 cm.

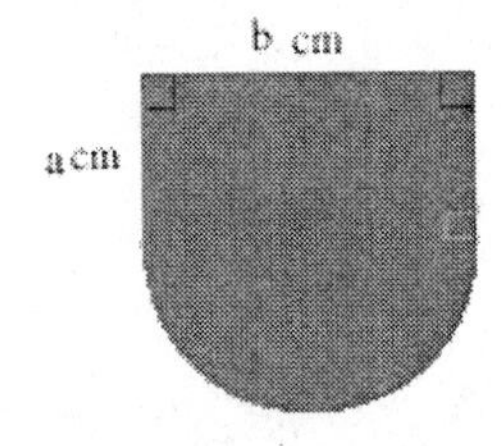

( ) 73.12 cm
( ) 98.24 cm
( ) 48 cm

22. The rotunda at a state capitol is a circular area 100 feet in diameter. The legislature wishes to appropriate money to have the floor of the rotunda tiled. The lowest bid is $95 per square yard, including installation.
How much must the legislature spend to tile the floor?

( ) $745750.00
( ) $331444.44
( ) $20715.28
( ) $82861.11

23. Find the volume of a rectangular solid with dimensions of 9 by 2 by 8 centimeters.

( ) 212 cm^3
( ) 144 cm^3
( ) 19 cm^3

24. Find the volume of a sphere with a radius of 2 inches.

( ) 100.48 $in.^3$
( ) 16.75 $in.^3$
( ) 10.67 $in.^3$
( ) 33.49 $in.^3$

25. Find the surface area of a rectangular solid with dimensions of 10 by 10 by 9 centimeters.

( ) 562 cm^2
( ) 560 cm^2
( ) 280 cm^2

Answers

1. *AGC*

2. 48

3. 36

4. 165

5. $\angle 4$ and $\angle 6$

6. 77°

7. 63°

8. 5°

9. 3

10. 57°

11. 49cm

12. $m(\angle 1) = 52^\circ$, $m(\angle 2) = 38^\circ$ and $m(\angle 3) = 52^\circ$.

13. 48°

14. 10

15. 7

16. 56

17. 21

18. radius

19. 254.34

20. 8 m

21. 73.12 cm

22. $82861.11

23. $144\ cm^3$

24. $33.49\ in.^3$

25. $560\ cm^2$

1. $\angle c$ and $\angle b$ are complementary angles. What is their sum?

( ) 180°
( ) 90°
( ) 360°

2. In the figure below *a*= 6, *b*= 5, and *c*= 22. What is the measure of angle *y*.

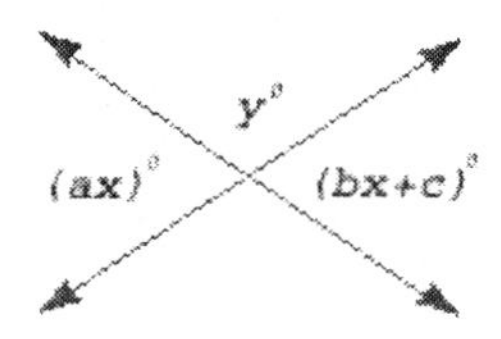

( ) 112
( ) 22
( ) 48

3. Which of the following angles are supplementary?

[ ] $88^{o}$and 2°
[ ] $20.5^{o}$and 159.5^{o}
[ ] $57^{o}$and 123°
[ ] $49^{o}$and 41°

4. In the figure below, choose the pair of corresponding angles.

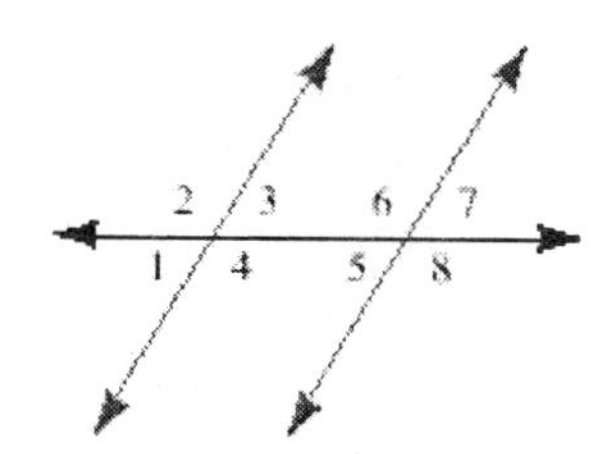

( ) $\angle 2$ and $\angle 1$
( ) $\angle 8$ and $\angle 5$
( ) $\angle 1$ and $\angle 5$

5. Using the figure below, find $\angle 6$ if l_1 is parallel to l_2 with $\angle 2 = 20^\circ$

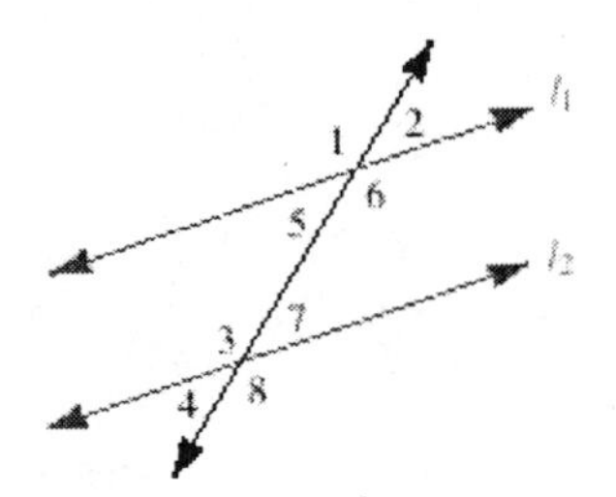

( ) 20°

( ) 160°

6. In the figure below, line AB is parallel to line DE. Find x, if $a = 5, b = -4, c = 3$ and $d = 6$.

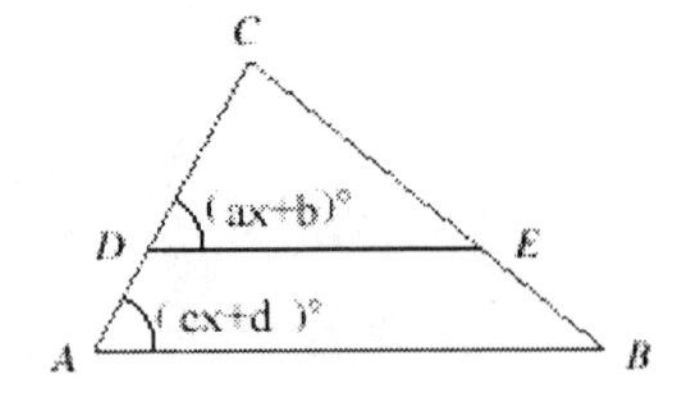

( ) 5°

( ) 85°

7. Find

$\angle 2$ if $\angle 1 = 56^{\circ}$

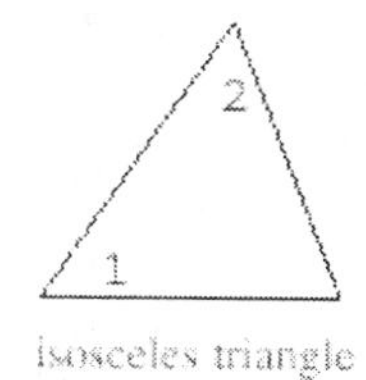

Choose your answer from below.

( ) 56°

( ) 57°

( ) 34°

8. Classify the following polygons:

1.

2.

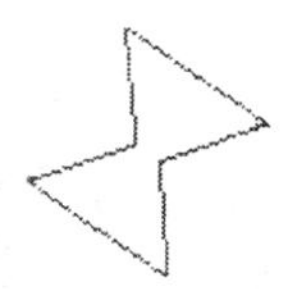

3.

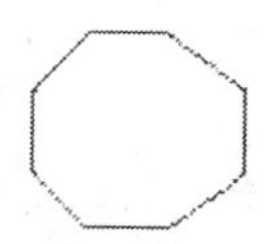

4.

5.

Choose your answer from below.

( ) Picture 1: quadrilateral; picture 2: pentagon; picture 3: octagon; picture 4: triangle and picture 5: hexagon.
( ) Picture 1: octagon; picture 2: hexagon; picture 3: quadrilateral; picture 4: triangle and picture 5: pentagon.
( ) Picture 1: quadrilateral; picture 2: octagon; picture 3: hexagon; picture 4: triangle and picture 5: pentagon.
( ) Picture 1: quadrilateral; picture 2: hexagon; picture 3: octagon; picture 4: triangle and picture 5: pentagon.
( ) Picture 1: quadrilateral; picture 2: triangle; picture 3: octagon; picture 4: hexagon and picture 5: pentagon.

9. Find $\overline{AB}$ if $\overline{AC} = 54$.

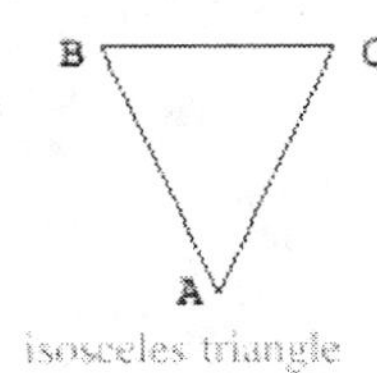

Choose the answer from below.

( ) 64cm
( ) 49cm
( ) 54cm

10. Refer to the illustration below to find $m(\overline{BD})$, if $m(\overline{AC}) = 9cm$.

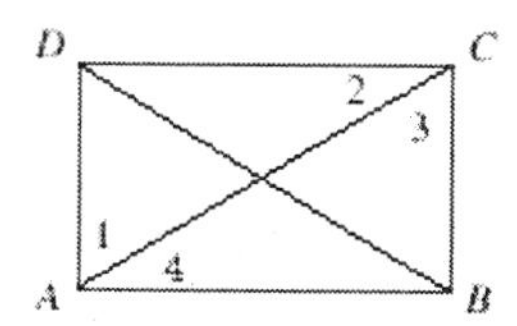

Choose the answer from below.

( ) 18 cm
( ) 9 cm
( ) 4.5 cm
( ) 7 cm

11. The angle*a*shown in the illustration is 44°. Find*b*, if the two triangles are similar. Choose your answer from below.

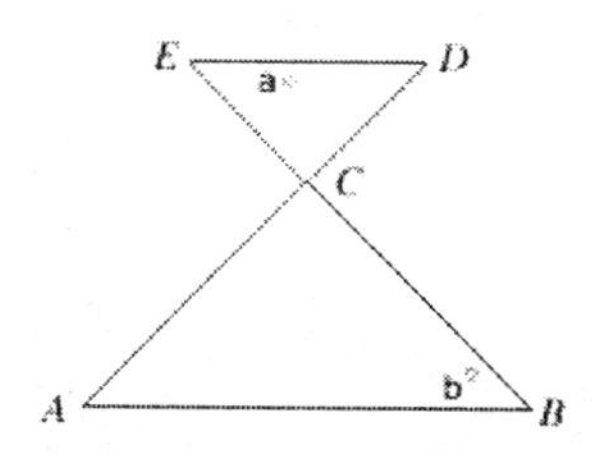

( ) 44°
( ) 88°
( ) 22°

12. The angles of the triangles shown in the illustration are $a = 52^{\circ}, b = 52^{\circ}$. The triangles are congruent because of what property?

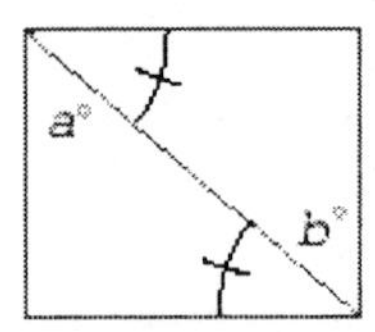

Choose the answer from below.

( ) SAS property
( ) ASA property
( ) SSS property

13. Find x if $a = 8, b = 15$, and $c = 17$. Choose the answer from below.

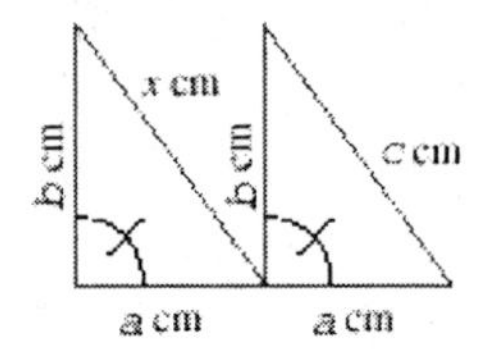

( ) 23
( ) 8
( ) 17
( ) 15

14. The airplane in the illustration ascends c = 700 feet as it flies a horizontal distance b = 3000 feet. How much altitude is gained as it flies a horizontal distance of a = 4 mi? Choose the answer from below.

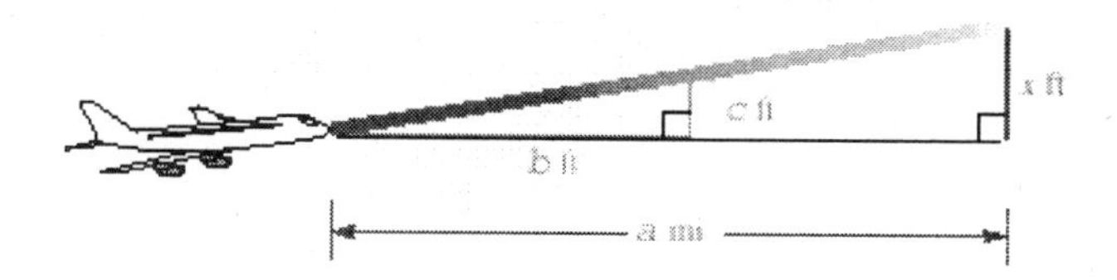

( ) $\frac{1}{4928}$

( ) 4928

( ) $\frac{1}{905.142857}$

( ) 905.142857

15. What size is the television screen shown in the illustration? Find d if a = 8 and b = 15. Choose the answer from below.

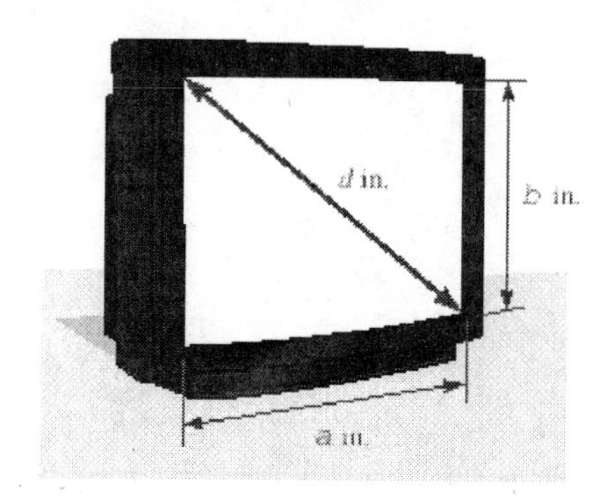

( ) 23

( ) $\sqrt{23}$

( ) $\sqrt{514}$

( ) 17

16. Find the perimeter of the figure if $a = 9, b = 8, c = 2$. Select the correct answer.

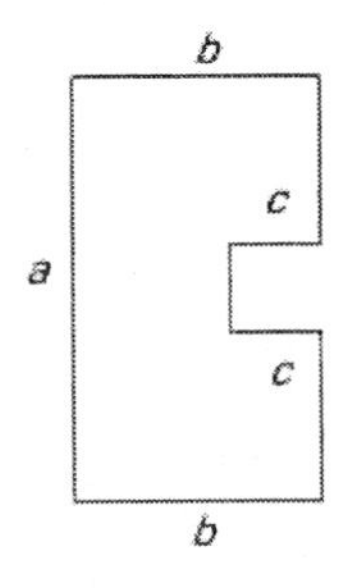

( ) 38
( ) 30
( ) 36

17. Find the area of the shaded part of the figure if $a = 6, b = 7, c = 3$. Select the correct answer.

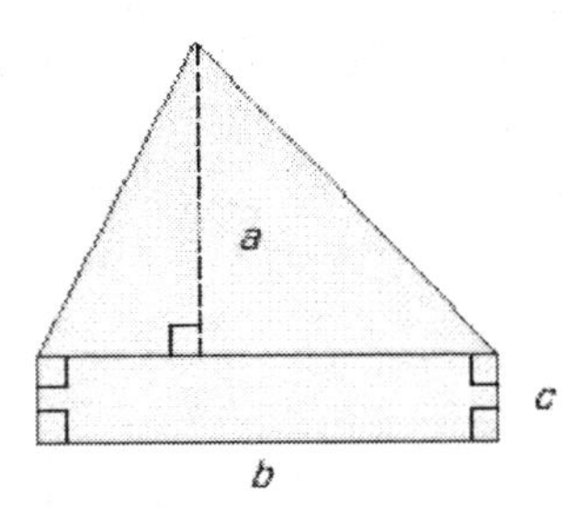

( ) 60
( ) 23
( ) 42

18. A rectangular living room measures 9 by 12 feet. At $29 per square yard, how much will it cost to carpet the room?

( ) $203
( ) $1044
( ) $348

19. What is an arc that is longer than a semicircle called?

( ) minor arc
( ) major arc
( ) chord
( ) semicircle

20. To the nearest hundredth, find the circumference of a circle that has a diameter of 15 inches, if $\pi = 3.14$.

( ) 47.115 in.
( ) 47.1 in.
( ) 61.95 in.
( ) 471 in.

21. Find the perimeter of the figure to the nearest hundredth, if $\pi = 3.14$, a= 11 m and b= 4 m.

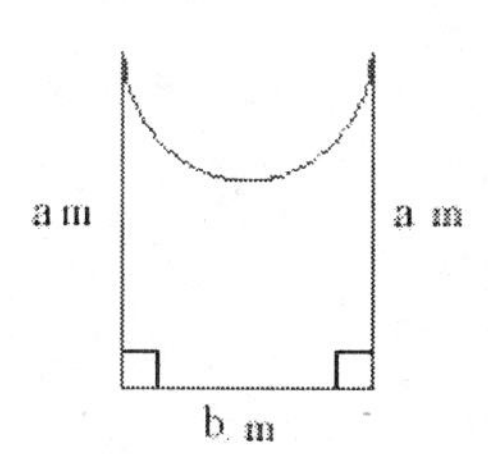

( ) 32.28 m
( ) 50.28 m
( ) 19.72 m
( ) 28.28 m

22. Joan wants to jog 14 miles on a circular track $\frac{1}{6}$ mile in diameter.

How many times must she circle the track?

( ) 13.38
( ) 26.75
( ) 4.46
( ) 53.50
( ) 1.49

23. Find the volume of a prism whose base is a right triangle with legs 9 and 6 meters long and whose height is 7 meters.

( ) 189 m^3
( ) 54 m^3
( ) 378 m^3

24. Find the volume of the figure if a= 3 cm, b= 6 cm.

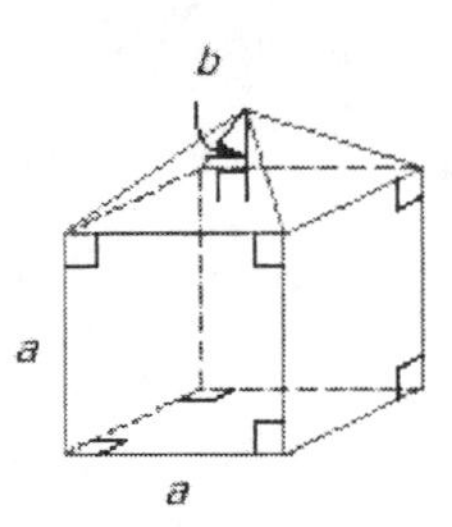

( ) 45 cm^3
( ) 27 cm^3
( ) 72 cm^3

25. A restaurant serves pudding in a conical dish that has a diameter of 9 inches. If the dish is 3 inches deep, how many cubic inches of pudding are in each dish?

() 381.78 $in.^3$

() 63.63 $in.^3$

() 763.56 $in.^3$

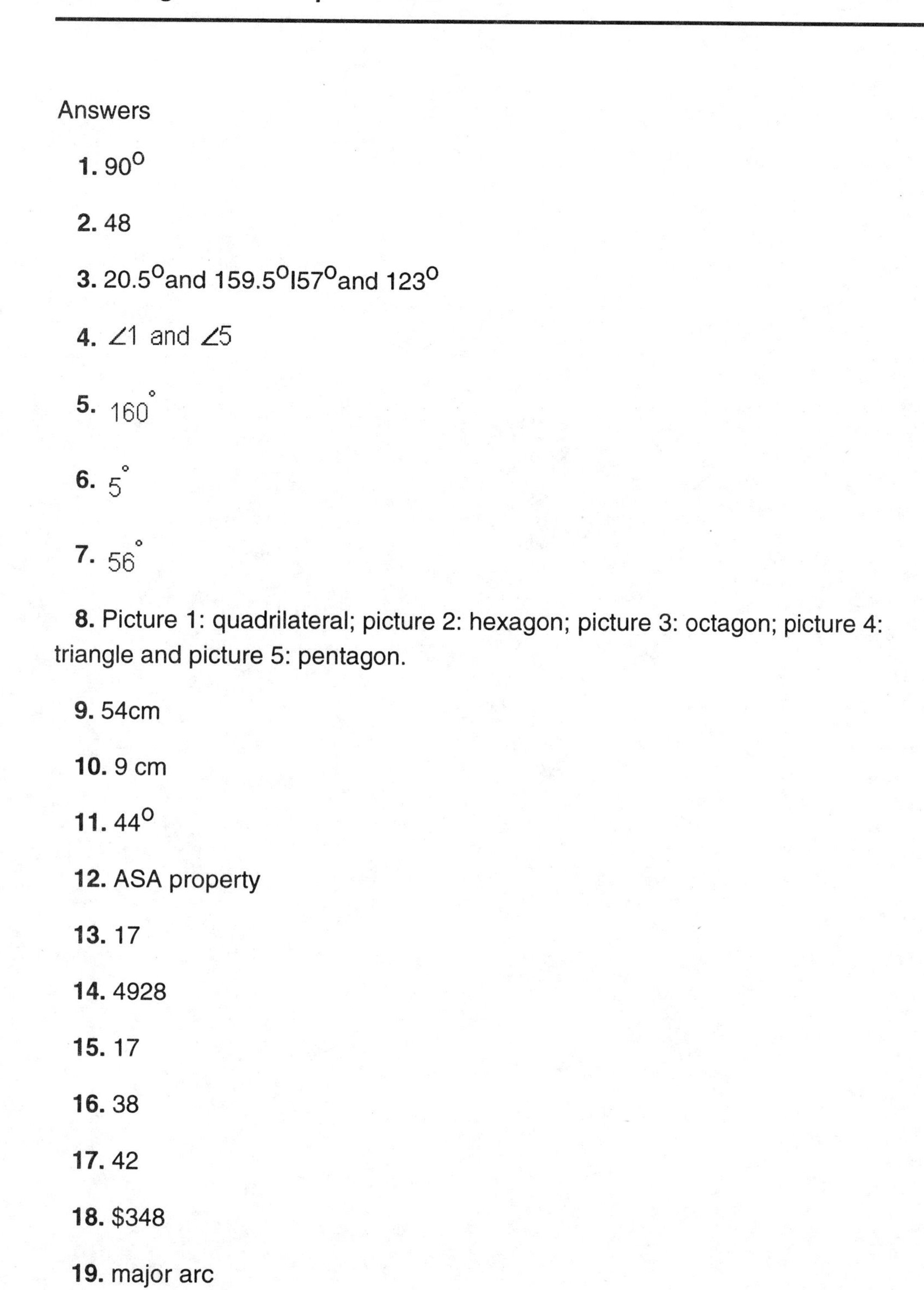

Answers

1. 90°

2. 48

3. $20.5^{\circ}$and $159.5^{\circ}157^{\circ}$and 123°

4. $\angle 1$ and $\angle 5$

5. 160°

6. 5°

7. 56°

8. Picture 1: quadrilateral; picture 2: hexagon; picture 3: octagon; picture 4: triangle and picture 5: pentagon.

9. 54cm

10. 9 cm

11. 44°

12. ASA property

13. 17

14. 4928

15. 17

16. 38

17. 42

18. $348

19. major arc

20. 47.1 in.

21. 32.28 m

22. 26.75

23. 189 m^3

24. 45 cm^3

25. 63.63 $in.^3$

1. A man places a mirror on the ground and sees the reflection of the top of a building, as shown in the illustration. Find the height of the man,*a*, if *b*= 24,*c*= 152, and*h*= 38.

Choose the answer from below.

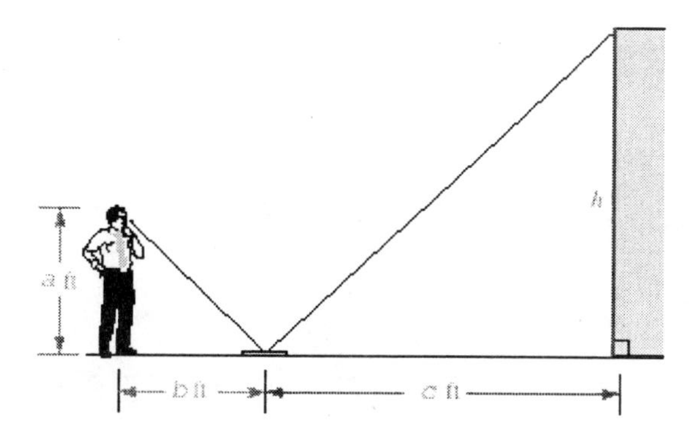

( ) $\frac{722}{3}$
( ) $\frac{1}{6}$
( ) 44
( ) 6

2. Find*c*if*a*= 40.

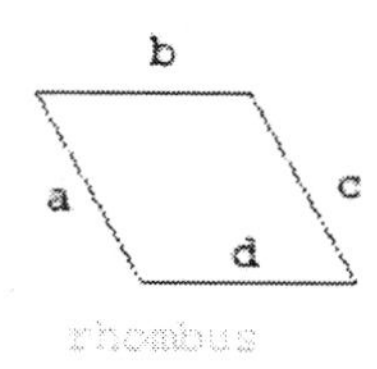

Choose your answer from below.

( ) 35cm
( ) 40cm
( ) 50cm

3. Using the figure below, find $\angle 6$ if l_1 is parallel to l_2 with $\angle 2 = 23^\circ$

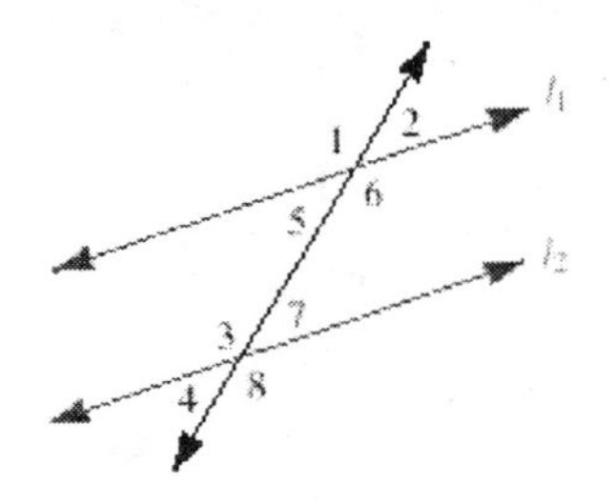

( ) 23°

( ) 157°

4. Find the area of the shaded part of the figure if $a = 5, b = 6$. Select the correct answer.

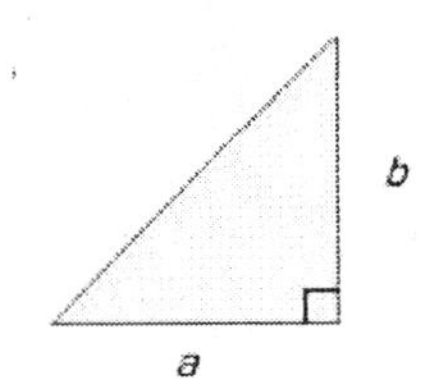

( ) 60
( ) 11
( ) 15

5. The triangles shown in the illustration are congruent. The sides of the triangles shown in the illustration are a= 8, b= 14, c= 8. True or False? d= 14.

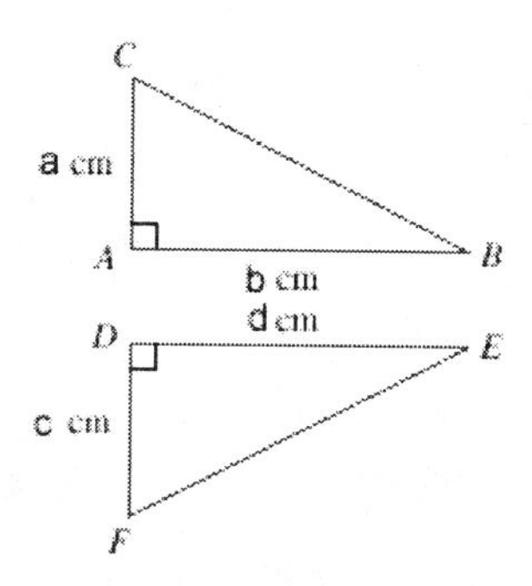

( ) True
( ) False

6. $\angle e$ and $\angle b$ are complementary angles. What is their sum?

( ) 90°
( ) 360°
( ) 180°

7. Find the volume of the figure if a= 16 cm, b= 5 cm.

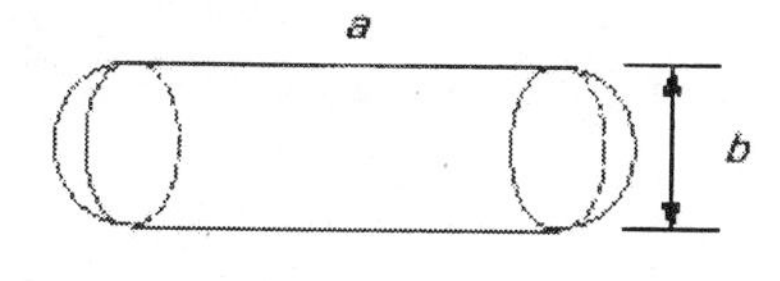

8. In the figure below angle a = 24°. What is the measure of anglex.

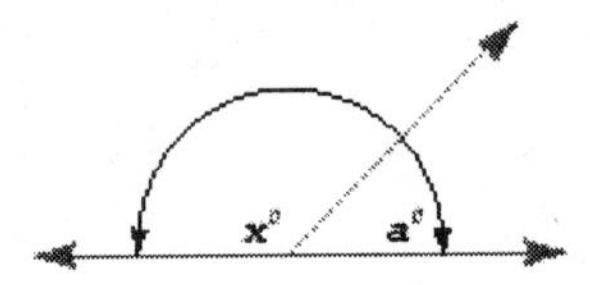

9. Find the volume of a cylinder with a height of 10 meters and a circular base with a radius of 10 meters.

10. How many interior angles are shown in the figure below?

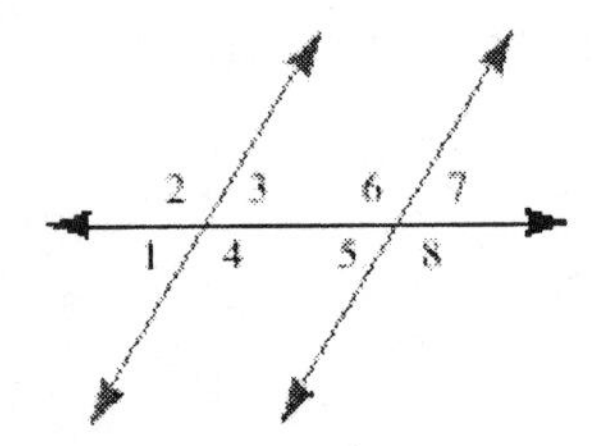

11. A classroom is 19 feet long, 7 feet wide, and 8 feet high. Find the number of cubic feet of air in the room.

( ) 34 ft^3

( ) 136 ft^3

( ) 1064 ft^3

12. The two triangles shown in the illustration are congruent. Find b, if angle a is 60°.

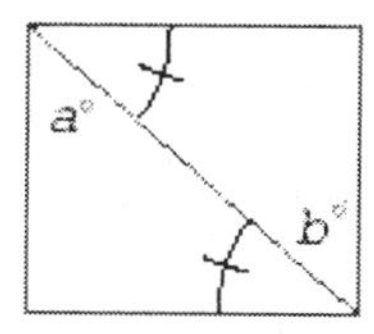

13. In the figure below, line AC is parallel to line BD. Find x, if $a = 6$, $b = -9$, $c = 3$ and $d = 12$.

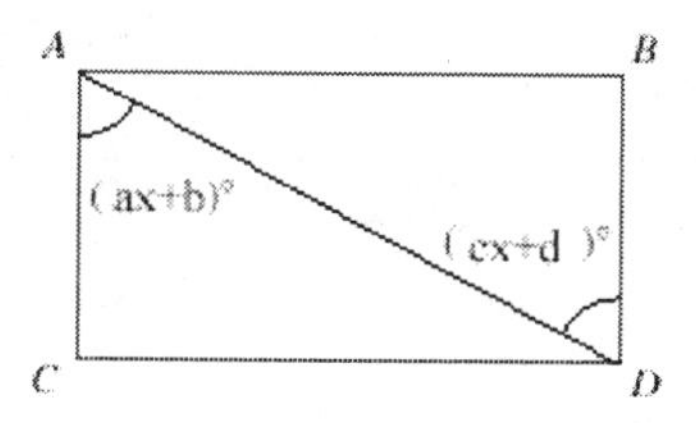

( ) 7°

( ) 53°

14. Find the area of the shaded part of the figure if $a = 7$, $b = 8$, $c = 2$.

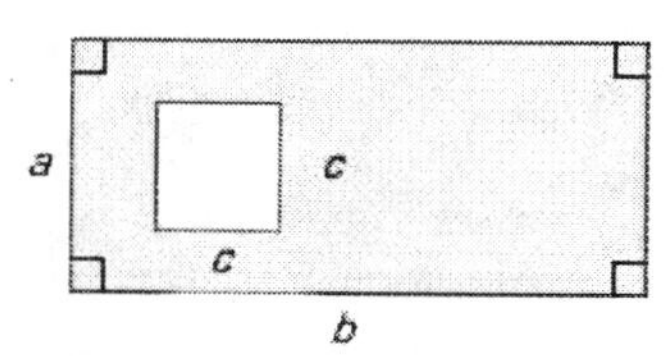

15. Find the total area of the shaded figure.

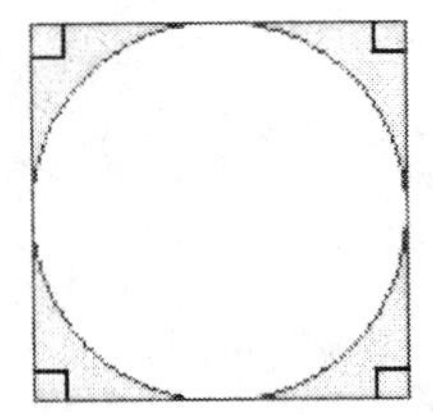

The side of the square is equal to 12.

( ) 113.1
( ) 1614.9
( ) 30.9
( ) 115.7

16. Match the sides of a right triangle with the lengths of the sides.

Least Leg	17
Hypotenuse	15
Greatest Leg	8

17. Look at the illustration. Find $m(\angle 2)$ if $m(\angle 1) = 59^{\circ}$

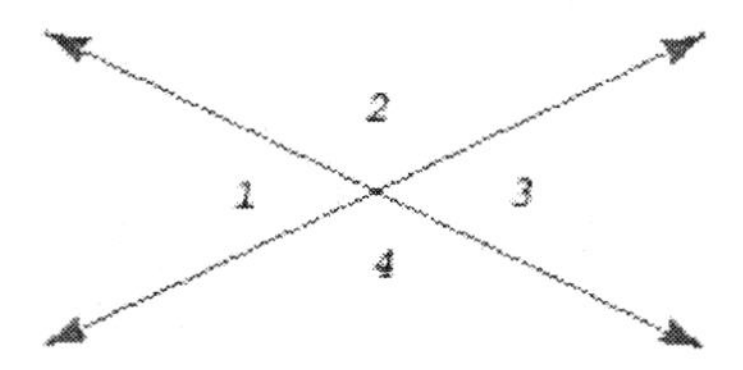

( ) 121
( ) 59
( ) 31

18. Find the perimeter of the figure to the nearest hundredth, if $\pi = 3.14$, *a*= 5 in. and *b*= 6 in.

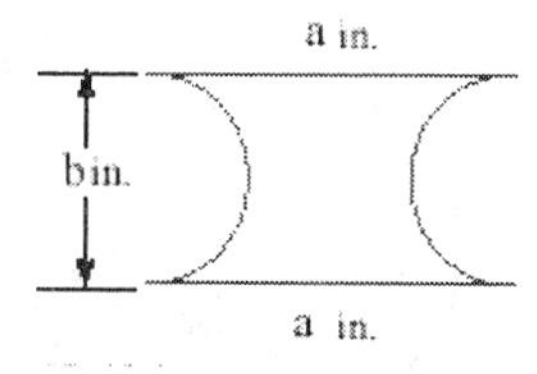

19. In the figure below, line AB is parallel to line DE. Find *x*, if *a*= 7, *b*= -8, *c*= 3 and *d*= 12.

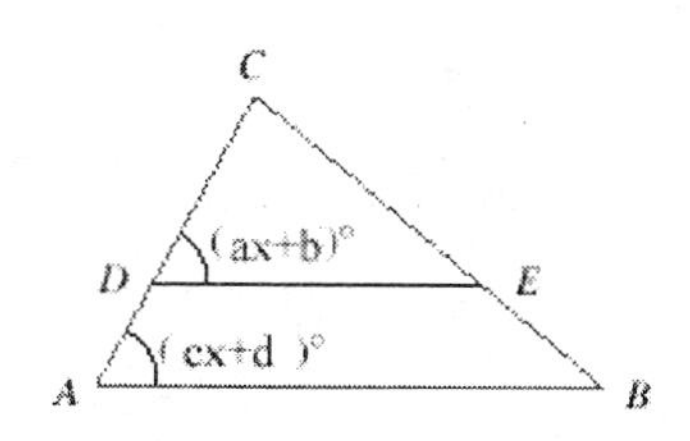

20. Find the perimeter of the figure if $a = 6$.

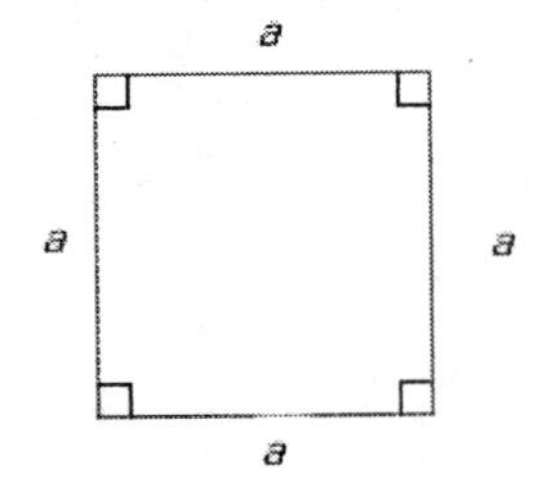

21. Find

$\angle 2$ if $\angle 1 = 59^\circ$

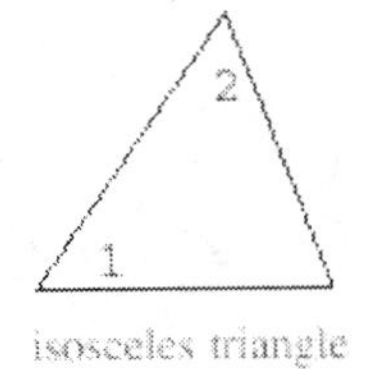

isosceles triangle

Choose your answer from below.

( ) 60°

( ) 31°

( ) 59°

22. Round π to the nearest hundredth.

23. In the figure below *a* = 47. How many degrees from the horizontal position are the wings of the airplane?

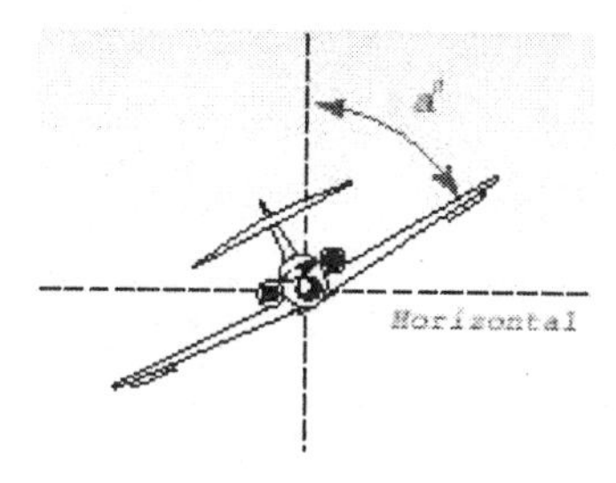

24. Refer to the illustration below to find $m(\overline{BD})$, if $m(\overline{AC}) = 14\text{cm}$.

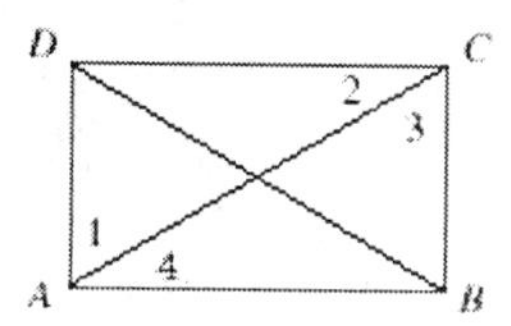

25. Refer to the illustration. How far does a point on the tip of a rotor blade travel when it makes one complete revolution?

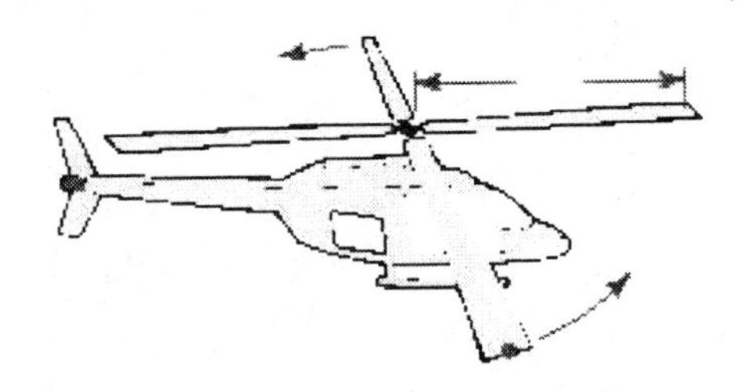

The length of the blade is equal to 21 feet.

( ) 1384.74 ft
( ) 65.94 ft
( ) 2769.48 ft
( ) 131.88 ft

Answers

1. 6

2. 40cm

3. 157°

4. 15

5. true

6. 90°

7. 379.42

8. 156

9. 3140.00

10. 4

11. 1064 ft^{3}

12. 60

13. 7°

14. 52

15. 30.9

16. Hypotenuse -> 17, Greatest Leg -> 15, Least Leg -> 8

17. 121

18. 28.84

19. 5

20. 24

21. 59°

22. 3.14

23. 43

24. 14

25. 131.88 ft

1. What is the sum of $\angle g$ and $\angle h$? They are complementary angles.

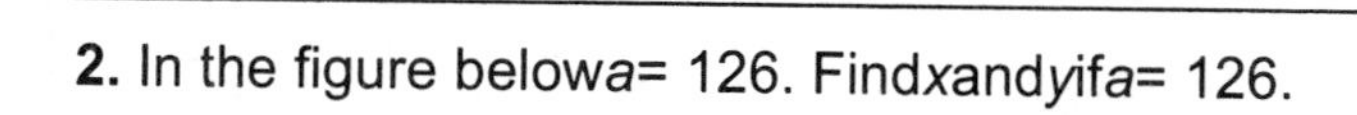

2. In the figure below*a*= 126. Find*x*and*y*if*a*= 126.

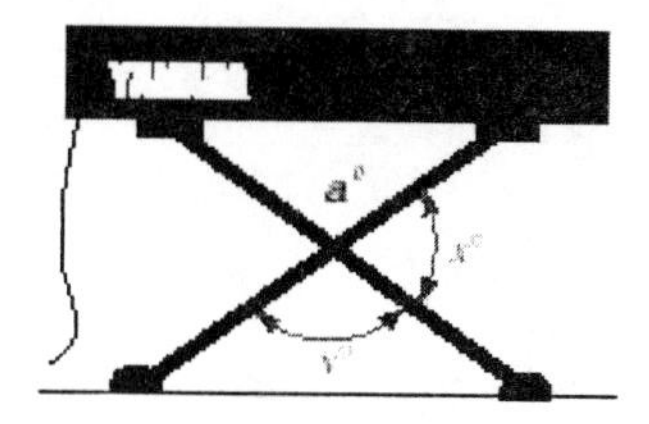

( ) *x*= 126,*y*= 54
( ) *x*= 54,*y*= 126
( ) *x*= 126,*y*= 126

3. In the figure below, find the corresponding angle that completes each pair.

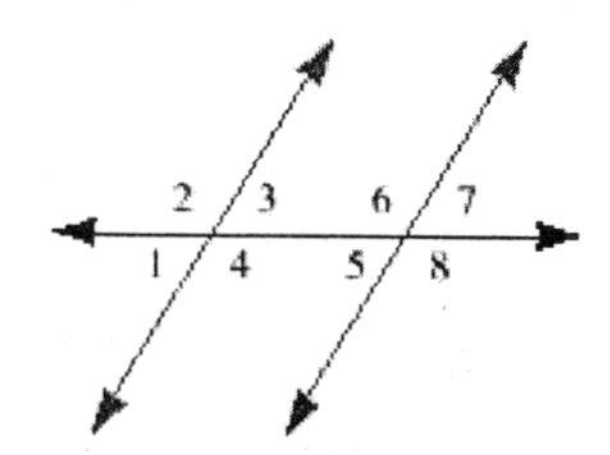

4	
2	

4. In the figure below, l_1 is parallel with l_2. Find x, if a= 5, b= -6, c= 2 and d= 9.

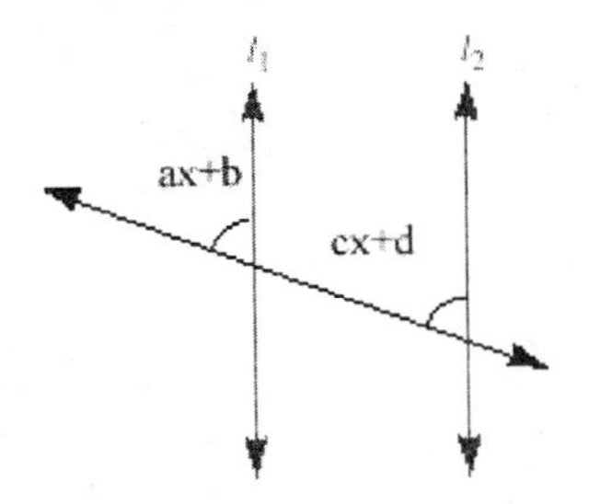

( ) 5°

( ) 175°

5. For many sign painters, the most difficult letter to paint is a capital *E*, because of all of the right angles involved. Look at the illustration carefully. How many right angles are there?

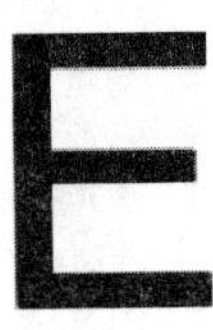

6. What is a triangle with three sides of equal length called? Select the answer from below.

( ) scalene
( ) right
( ) isosceles
( ) equilateral

7. Classify the following triangles:

1.

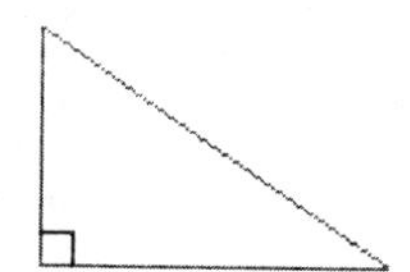

2.

3.

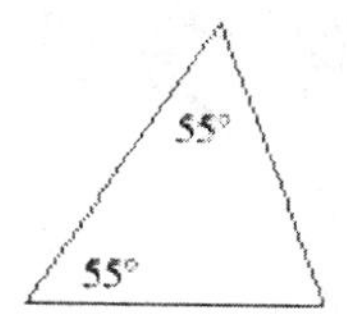

4.

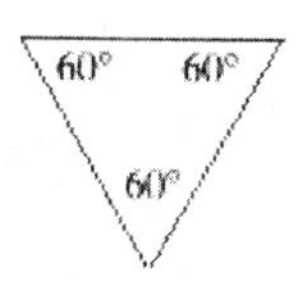

Picture 1	Right triangle
Picture 2	Equilateral triangle
Picture 4	Scalene triangle
Picture 3	Isosceles triangle

8. The measures of two angles of $\triangle ABC$ (shown in illustration) are given. Find the measure of the third angle, if

$m(\angle A) = 38^{\circ}$ and

$m(\angle B) = 73^{\circ}$.

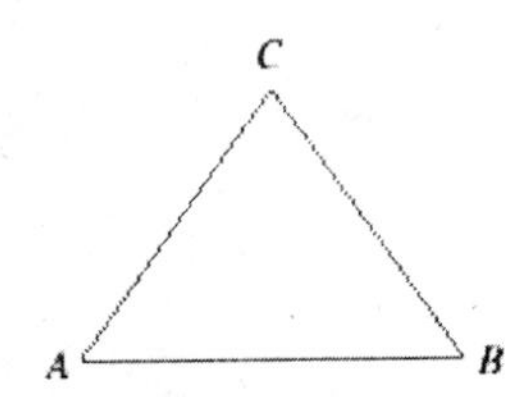

Choose the answer from below:

( ) 79°

( ) 249°

( ) 69°

( ) 68°

9. Find the sum of the angles in a polygon with 18 sides.

10. The angle*a*shown in the illustration is 34°. Find*b*, if the two triangles are similar. Choose your answer from below.

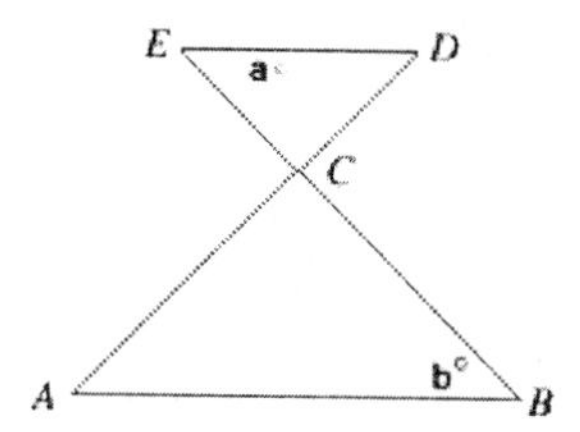

( ) 68°
( ) 17°
( ) 34°

11. Find*x*if*a*= 6,*b*= 8, and*c*= 10.

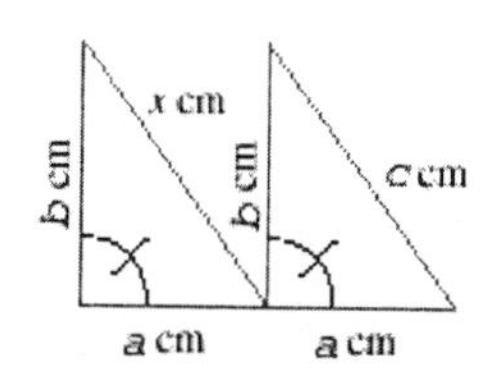

12. The lengths of the three sides of a triangle are given. Determine whether the triangle is a right triangle (true) or not (false).
a= 8,*b*= 15,*c*= 17.

( ) True
( ) False

13. If segmentDEin the illustration is parallel to segmentAB, then $\triangle ABC$ is similar to $\triangle DEC$. Assuming this is the case, find$x$if$a$= 80 ,b= 40 , and$c$= 24.

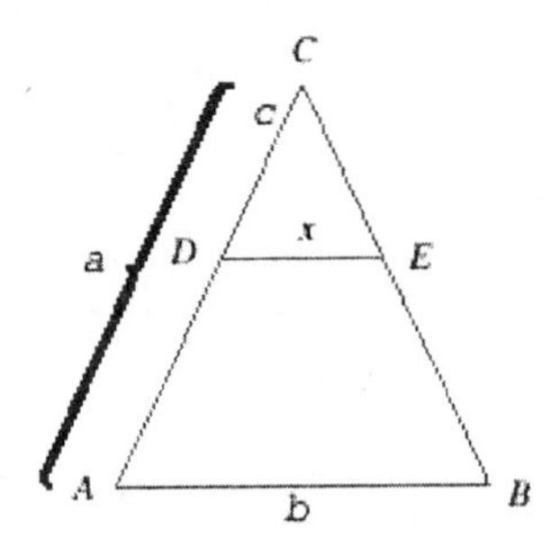

14. Find the perimeter of the figure if$a$= 10,b= 3,c= 2. Select the correct answer.

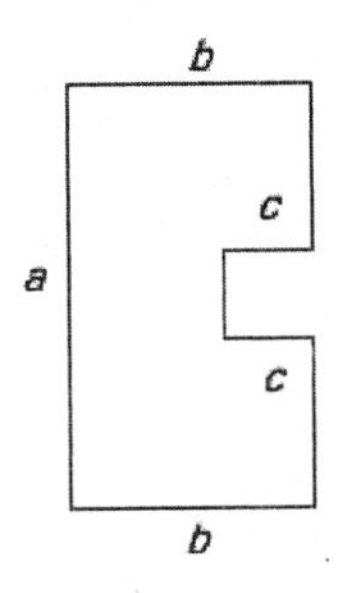

( ) 30
( ) 28
( ) 27

15. Find the area of the shaded part of the figure if $a = 18, b = 8$.

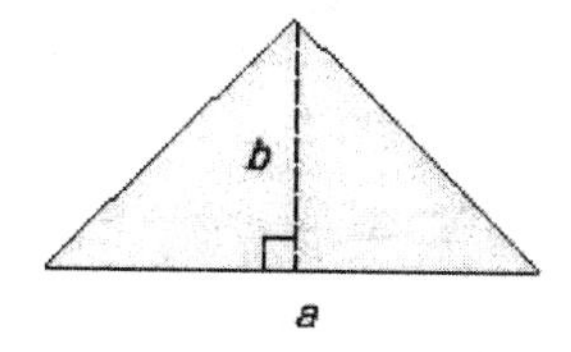

16. Find the area of the shaded part of the figure if $a = 6, b = 10, c = 4$. Select the correct answer.

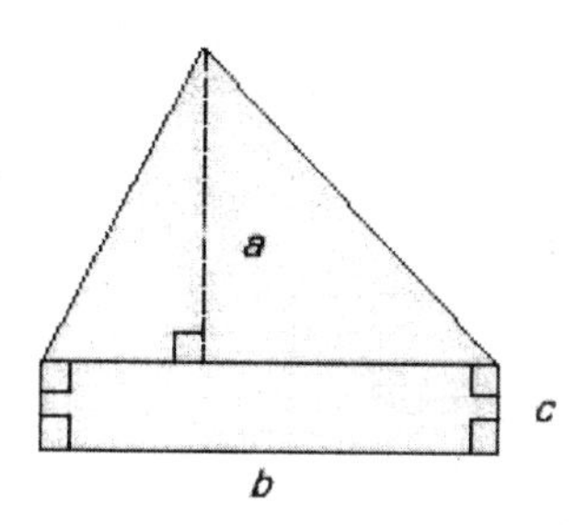

( ) 30
( ) 70
( ) 84

17. A rectangular living room measures 12 by 6 feet. At $34 per square yard, how much will it cost to carpet the room?

18. Find the radius of the circle, if the diameter is 10.

( ) 5
( ) 20
( ) 2.5

19. Find the perimeter of the figure to the nearest hundredth, if $\pi = 3.14$, a= 10 m and b= 4 m.

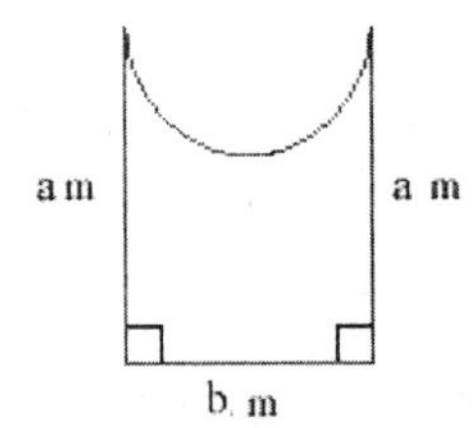

20. Find the total area of the figure and round answer to the nearest tenth.

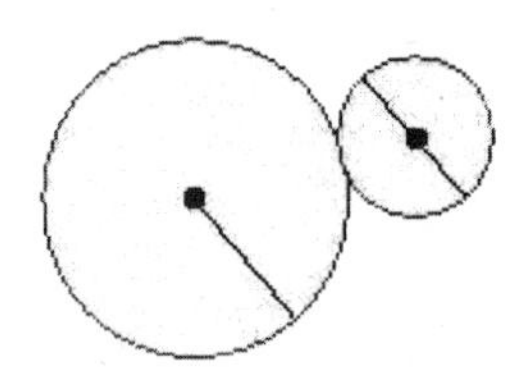

The radius of the larger circle is equal to the diameter of the smaller circle and is equal to 4.

( ) 50.3 $in.^2$
( ) 62.8 $in.^2$
( ) 100.5 $in.^2$
( ) 12.6 $in.^2$

21. Joan wants to jog 16 miles on a circular track $\frac{1}{2}$ mile in diameter. How many times, to the nearest hundredth, must she circle the track?

22. Find the volume of a prism whose base is a right triangle with legs 3 and 6 meters long and whose height is 2 meters.

( ) 18 m^3

( ) 18 m^3

( ) 36 m^3

23. Find the surface area of a cube with a side 10 centimeters long.

24. Find the volume of the figure if *a*= 60 in., *b*= 4 in..

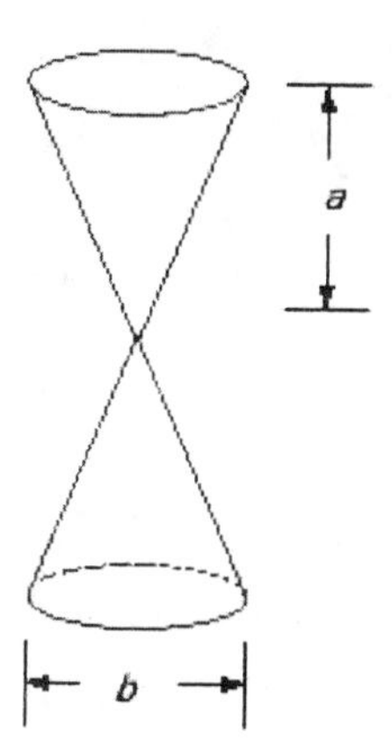

( ) 3014.40 $in.^3$

( ) 502.40 $in.^3$

( ) 160 $in.^3$

25. The lifting power of a spherical balloon depends on its volume. How many cubic feet of gas will a balloon hold if it is 6 feet in diameter? If an answer is not exact, round to the nearest hundredth.

Answers For

1. 90

2. $x = 54, y = 126$

3. 4, 8, 2, 6

4. 5°

5. 12

6. equilateral

7. Picture 1 -> Right triangle, Picture 2 -> Scalene triangle, Picture 3 -> Isosceles triangle, Picture 4 -> Equilateral triangle

8. 69°

9. 2880

10. 34°

11. 10

12. true

13. 12

14. 30

15. 72

16. 70

17. $272

18. 5

19. 30.28

20. 62.8 in.^2

21. 10.19

22. 18 m^3

23. 600

24. 502.40 $in.^3$

25. 113.04

1. Look at the illustration and match each angle with its type. $\angle 1 = 79^{\circ}$ and $\angle 2 = 11^{\circ}$.

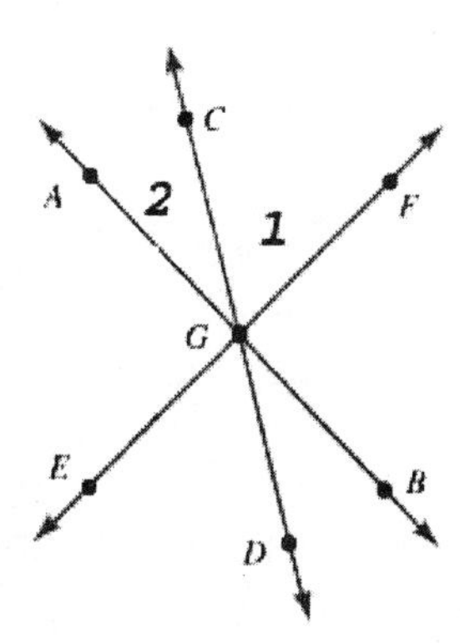

AGC	obtuse
FGD	acute
BGE	straight
BGA	right

2. Which of the following angles are supplementary?

[ ] $61^{\circ}$and 29°
[ ] $8^{\circ}$and 82°
[ ] $170^{\circ}$and 10°
[ ] $165^{\circ}$and 15°

3. In the figure below $m(\angle 1) = 53^\circ$

Find $m(\angle 2) + m(\angle 3) + m(\angle 4)$

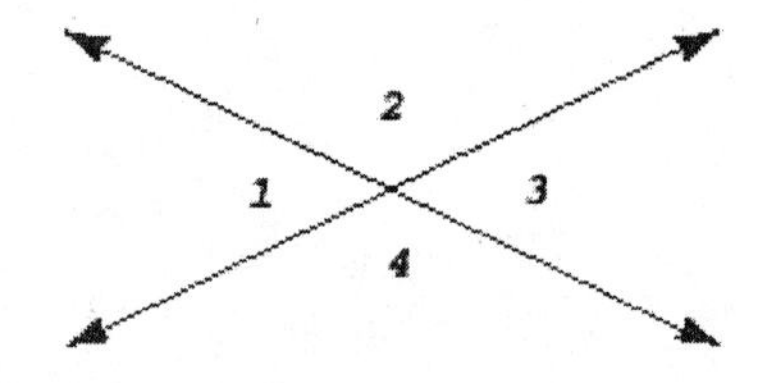

4. Which of the following angles cannot have a complement?

( ) 35°
( ) 95°
( ) 32°

5. In the figure below, match the corresponding statements.

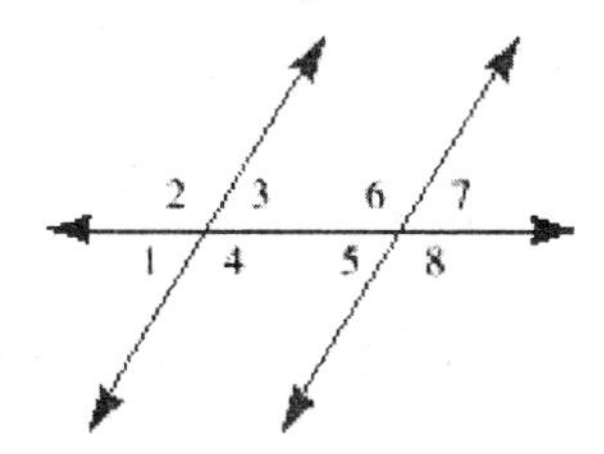

4 and 6	alternate interior angles
3 and 7	corresponding angles

6. Using the figure below, find $\angle 3$ if l_1 is parallel to l_2 with $\angle 2 = 21^\circ$

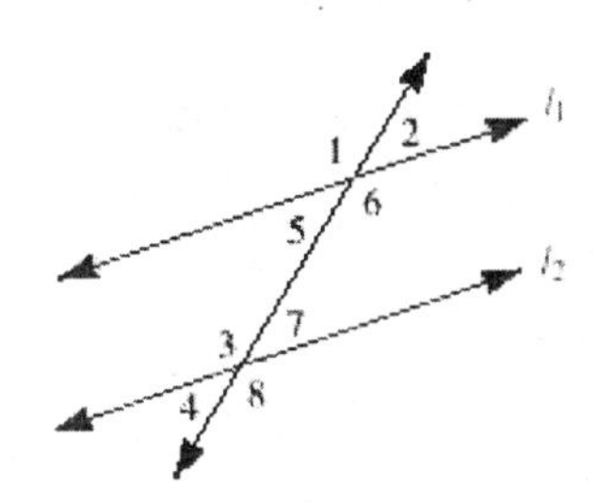

( ) 159°

( ) 21°

7. In the figure below, l_1 is parallel with l_2. Find x, if $a = 3$, $b = 2$ and $c = 34$.

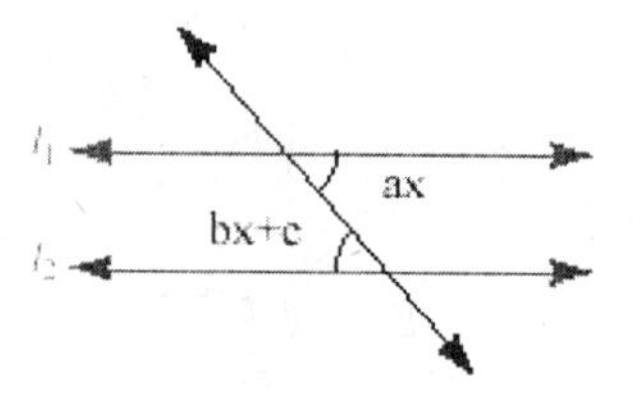

8. In the figure below, line AC is parallel to line BD. Find x, if $a = 6$, $b = -6$, $c = 3$ and $d = 15$.

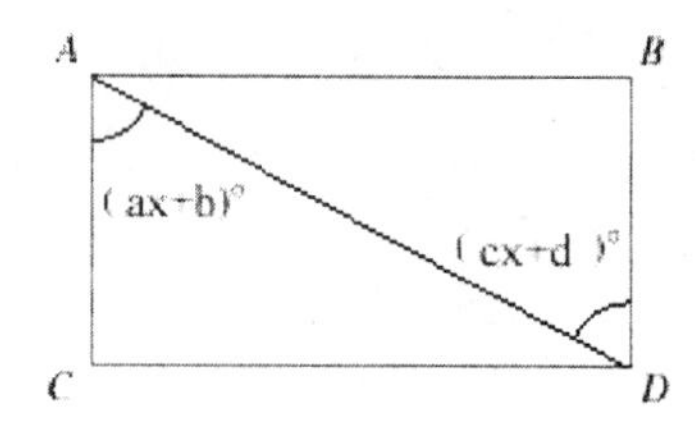

( ) 7°

( ) 53°

9. What is a triangle with exactly two angles of equal measure called?

10. Find $\angle 2$ if

$\angle 1 = 36^{\circ}$.

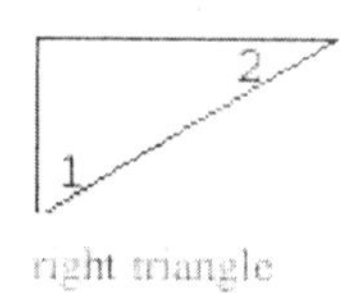

Choose your answer from below.

() 55°

() 54°

() 36°

11. Fill in the table by referring to the rectangle ABCD, shown below, where

$m(\angle 4) = 38^{\circ}$

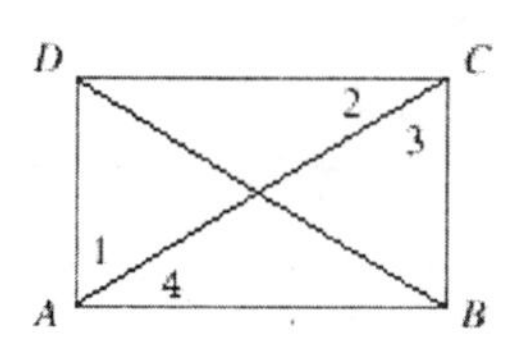

Angle	Measure
1	
2	
3	

12. How many sides does a polygon have if the sum of its angles is

1620°?

Choose the answer from below.

( ) 11 sides
( ) 9 sides
( ) 12 sides
( ) 15 sides

13. The triangles shown in the illustration are congruent. The sides of the triangles are $a = 9, b = 15, c = 9$. Find d.

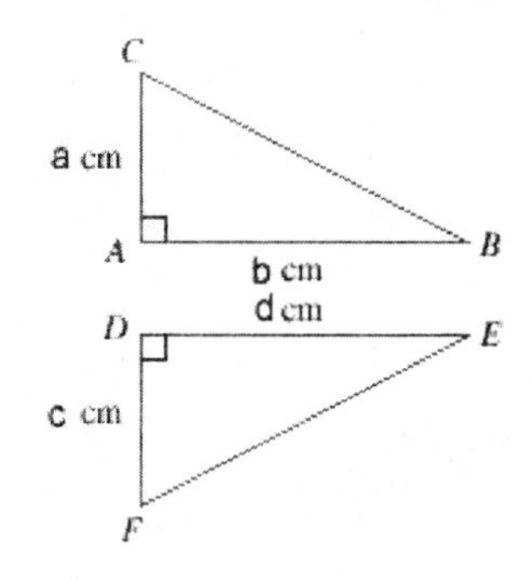

14. Find x if $a = 9, b = 11$, and $C = 40^{\circ}$. Choose the answer from below.

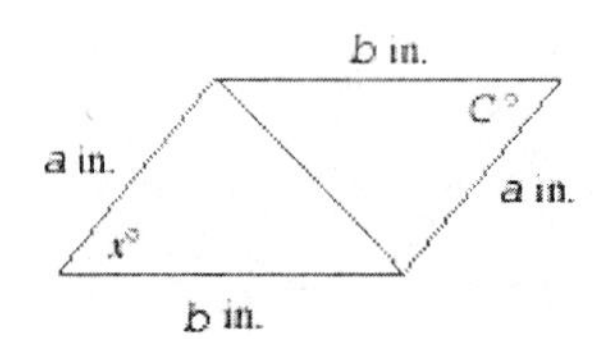

( ) 9°
( ) 40°
( ) 20°
( ) 140°
( ) 11°

15. The tree in the illustration casts a shadow c= 9 feet long while a person a= 4 feet tall casts a shadow b= 6 feet long. Find the height of the tree.

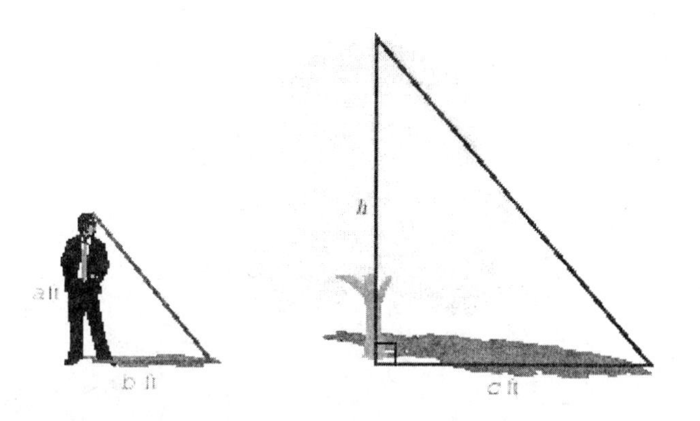

16. After joining two pieces of picture frame molding together, a frame maker checks her work by making a diagonal measurement (see the illustration). If the sides of the frame that form a right angle are a= 8 and b= 15, what measurement should the frame maker read on the yardstick? Choose the answer from below.

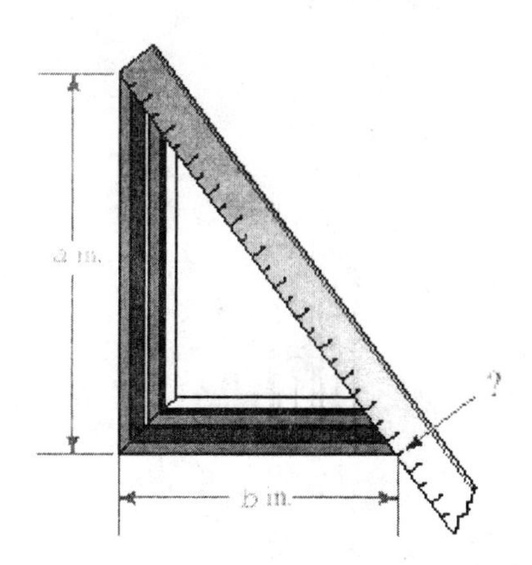

( ) 17
( ) 23
( ) $\sqrt{23}$
( ) $\sqrt{514}$

17. Find the perimeter of the figure if $a = 5$, $b = 3$.

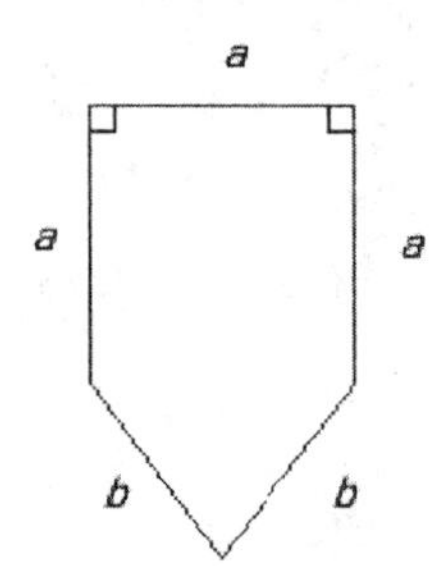

18. Find the area of the shaded part of the figure if $a = 7$, $b = 8$. Select the correct answer.

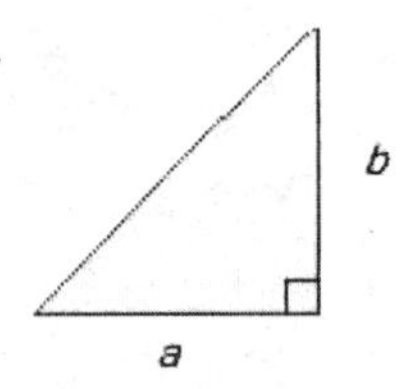

( ) 112
( ) 15
( ) 28

19. Find the area of the shaded part of the figure if $a = 8$, $b = 4$.

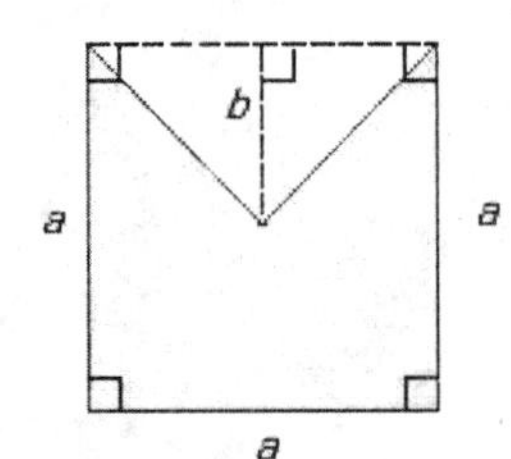

20. If nylon is $14 per square yard, how much would the fabric cost to make a triangular sail with a base of 30 feet and a height of 36 feet?

( ) $840
( ) $7560
( ) $15120

21. Match the corresponding statements.

an arc longer than a semicircle	major
an arc shorter than a semicircle	minor

22. To the nearest hundredth, find the circumference of a circle that has a diameter of 19 inches, if $\pi = 3.14$.

( ) 78.47 in.
( ) 59.679 in.
( ) 59.66 in.
( ) 596.6 in.

23. A round lake has a circular shoreline that is 6 miles in diameter. Find the area of the lake.

24. Find the volume of a cylinder with a height of 6 meters and a circular base with a radius of 5 meters.

( ) 78.50 m^3

( ) 47.77 m^3

( ) 471.00 m^3

25. A box of cereal measures 8 by 7 by 8 inches. The manufacturer plans to market a smaller box that measures 5 by 2 by 7 inches. By how much will the volume be reduced?

Answers For

1. AGC -> acute, FGD -> obtuse, BGE -> right, BGA -> straight

2. $170^\circ$and 10°|$165^\circ$and 15°

3. 307

4. 95°

5. 4 and 6 -> alternate interior angles, 3 and 7 -> corresponding angles

6. 159°

7. 34

8. 7°

9. isosceles

10. 54°

11. 1, 52, 2, 38, 3, 52

12. 11 sides

13. 15

14. 40°

15. 6

16. 17

17. 21

18. 28

19. 48

20. $840

21. an arc shorter than a semicircle -> minor, an arc longer than a semicircle -> major

22. 59.66 in.

23. 28.26

24. 471.00 m^3

25. 378

1. PRESIDENTS The following list shows 5 of the youngest U.S. presidents and their ages (in years/days) when they took office. Complete the table below presenting the data in order, beginning with the youngest president.

President Kennedy 43 yr/236 days
President Cleveland 47 yr/351 days
President Grant 46 yr/236 days
President Roosevelt 42 yr/322 days
President Clinton 46 yr/154 days

	President
youngest	
2	
3	
4	
oldest	

2. A rock band gave two concerts in 45 cities. Approximately 1900 fans attended each concert. How many persons heard the group?

3. Write 392 in prime-factored form.

4. Evaluate the following expression:

$$\frac{13 + 5}{5 - 3}$$

5. Find the solution of the equation:

$37 = 25 + z$

6. Simplify the expression.

$-|10|$

7. Use the division or the multiplication property of equality to solve the equation.

$$251 = \frac{a}{3}$$

8. Evaluate the expression:

$-6 - (12 - 31)$.

9. Evaluate the expression: $(-5)(-7)(-3)$

10. Find the following sum:

$-7 + (-21)$.

11. The following bar chart shows the daily high temperature in degrees Fahrenheit. Fill the table with values of the temperature for each month to obtain a line graph of the same information.

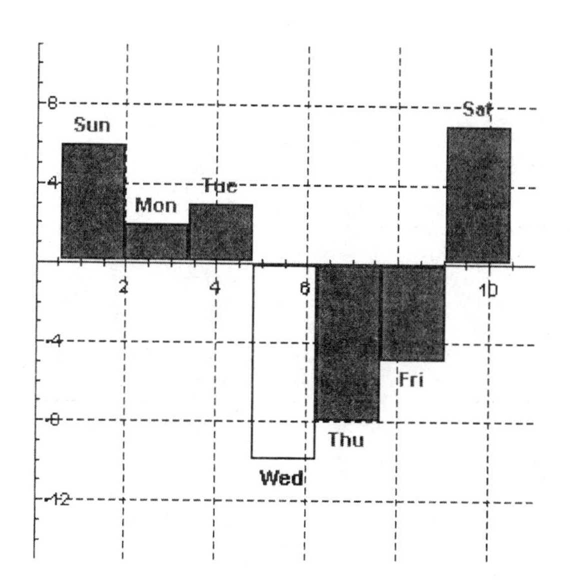

Day	Temperature
Sun	
Mon	
Tue	
Wed	
Thu	
Fri	
Sat	

12. Divide 18 by -6.

13. Evaluate: $8 + \frac{30}{-10} + 8 \cdot 6$

14. Solve the equation:

$\frac{h}{-7} + 9 = 8$.

15. After its first year of business, a manufacturer of smoke detectors found its market share 45 points behind the industry leader. Five years later, it trailed the leader by only 8 points. How many points of market share did the company pick up over this five-year span?

16. A graduating class of w people took buses that held 50 students each to an all night graduation party. How many buses were needed to transport the class?

17. Evaluate the algebraic expression:

$x^2 - s^2$ for $x = 3$ and $s = 7$

18. Simplify the following expression. Use the distributive property to remove the parentheses.

$2(7x + 9y + 10r)$

19. Simplify the following expression by combining like terms, if possible.

$9(9a + 5) - 4(9a + 7)$

20. Solve the equation by eliminating a variable term on one side of the equation.

$7y + 20 = 9y$

21. The daily listening audience of an AM radio station is 3 times as large as that of its FM sister station. If 100000 people listen to these two radio stations, how many listeners does the FM station have?

22. Multiply and express the product in two ways.

$\frac{43}{6} \cdot b$.

23. Find the quotient.

$\frac{11t}{5b} \div \frac{7t}{11b}$.

24. Complete the operation and simplify if necessary.

$\frac{3}{5} - \frac{4x}{7}$

25. Complete the operation and simplify if necessary.

$\frac{4}{y} + \frac{10}{11}$

26. Evaluate the power and write your answer as an improper fraction.

$$\left(3\frac{6}{7}\right)^2$$

27. AIR TRAVEL

A businesswoman's flight leaves Miami at 3 P.M. and arrives in Boston at 8:15 P.M. Express the duration of the flight as a mixed number.

28. Evaluate the expression and simplify if necessary.

$$\frac{\frac{1}{8}+\left(-\frac{3}{4}\right)}{2\frac{3}{4}}$$

29. Solve the equation: $x - \frac{3}{11} = \frac{1}{7}$

30. The amount of sunlight that comes into a room depends on the area of the windows in the room. What is the area of the window in the illustration?

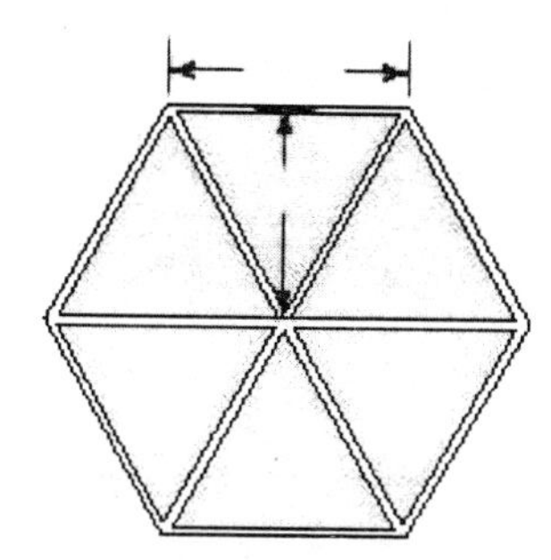

The height of the triangular pane is 4.7 inches and the width is 6 inches.

31. Combine like terms in the following expression:

$14.3a + 15.9 - 5.9a + 0.3$

32. What is the value of x in the following equation?

$0.5x - 5.9 + 0.9x = -2.68$

33. Use the imaginary triangles set up by a surveyor in the illustration below to find the length of the lake.

$L = \sqrt{585225}$ meters

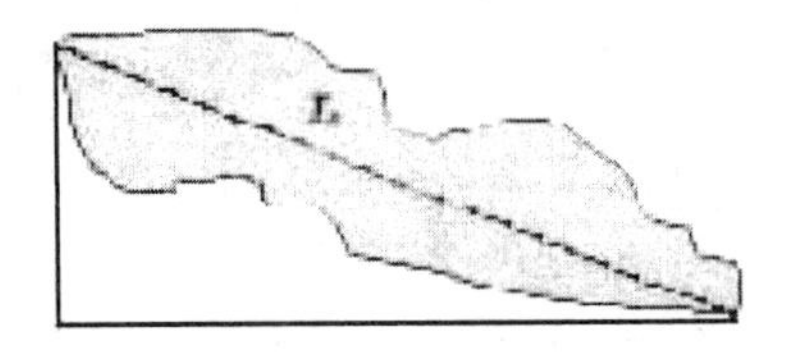

34. Complete the table.

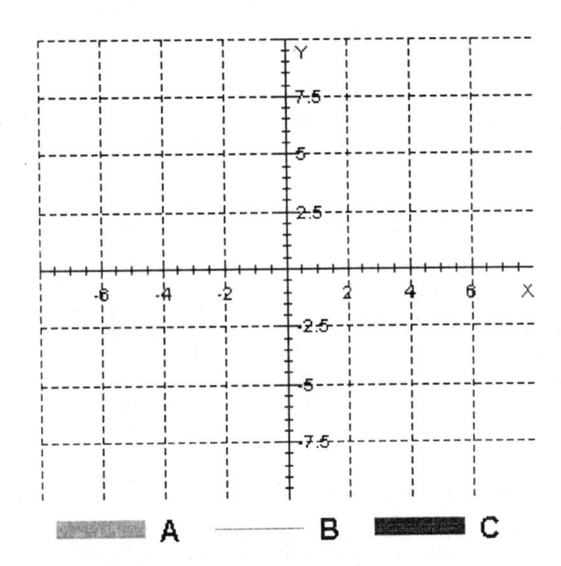

Point	x	y
A		
B		
C		

35. Find the coordinates of the x- and y-intercepts of the graph for the equation $x+y=7$.

36. The graph of the equation $y=ax+-2$ is given. Find a.

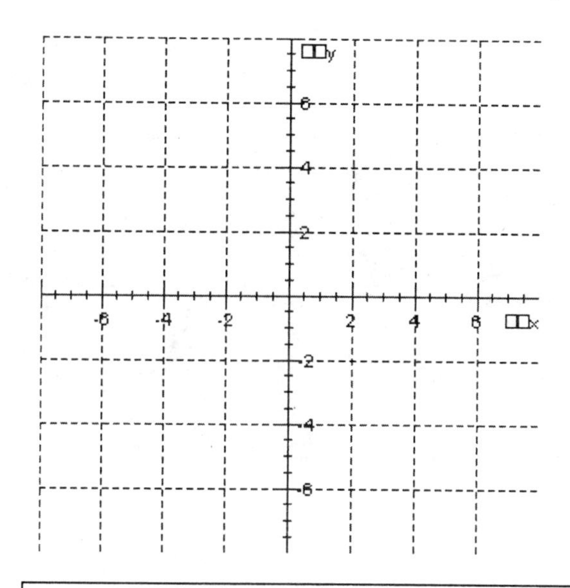

37. Simplify the product:

$y^2 \cdot b^2 y^4$

38. Evaluate the polynomial $2.25x^2 + 0.75x - 12.75$ for each given value and complete the table.

x	answer
6	
4	
8	

39. Subtract the polynomials:

$(9z^2+4z+4)-(3z^2-8z+2)$.

40. Find the product:

$-5y(10y^9-8y+5)$.

41. Change the following percent to a fraction. Simplify when necessary.

59%

42. Change the following decimal to a percent.

0.83 = ____ %

43. Change the following fraction to a percent.

$\frac{7}{8}=$ __%

44. What number is 27% of 250?

45. In one state, a gallon of unleaded gasoline sells for $2.38. This price includes federal and state taxes that total approximately $0.68 per gallon. Therefore, the price of a gallon of gasoline, before taxes, is about $1.70. What is the tax rate on gasoline?

___%

46. Because of a heavy spring runoff, the shoreline of a lake increased from 7.1 miles to 8.52 miles. What was the percent of increase in the shoreline?

___%

47. A developer promised a return of 2% annual interest on an investment of $20000 in her company. How much interest could an investor expect to make in the first year?

48. A driver pumped 15 gallons of gasoline into his tank at a total cost of $34.5. Find the cost per gallon of gasoline.

49. An 23000-gallon tank can be emptied in 50 minutes. Find the rate of flow in gallons per minute.

50. Solve for the variable in the proportion: $\frac{x + 1}{24} = \frac{-9}{3}$

51. Convert 36960 feet to miles.

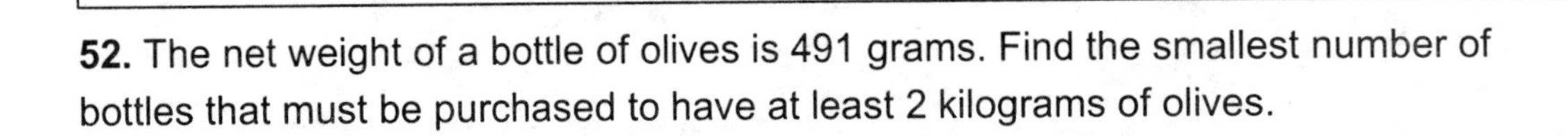

52. The net weight of a bottle of olives is 491 grams. Find the smallest number of bottles that must be purchased to have at least 2 kilograms of olives.

53. POSTAL REGULATIONS: You can mail a package weighing up to 70 pounds via priority mail. Can you mail a package that weighs 37 kilograms by priority mail? If the answer is yes enter a 1; if the answer is no, enter 0.

54. In the figure below$a$= 9,b= 3,c= 4, and$d$= 108. Find$x$.

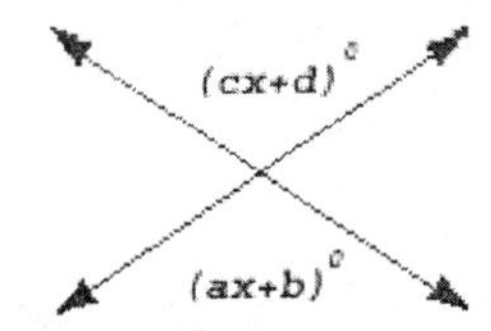

In the figure below,$l_1$is parallel withl_2. Find$x$, if$a$= 6,b= -4,c= 4 and$d$= 6.

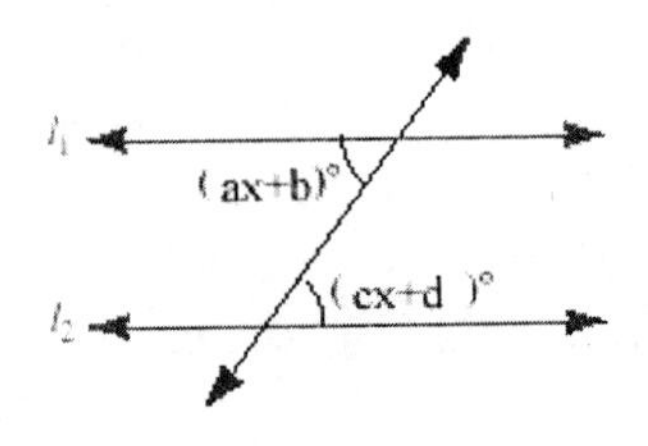

55. Find

$\angle 2$ if $\angle 1 = 17^\circ$.

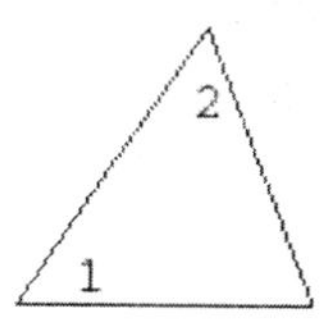

isosceles triangle

56. Find x, if a = 10 and b = 11.

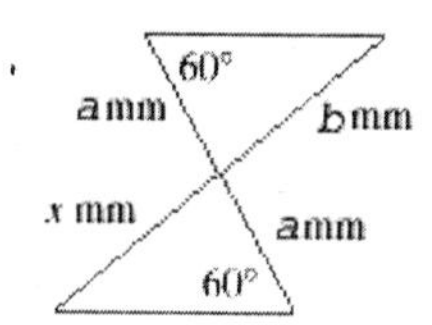

57. Find the area of the shaded part of the figure if a = 5, b = 10, c = 2.

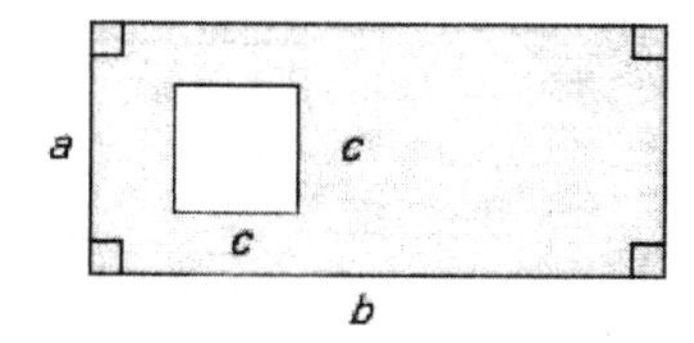

58. The rotunda at a state capitol is a circular area 112 feet in diameter. The legislature wishes to appropriate money to have the floor of the rotunda tiled. The lowest bid is \$81 per square yard, including installation.
How much must the legislature spend to tile the floor?

59. Find the volume of a prism whose base is a right triangle with legs 3 and 7 meters long and whose height is 8 meters.

Answers

1. youngest, Roosevelt, 2, Kennedy, 3, Clinton, 4, Grant, oldest, Cleveland

2. 171000

3. $2^3 \cdot 7^2$

4. 9

5. z=12

6. -10

7. 753

8. 13

9. -105

10. -28

11. Sun, 6, Mon, 2, Tue, 3, Wed, -10, Thu, -8, Fri, -5, Sat, 7

12. -3

13. 53

14. h=7

15. 37

16. $\frac{w}{50}$

17. -40

18. $14x + 18y + 20r$

19. $45a + 17$

20. 10

21. 25000

22. $\frac{43b}{6}, \frac{43}{6}b$

23. $\frac{121}{35}$

24. $\frac{(21-20x)}{35}$

25. $\frac{(44+10y)}{(11y)}$

26. $\frac{729}{49}$

27. $5\frac{1}{4}$

28. $\frac{-80}{352}$

29. $\frac{32}{77}$

30. 84.6

31. $8.4a+16.2$

32. 2.3

33. 765

34. A, 6, 8, B, -2, -4, C, 2, -9

35. (0,-7), (-7,0)

36. 1

37. $y^6 b^2$

38. 6, 72.75, 4, 26.25, 8, 137.25

39. $6z^2 + 12z + 2$

40. $-50y^{10} + 40y^2 - 25y$

41. $\frac{59}{100}$

42. 83

43. 87.5

44. 67.5

45. 40

46. 20

47. 400

48. $2.3

49. 460

50. -73

51. 7

52. 5

53. 0

54. 21

55. 17

56. 11

57. 46

58. 88623.36

59. 84

1. The amount of electricity used in a household is measured by a meter in kilowatt hours (kwh). Determine the reading on the meter shown in the illustration. (When the pointer is between two numbers, read the lower number.)

( ) 6540kwh
( ) 5604kwh
( ) 6504kwh

2. A first grade class received 173 halfpint cartons of milk to distribute evenly to the 21 students. How many cartons were left over?

Select the correct answer:

( ) 4
( ) 0
( ) 5
( ) 7

3. Write 1125 in prime-factored form.

Select the correct answer:

( ) $5^4 \cdot 4^2$
( ) $5^4 \cdot 3^3$
( ) $5^3 \cdot 3^2$
( ) $5^4 \cdot 3^2$

4. Evaluate the following expression:

$$16 - \frac{56}{7} + 3 \cdot 9$$

Select the correct answer:

( ) 37
( ) 34
( ) 35
( ) 30
( ) 45

5. Find the solution of the equation:

$39 = 33 + z$

Select the correct answer.

( ) $z = 72$
( ) $z = -72$
( ) none of these choices
( ) $z = 6$

6. Use the division or the multiplication property of equality to solve the equation. What is the result?

$$12 = \frac{y}{12}$$

( ) 0.083333
( ) 1
( ) 143
( ) 144

7. Simplify the expression.

$|-1|$

( ) -1
( ) 1
( ) -|-1|

8. The following bar chart shows the daily high temperature in degrees Fahrenheit.

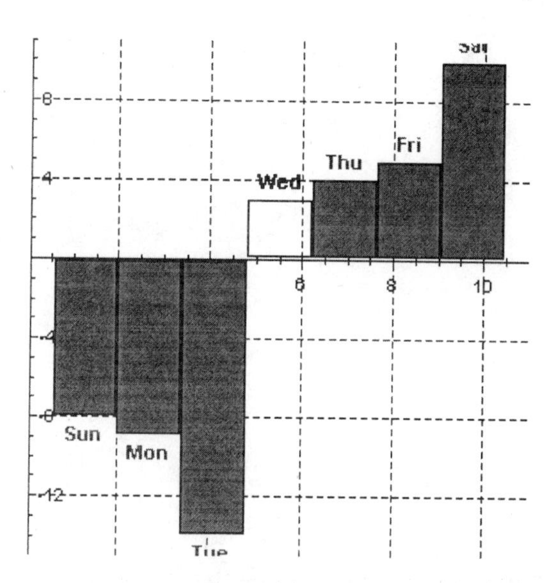

What was the high temperature for Monday?

( ) -8
( ) 5
( ) -9
( ) 4
( ) -14
( ) 10
( ) 3

9. Find the sum of**18 + (-28)**.

( ) -9
( ) 10
( ) -10
( ) 46

10. Evaluate the expression:

- 9 - (- 9) - 20.

( ) -2
( ) - 38
( ) -20
( ) 20

11. Evaluate: $(5 - 9)^2 - (10 - 8)^2$

( ) 19
( ) 7
( ) 23
( ) 15
( ) 12
( ) 0
( ) 3

12. Divide 14 by -2.

( ) 28
( ) -2
( ) 2
( ) -7
( ) -28
( ) 7

13. Evaluate the expression: $(-8)(-9)(-7)$

( ) -504
( ) 506
( ) 504
( ) -506

14. Solve the equation: $0=\frac{x}{12}$.

( ) x = - 12
( ) x = 12
( ) $x=\frac{1}{12}$
( ) x = 0

15. Six months before an election, a political candidate was 38 points behind in the polls. Two days before the election, polls showed that his support had skyrocketed; he found himself only 2 points behind.

How much support had he gained over the six-month period?

( ) 40 points
( ) - 40 points
( ) 33 points
( ) -38 points
( ) 36 points
( ) 39 points

16. A graduating class of w people took buses that held 35 students each to an all night graduation party. How many buses were needed to transport the class?

Select the correct answer.

( ) $\frac{35}{w}$
( ) $\frac{w}{35}$
( ) $35w$

17. Evaluate the expression:

$|3x - 19|$ for $x = 6$

Select the correct answer.

( ) -1
( ) 1
( ) 13

18. Simplify the following expression. Use the distributive property to remove the parentheses.

$2(10m + 9u - 3c)$

Select the correct answer.

( ) $20m - 6u + 18c$
( ) $6m - 18u + 20c$
( ) $20m + 18u - 6c$
( ) $18m + 20u - 6c$
( ) $6m - 20u + 18c$
( ) $18m + 6u - 20c$

19. Simplify the following expression by combining like terms, if possible.

$6(6y+9) - 2(7y+4)$

Select the correct answer.

( ) $22y - 62$
( ) $50y + 46$
( ) $22y + 46$
( ) none of these

20. Solve the equation.

$-4s + 28 = 3s$

Select the correct answer.

( ) $s = -4$
( ) $s = 16$
( ) $s = 4$

21. The daily listening audience of an AM radio station is 2 times as large as that of its FM sister station. If 72000 people listen to these two radio stations, how many listeners does the FM station have?

Select the correct answer.

( ) 17800
( ) 24000
( ) 7800
( ) 5800
( ) 22800
( ) 14800

22. Select all of the following expressions that correctly express the product of this multiplication problem.

$\frac{73}{8} \cdot c$.

[ ] $\frac{73}{8}c$

[ ] $\frac{73}{8c}$

[ ] $\frac{73c}{8}$

23. Find the quotient and select the correct answer.

$\frac{5m}{13s} \div \frac{11m}{2s}$.

( ) $\frac{12}{148}$

( ) $\frac{5}{142}$

( ) $\frac{9}{147}$

( ) $\frac{15}{138}$

( ) $\frac{14}{145}$

( ) $\frac{10}{143}$

24. Complete the operation and simplify if necessary.

$$\frac{1}{5} - \frac{8c}{13}$$

Select the correct answer.

( ) $\dfrac{13 - 40c}{65}$

( ) $\dfrac{13 - 40c}{13}$

( ) $\dfrac{13 + 40c}{65}$

25. What is the sum of $\dfrac{3}{15}$ and $\dfrac{1'}{2'}$ decreased by $\dfrac{29}{30}$?

( ) $\dfrac{-51}{210}$

( ) $\dfrac{-271}{210}$

( ) $\dfrac{-51}{105}$

( ) $\dfrac{355}{210}$

( ) $\dfrac{-15}{210}$

26. Divide.

$-1\frac{1}{5} \div 2\frac{1}{4}$

Select the correct answer.

( ) $\frac{24}{45}$

( ) $\frac{20}{40}$

( ) $-\frac{20}{40}$

( ) $-\frac{24}{45}$

27. AIR TRAVEL

A businesswoman's flight leaves Atlanta at 3 P.M. and arrives in New York at 7:45 P.M. Express the duration of the flight as a mixed number. Check your answer below.

( ) $10\frac{3}{4}$

( ) $4\frac{3}{4}$

( ) $5\frac{3}{4}$

( ) $4\frac{0}{4}$

28. Evaluate the expression: $\dfrac{\frac{3}{5}+\frac{1}{2}}{\frac{3}{5}-\frac{1}{2}}$

( ) $\frac{11}{6}$

( ) $\frac{1}{13}$

( ) $\frac{1}{11}$

( ) $\frac{13}{1}$

( ) $\frac{11}{1}$

29. Solve the equation: $5a - \frac{3}{2} = \frac{11}{7}$

( ) $-\frac{47}{70}$

( ) $\frac{83}{14}$

( ) $-\frac{43}{70}$

( ) $\frac{43}{70}$

( ) $\frac{47}{70}$

( ) $\frac{36}{14}$

30. Use a calculator evaluate: $2491.013 + 5890.5605$

Select the correct answer:

( ) 8382.5735
( ) 8381.3735
( ) 8392.6735
( ) 8377.5735
( ) 8381.5735

31. Combine like terms in the following expression:

$12.7a + 9.5 - 6.1a + 2.5$

Select the correct answer:

( ) 6.6 a + 12
( ) 6.6 a - 12
( ) 18.8 a + 12

32. Solve the following equation:

$c + 7.5 = 5.7$

Select the correct answer:

( ) $c = 13.2$
( ) $c = -13.2$
( ) $c = -1.8$
( ) $c = -18.9$
( ) $c = 1.8$

33. Find the length of the slanted side of the following roof truss, c, where $a= 5$, $b= 7$ and $c = \sqrt{121}$.

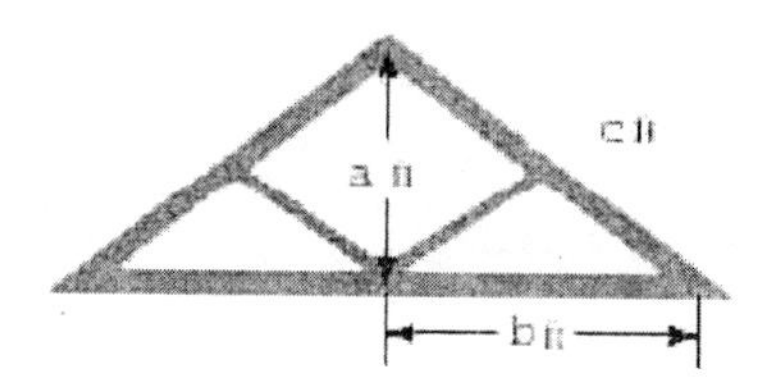

Select the correct answer:

( ) 11 ft
( ) 23 ft
( ) 5 ft
( ) 7 ft

34. Which of the points below has the coordinates $(-6,2)$?

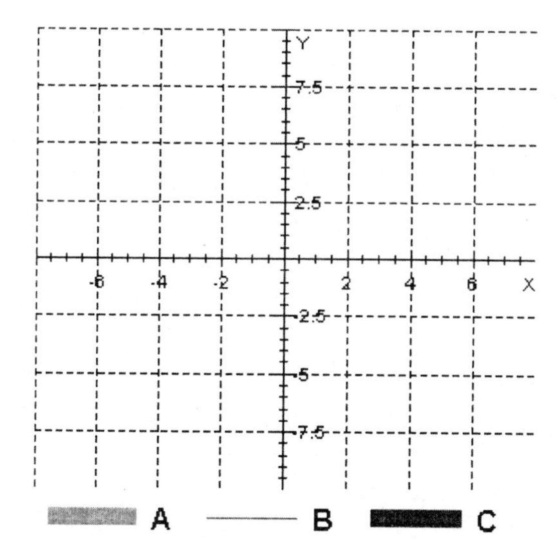

( ) C
( ) A
( ) B

35. Choose the equation whose solution is (9, -43).

( ) $y = -5x + 2$
( ) $-10y = -5x + 3$
( ) $y = -4x - 4$

36. Which line in the following graph is the graph of equation $y = -3x$?

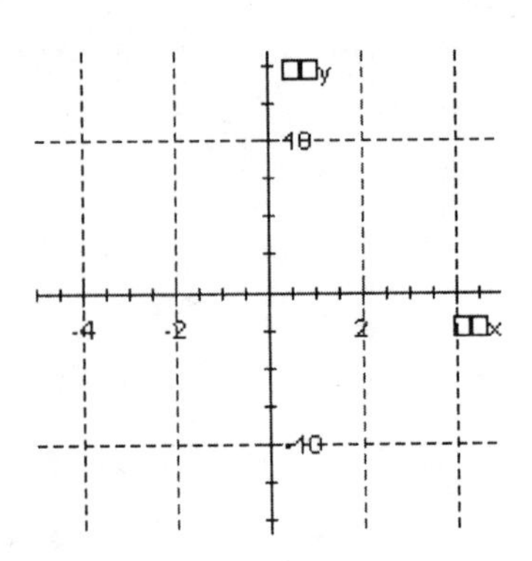

( ) Blue
( ) Red

37. Simplify the product:

$$-3s^2t^3(-3t^2s^3)$$

( ) $9s^5t^5$
( ) $-9s^3t^5$
( ) $3s^5t^2$

38. Evaluate the polynomial $-9b^2 - 5b + 10$ for $b = 5$.

( ) -240
( ) -260
( ) -190

39. Choose the correct answer for subtracting the polynomials:

$$\begin{array}{r} 4x^2+8x+9 \\ -(-9x^2-4x+5) \\ \hline \end{array}$$

( ) $13x^2+4x$

( ) $13x^2+4x+14$

( ) $13x^2+4x-14$

( ) $13x^2+12x+4$

40. Choose the correct answer for the product:

$10s(4s^{10} - s + 5)$.

( ) $10s^{11} - 10s^2 + 5s$

( ) $4s^{10} - 10s^2 - 10s$

( ) $40s^{11} - 10s^2 + 50s$

41. Change the following percent to a fraction. Select the correct answer.

3.1%

( ) $\frac{31}{100}$

( ) $\frac{31}{1000}$

42. Change the following decimal to a percent. Select the correct answer.

0.81

( ) 8.1%

( ) 81%

( ) 0.0081%

43. Change the following fraction to a percent. Select the correct answer.

$\frac{6}{25}$

( ) 24%

( ) 60%

44. 194 is 97% of what number? Select the correct answer.

( ) 400
( ) 200
( ) 300

45. While examining the monthly telephone bill, a women noticed an additional charge of $1.14 labeled federal excise tax. If the basic service charges for that billing period were $38, what is the federal excise tax rate? Select the correct answer.

( ) 97%
( ) 30%
( ) 3%
( ) 43.32%

46. Because of a heavy spring runoff, the shoreline of a lake increased from 7.9 miles to 10.27 miles. What was the percent of increase in the shoreline? Select the correct answer.

( ) 129 %
( ) 30 %
( ) 130 %

47. In order to meet month's end payroll obligations, a small business had to borrow $6000 for 20 days. How much did the business have to repay if the interest rate was 14%? Round the result to the nearest cent. Select the correct answer.

( ) $6046.02
( ) $6056.03
( ) $6046.03
( ) $5946.01
( ) $6156.04

48. A 10 pound bag of flower seed costs $46. Find the cost per pound of flower seed. Choose your answer from below.

( ) $9.2
( ) $4.6
( ) $13.8

49. In one community, a bill for 610 kilowatt hours of electricity is $55. In a second community, a bill for 865 kwh is $48. In which community is the unit cost of electricity cheaper? Choose your answer from below.

( ) In the second community the unit cost of electricity is cheaper.
( ) In the first community the unit cost of electricity is cheaper.
( ) In both communities the unit costs of electricity are the same.

50. Solve for the variable in the proportion: $\frac{s + 4}{14} = \frac{-5}{2}$.

Choose your answer from below.

( ) -31

( ) 39

( ) -9

( ) -39

51. AMELIA EARHART: In 1932, Amelia Earhart became the first woman to fly across the Atlantic Ocean alone, establishing a new record for the crossing: 13 hours and 30 minutes. How many minutes is this? Choose your answer frow below.

( ) 810 minutes
( ) 809
( ) 793 minutes

52. A baby weighs 4.004 kilograms. Give this weight in centigrams. Choose your answer from below.

( ) 40040 cg
( ) 0.04004 cg
( ) 400400 cg
( ) 4004 cg

53. POSTAL REGULATIONS: You can mail a package weighing up to 70 pounds via priority mail. Can you mail a package that weighs 35 kilograms by priority mail? Choose your answer from below.

( ) no
( ) I don't know
( ) yes

54. Which of the following angles are supplementary?

[ ] $10.5^{o}$and 79.5^{o}
[ ] $97.5^{o}$and 82.5^{o}
[ ] $114.5^{o}$and 65.5^{o}
[ ] $59.5^{o}$and 30.5^{o}

55. In the figure below,$l_1$is parallel withl_2. Find*x*, if*a*= 4,*b*= -4,*c*= 2 and*d*= 6.

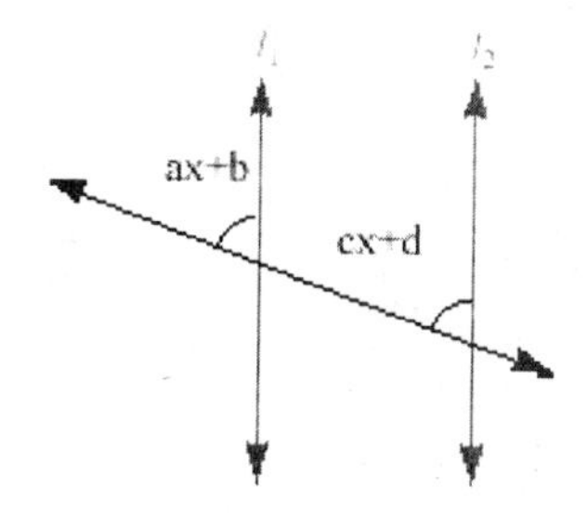

( ) 5°
( ) 175°

56. Classify the following polygons:

1.

2.

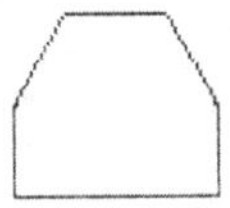

3.

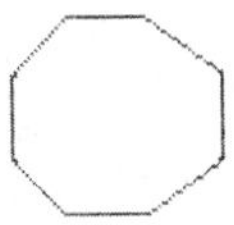

4.

5.

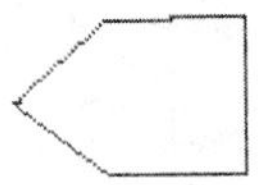

Choose your answer from below.

( ) Picture 1: quadrilateral; picture 2: octagon; picture 3: hexagon; picture 4: triangle and picture 5: pentagon.
( ) Picture 1: quadrilateral; picture 2: triangle; picture 3: octagon; picture 4: hexagon and picture 5: pentagon.

( ) Picture 1: octagon; picture 2: hexagon; picture 3: quadrilateral; picture 4: triangle and picture 5: pentagon.
( ) Picture 1: quadrilateral; picture 2: hexagon; picture 3: octagon; picture 4: triangle and picture 5: pentagon.
( ) Picture 1: quadrilateral; picture 2: pentagon; picture 3: octagon; picture 4: triangle and picture 5: hexagon.

57. The angles of the triangles shown in the illustration are $a= 60^{o}, b= 60^{o}$. The triangles are congruent because of what property?

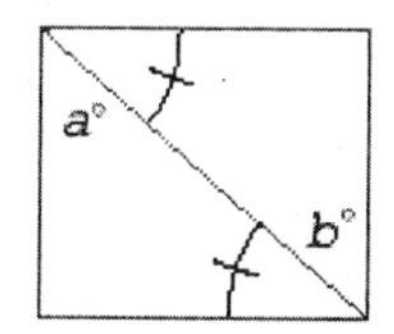

Choose the answer from below.

( ) SAS property
( ) SSS property
( ) ASA property

58. Find the area of the shaded part of the figure if $a= 7, b= 10, c= 3$. Select the correct answer.

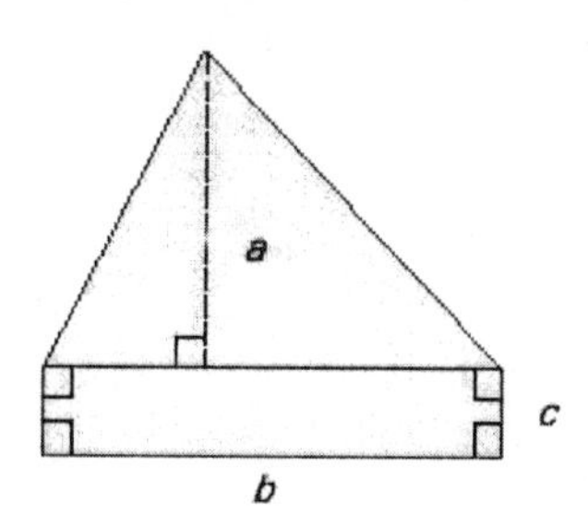

( ) 65
( ) 91
( ) 30

59. Refer to the illustration. How far does a point on the tip of a rotor blade travel when it makes one complete revolution?

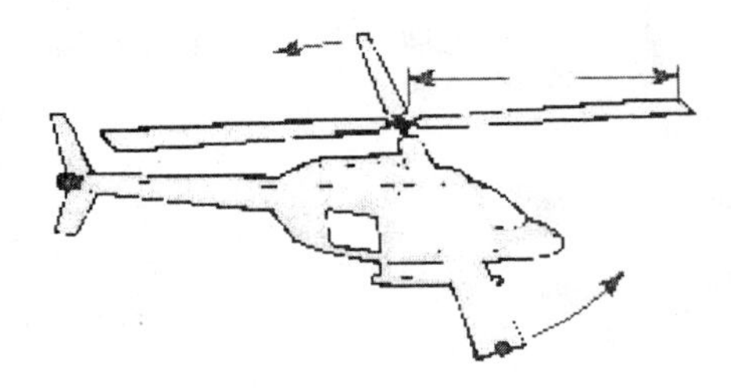

The length of the blade is equal to 20 feet.

( ) 1256 ft
( ) 2512 ft
( ) 125.6 ft
( ) 62.8 ft

60. Find the volume of a cylinder with a height of 10 meters and a circular base with a radius of 4 meters.

( ) 502.40 m^3
( ) 50.96 m^3
( ) 50.24 m^3

Answers

1. 6504kwh

2. 5

3. $5^3 \cdot 3^2$

4. 35

5. z = 6

6. 144

7. 1

8. -9

9. -10

10. -20

11. 12

12. -7

13. -504

14. x = 0

15. 36 points

16. $\frac{w}{35}$

17. 1

18. $20m + 18u - 6c$

19. $22y + 46$

20. $s = 4$

21. 24000

22. $\frac{73}{8}c$ | $\frac{73c}{8}$

23. $\frac{10}{143}$

24. $\frac{13 - 40c}{65}$

25. $\frac{-51}{210}$

26. $-\frac{24}{45}$

27. $4\frac{3}{4}$

28. $\frac{11}{1}$

29. $\frac{43}{70}$

30. 8381.5735

31. 6.6 a + 12

32. c= -1.8

33. 11 ft

34. A

35. y= -5x+ 2

36. Red

37. $9s^5t^5$

38. -240

39. $13x^2 + 12x + 4$

40. $40s^{11} - 10s^2 + 50s$

41. $\frac{31}{1000}$

42. 81%

43. 24%

44. 200

45. 3%

46. 30 %

47. $6046.03

48. $4.6

49. In the second community the unit cost of electricity is cheaper.

50. -9
|-39

51. 810 minutes

52. 400400 cg

53. no

54. 97.5°and 82.5°|114.5°and 65.5°

55. 5°

56. Picture 1: quadrilateral; picture 2: hexagon; picture 3: octagon; picture 4: triangle and picture 5: pentagon.

57. ASA property

58. 65

59. 125.6 ft

60. 502.40 m^3

1. The speed of light in a vacuum is 299,792,458 meters per second.

The nearest hundred thousand meters per second is 299,800,000 m/s.
True or False?

( ) True
( ) False

2. A first grade class received 140 halfpint cartons of milk to distribute evenly to the 15 students. How many cartons were left over?

3. Write 16875 in prime-factored form.

4. Evaluate the following expression:

$$\frac{15 - 3^2}{(4 - 3)^2}$$

Select the correct answer:

( ) 16
( ) 4
( ) 7
( ) 6
( ) 5

5. Find the solution of the equation:

$50 = 30 + x$

6. True or False:
In 2000, three Americans were awarded a cash prize for work in Physics. They shared the prize money. If each person received $198969, the total cash prize was $397938.

( ) True
( ) False

7. Evaluate the following expression:

19 + (-13) - (-30) - 11.

8. Evaluate the expression: $(-6)(-9)(-4)$

9. True or False:

Simplifying the expression $-(-11)$ we get 11.

( ) True
( ) False

10. The bar chart below shows a week of daily reports listing the height of a river in comparison to flood stage. Fill the table with values of the daily height in relation to the flood stage using signed numbers.

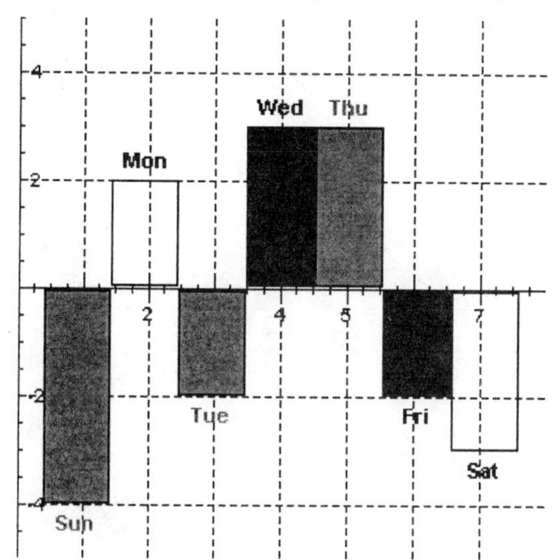

Day	Height
Sun	
Mon	
Tue	
Wed	
Thu	
Fri	
Sat	

11. Evaluate the expression:

- 15 - (11 - 57).

( ) 31
( ) 61
( ) -61
( ) -31
( ) 53
( ) -53

12. True or False:

The quotient of $\frac{-160}{40}$ is 4.

( ) True
( ) False

13. Evaluate: $3 + 10[2 - (6 - 9)]$

14. True or False:

The solution of the equation:

$\frac{h}{-7} + 9 = 2$ is ***h*= 49**.

( ) True
( ) False

15. Six months before an election, a political candidate was 35 points behind in the polls. Two days before the election, polls showed that his support had skyrocketed; he found himself only 7 points behind. How much support had he gained over the six-month period?

16. The height of a hedge was*w*feet before a gardener cut 4 feet off of the top.

Write an algebraic expression that describes the new height of the trimmed hedge.

17. True or False:

$\frac{9x - 6b}{-10} = -9$ for$x$= 10 and$b$= 30

( ) True
( ) False

18. Simplify the following expression. Use the distributive property to remove the parentheses.

$7(2m- 6n- 5)$

19. Simplify the following expression by combining like terms, if possible.

$10x+ 5 - 2y- 7x+ 10$

Select the correct answer.

( ) $3x- 2y+ 15$
( ) $17x- 2y+ 5$
( ) none of these
( ) $8x- 3y+ 14$

20. Solve the equation by eliminating a variable term on one side of the equation:

$8s - 24 = 5s - 12$

21. In an effort to cut costs, a corporation has decided to lay off 2 employees every month until the number of employees totals 130. If 250 people are now employed, how many months will it take to reach the employment goal?

22. Multiply and express the product in two ways.

$\frac{31}{6} \cdot x$.

23. Find the quotient and select the correct answer.

$\frac{2}{13a} \div \left(-\frac{1}{7}\right)$

( ) $-\frac{19}{11a}$

( ) $-\frac{17}{14a}$

( ) $-\frac{15}{18a}$

( ) $-\frac{11}{16a}$

( ) $-\frac{12}{10a}$

( ) $-\frac{14}{13a}$

24. Complete the operation and simplify if necessary.

$\frac{7}{a} + \frac{7}{13}$

25. What is the sum of $\frac{17}{21}$ and $\frac{3}{15}$ decreased by $\frac{17}{42}$?

( ) $\frac{297}{210}$

( ) $\frac{127}{210}$

( ) $\frac{127}{105}$

( ) $\frac{43}{210}$

( ) $\frac{3}{210}$

26. Divide.

$-5\frac{1}{5} \div 2\frac{1}{2}$

27. AIR TRAVEL

A businesswoman's flight leaves Miami at 2 P.M. and arrives in New York at 7:15 P.M. Express the duration of the flight as a mixed number. Check your answer below.

( ) $6\frac{1}{4}$

( ) $5\frac{1}{4}$

( ) $9\frac{1}{4}$

( ) $5\frac{3}{4}$

28. Evaluate the expression and simplify if necessary.

$$\frac{\frac{3}{4}+\left(-\frac{1}{8}\right)}{2\frac{1}{2}}$$

29. Combine like terms in the following expression:

$6.7\ (18 - d) + 14.7d$

30. What is the value ofxin the following equation?

$-7.1x - 6.9 + 7.3x = -5.36$

31. Solve the equation: $2x - \frac{11}{3} = \frac{7}{2}$

( ) $-\frac{83}{12}$

( ) $\frac{43}{12}$

( ) $\frac{83}{12}$

( ) $\frac{41}{6}$

( ) $\frac{47}{6}$

( ) $-\frac{43}{12}$

32. The amount of sunlight that comes into a room depends on the area of the windows in the room. What is the area of the window in the illustration?

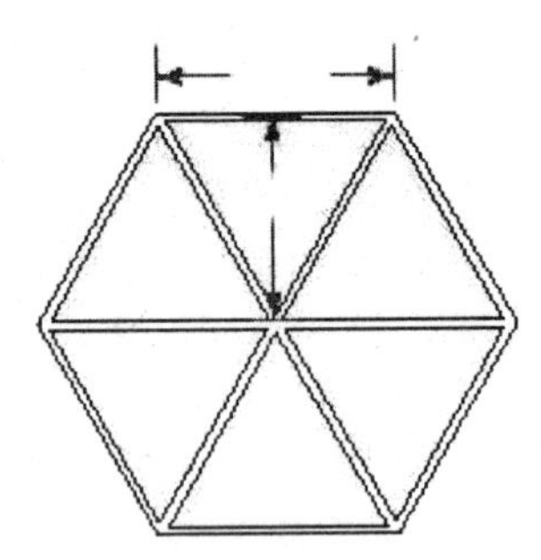

The height of the triangular pane is 4.9 inches and the width is 4 inches.

Select the correct answer:

( ) 58.8 in^2

( ) none of these

( ) 19.6 in^2

( ) 9.8 in^2

( ) 117.6 in^2

33. The picture screen on a television set is measured diagonally, as shown in illustration below. Match values of a (left column) with corresponding size screen. (All measurements are in inches.)

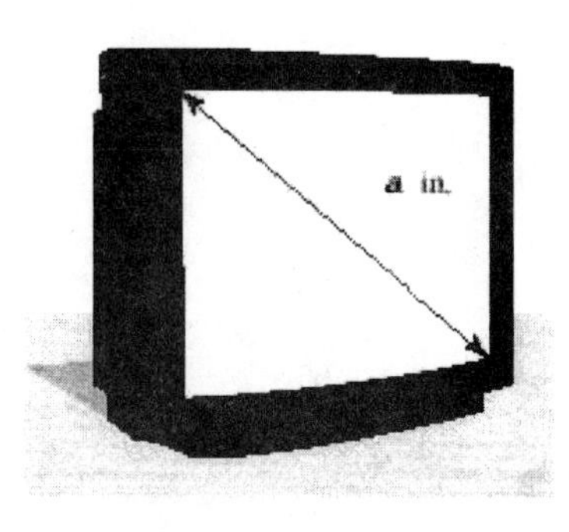

$\sqrt{2304}$	30
$\sqrt{900}$	49
$\sqrt{2401}$	48

34. Find the coordinates of the x- and y-intercepts of the graph for the equation $x+y=1$.

35. Complete the table.

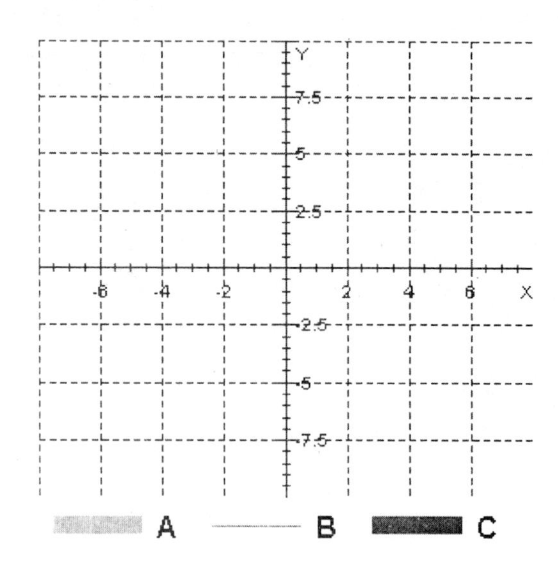

Point	x	y
A		
B		
C		

36. Complete the table and graph the equation $y = 5x$.

x	y
-10	
-7	
2	
10	

37. Rewrite the following expression using only one exponent:

$5c^4(4c^4)2c^2$

38. Given the polynomial $2b^2 - 6b + 4$, match the values ofbon the left with the corresponding solution on the right.

-4	144
10	40
6	24
-2	60

39. Subtract the polynomials:

$(5z^2+9z+5)-(7z^2-3z+8)$.

40. Choose the correct answer for the product:

$4(2c^8 - c)c$.

( ) $8c^9 - 4c^2$

( ) $4c^9 - 4c$

( ) $4c^8 - 2c$

41. Change the percent to a fraction. Simplify if necessary.

125%

42. Change the following decimal to a percent. Select the correct answer.

0.46

( ) 0.0046%

( ) 46%

( ) 4.6%

43. Express the following fraction as a percent. Round to the nearest hundredth.

$\frac{1}{8} = \_\_\%$

44. 396 is 99% of what number? Select the correct answer.

( ) 400
( ) 500
( ) 800

45. NURSERY CENTER				
3	@	3.42	PLANTING MIX	$10.26
1	@	9.18	GROUND COVER	$9.18
2	@	13.25	SHRUBS	$26.50

Complete the sales receipt by finding the subtotal, the sales tax, and the total, if sales tax is 8%.

Sum	$
SUBTOTAL	
TAX	
TOTAL	

46. After flooding damaged much of the crop, the cost of a head of lettuce jumped from $0.50 to $1.20. What percent of increase is this? Select the correct answer.

( ) 140 %
( ) 240 %
( ) 42.16 %
( ) 142.16 %

47. A farmer borrowed $8000 from a credit union. The money was loaned at 8.1% annual interest. How many months was the money loaned for, if the credit union charged him $864 for the use of the money?

48. An airline had 3.7 complaints for every 500 passengers. Write this rate as a fraction in simplified form.

49. Ricardo worked for 30 hours to help insulate a hockey arena. For his work, he received $390. Find his hourly rate of pay. Choose your answer from below.

( ) 26
( ) 13
( ) 39

50. Solve for the variable in the proportion: $\frac{a + 9}{24} = \frac{-5}{4}$.

Choose your answer from below.

( ) -39

( ) -14

( ) -21

( ) 39

51. Convert 180 minutes to hours.

52. A bottle of hydrochlorothiazine contains 30 tablets. If each tablet contains 70 milligrams of the active ingredient, how many grams of the active ingredient are in the bottle?

53. HAIR GROWTH: When hair is short, its rate of growth averages about 0.7 inch per month. How many centimeters is this a month? Choose your answer from below.

( ) 17.78 cm.
( ) 0.1778 cm.
( ) 1.778 cm.

Find the complement of each angle and complete the table.

Measure of x	Measure of complement of x
65.5	
89	
36.5	
73	

54. In the figure below, line AB is parallel to line DE. Find x, if a= 5, b= -4, c= 3 and d= 6.

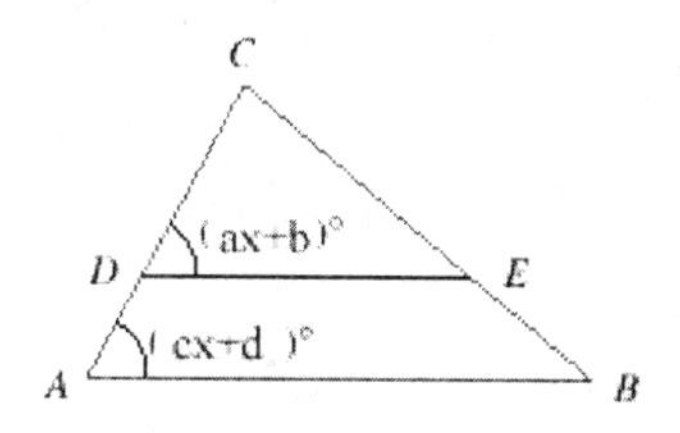

55. How many sides does the following polygon have?

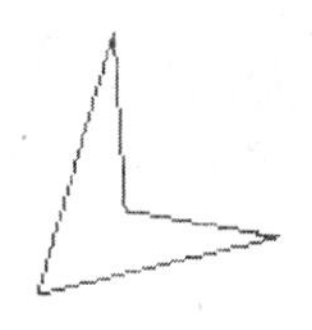

56. The two triangles shown in the illustration are congruent. Find b, if angle a is 56°.

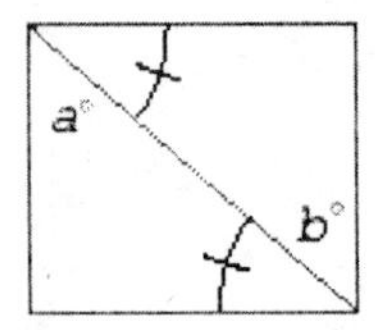

57. Find the area of the shaded part of the figure if $a = 6, b = 8, c = 2$. Select the correct answer.

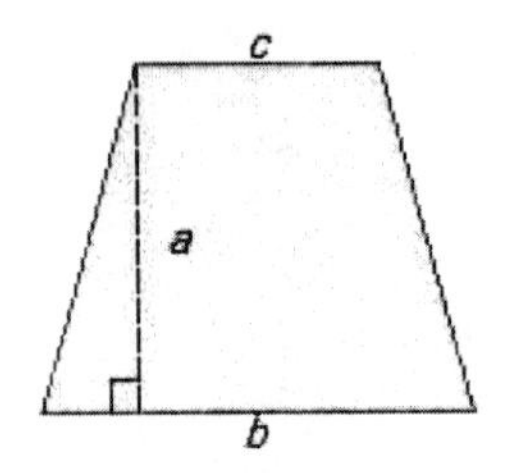

( ) 96
( ) 60
( ) 30

58. Refer to the illustration. How far does a point on the tip of a rotor blade travel when it makes one complete revolution?

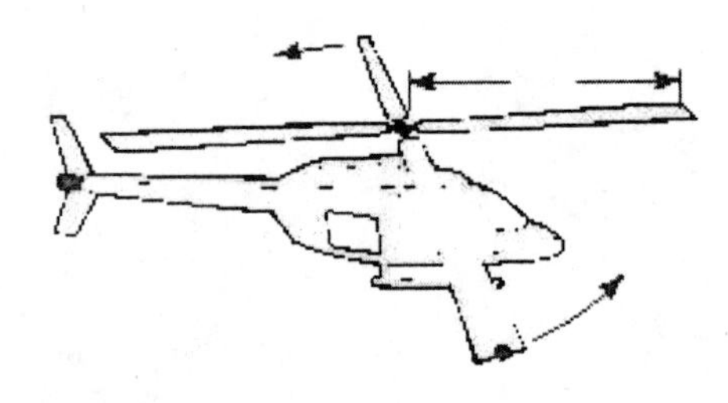

The length of the blade is equal to 18 feet.

59. Find the volume of a rectangular solid with dimensions of 4 by 6 by 7 centimeters.

( ) 17 cm^3

( ) 188 cm^3

( ) 168 cm^3

Answers

1. (none)

2. 5

3. $3^3 \cdot 5^4$

4. 6

5. x=20

6. false

7. 25

8. -216

9. true

10. Sun, -4, Mon, 2, Tue, -2, Wed, 3, Thu, 3, Fri, -2, Sat, -3

11. 31

12. false

13. 53

14. true

15. 28

16. w-4

17. true

18. $14m - 42n - 35$

19. $3x - 2y + 15$

20. 4

21. 60

22. $\frac{31x}{6}, \frac{31}{6}x$

23. $-\frac{14}{13a}$

24. $\frac{(91+7a)}{(13a)}$

25. $\frac{127}{210}$

26. $-\frac{52}{25}$

27. $5\frac{1}{4}$

28. $\frac{40}{160}$

29. $8d + 120.6$

30. 7.7

31. $\frac{43}{12}$

32. 58.8 in^2

33. sqr(2304) -> 48, sqr(2401) -> 49, sqr(900) -> 30

34. (0,-1), (-1,0)

35. A, -4, -9, B, 4, -7, C, 0, -8

36. -10, -50, -7, -35, 2, 10, 10, 50

37. $40c^{10}$

38. 10 -> 144, -4 -> 60, -2 -> 24, 6 -> 40

39. $-2z^{2} + 12z + -3$

40. $8c^{9} - 4c^{2}$

41. $\frac{5}{4}$

42. 46%

43. 12.5

44. 400

45. SUBTOTAL, 45.94, TAX, 3.68, TOTAL, 49.62

46. 140 %

47. 16

48. $\frac{37}{5000}$

49. 13

50. -39

|-14

51. 3

52. 2.1

53. 1.778 cm.

54. 5

55. 4

56. 56

57. 30

58. 113.04

59. 168 cm^3